REPRODUCTIVE PHYSIOLOGY

A Series of Books in AGRICULTURAL SCIENCE

ANIMAL SCIENCE

Editors: G. W. SALISBURY AND E. W. CRAMPTON

Applied Animal Nutrition: *The Uses of Feedstuffs in the Formulation of Livestock Rations*

E. W. CRAMPTON

Reproductive Physiology: *Comparative Reproductive Physiology of Domestic Animals, Laboratory Animals and Man* (Second Edition)

A. V. NALBANDOV

The Science of Meat and Meat Products

AMERICAN MEAT INSTITUTE FOUNDATION

Fundamentals of Nutrition

E. W. CRAMPTON AND L. E. LLOYD

Physiology of Reproduction and Artificial Insemination of Cattle

G. W. SALISBURY AND N. L. VANDEMARK

Introduction to Livestock Production: Including Dairy and Poultry

H. H. COLE, EDITOR

PLANT AND SOIL SCIENCE

Editors: IVER JOHNSON AND M. B. RUSSELL

Crop Adaption and Distribution

CARROLL P. WILSIE

Horticultural Science

JULES JANICK

REPRODUCTIVE PHYSIOLOGY

*Comparative Reproductive
Physiology of Domestic Animals
Laboratory Animals, and Man*

A. V. NALBANDOV
University of Illinois

SECOND EDITION

89   94

W. H. FREEMAN and COMPANY
San Francisco and London

Printed in the United States of America
Library of Congress Catalogue Card Number: 64-24554

Preface to the Second Edition

In preparing the second edition of *Reproductive Physiology*, I have tried to correct some of the errors of the first edition, bring the text up-to-date, and take into account the criticisms I have received. Of the many who volunteered suggestions, about half liked the manner of presentation especially because the flow of thought was not interrupted by references to numbers or names. This exclusion of references, they felt, made for ease of reading and above all stimulated the reader to seek documentation of the statements in the many excellent reference works which should be consulted by the interested student. Pedagogically I think they are right; it is all too easy to be convinced by the sheer authority of a well-known name that a statement must be true. Accordingly, I have again decided to leave the text uncluttered by references, in the hope that the serious student will want to find the necessary documentation himself and in the process learn more than he could simply by accepting a stated fact. A short list of essential references is given at the end of most chapters.

Some readers found irritating my willingness to speculate freely, but the majority welcomed it as a challenge for reflection and class discussion and, in some instances, as a stimulus for further research. In general, it was clear that about equal numbers of readers would be pleased or displeased by major changes. For lack of really compelling reasons, the format and style of the second edition remain essentially unchanged.

A majority of readers felt that one of the attractive features of the book was its compactness. To preserve the brevity without ignoring the many important advances in the field, is one of the aims of the second edition. Thus, for instance, the new concepts of corpus luteum maintenance, the role of releasing factors in hypophyseal control, and the newest work on the relationship between hormones and psychosomatic behavior (including pheromones), are far too important to be ignored; these topics form the bulk of the new material. Many other sections have been amplified or revised to take into account newer findings. Many of the older illustrations were replaced by new ones using later and—hopefully—more informative data.

Finally, I want to thank the many persons who have taken the time and trouble to make constructive criticisms. Among them, Drs. L. E. Casida and R. M. Melampy deserve special thanks.

January 1964   A. V. NALBANDOV

Preface to the First Edition

This book grew out of several years of giving a lecture course in the physiology of reproduction of animals. Since the preparation of the listeners was as varied as their fields of specialization (which included agriculture, zoology, veterinary and human medicine, physiology, nutrition, and even home economics), I could not presume adequate knowledge of the sciences on which the physiology of reproduction is based. I could not omit histology, embryology, and the anatomy of the reproductive systems, but neither could I discuss them in detail. I found it best, therefore, to review the basic information briefly and to leave it to the student to refresh his memory or to make up his deficiencies by referring to more detailed discussions in pertinent textbooks. The present book follows this general plan, which was found to work well when I gave the course.

Two subjects, on the other hand, I found it desirable to discuss in detail: (1) the endocrine glands and their relation to reproduction; (2) the problems of fertility and sterility, the presentation of which, so far as possible, was supported by experimental evidence. These subjects were discussed in detail because the information presented was not all generally available in one place, because they were found to be of the greatest interest to the audiences, and because they represented whatever sphere of competence the author might have.

Early in the organization of these lectures I became painfully aware that students in general, and graduate students in particular, become specialists at what seems to me an unwisely early stage of their training. Some of them, with apparent ardor, profess interest only in the aspects of the field that apply to the human animal; others want to concern themselves only with the reproduction of the rat; and still others are content to learn all there is to know about the cow. This attitude is frequently carried over into their productive scientific careers: at scientific meetings, gynecologists walk out when papers on the reproduction of sheep are read, "sheep men" retaliate by walking out when "rat men" are reading, and "rat men" are content to listen only to one another. And yet, as more is learned of reproduction, it becomes increasingly obvious that a comparative approach to the problem is the most fruitful for all concerned. It is for this reason that I have chosen to present the subject comparatively, using whatever good data there are on domestic animals (including chickens), laboratory animals, and primates. Please note the phrase "whatever *good* data there are." It is possible, to be sure, that I have omitted pertinent data simply because I was unaware of them; as a rule, however, I have omitted such data because they did not seem sufficiently well documented or were not based on well-designed or well-controlled experiments. I take full responsibility for deliberate omissions, and I apologize for inadvertent ones. I hope that my attention will be called to the latter.

Certain sections of this book contain much speculation. I do not apologize for these attempts to fill the gaps in our knowledge, for I agree with Dobzhansky's statement that, "while it is dangerous to forget the extent of our ignorance, it is foolish to neglect what we know." Provocative speculations may lead bright students to do further reading and research and will provide instructors with an opportunity to discuss controversial points in their lectures.

I have made no attempt to document all or even most of the statements. I have provided each chapter with a few references, usually to review articles or to books, which provide points of departure for further reading or contain more detailed information on, or documentation of, the statements made in this book. The papers from which many of the tables and graphs were adapted will furnish valuable additional source material and should be consulted for details.

I am grateful to Dr. O. G. Nalbandov, who wrote most of Chapter 6, and Dr. Ari van Tienhoven, who collected all of the information on the relation of the thyroid to reproduction that appears in Chapter 3. I am deeply grateful to Professor E. C. Amoroso, F. R.S., for permitting me to use the excellent pictures that illustrate Chapter 9. I am indebted to the graduate students who listened to me talk and talked back; they collected many of the data used in this book.

Finally, I want to thank Dr. L. E. Casida, who read the manuscript and made many suggestions for its improvement—as did, indeed, the other reviewers, whose names are unknown to me. Dr. P. J. Dziuk and Dr. Ari van Tienhoven read the whole manuscript, and Dr. R. M. Fraps read parts of it, and all contributed to its improvement.

April 1958   A. V. NALBANDOV

Contents

Introduction

Physiology of reproduction, the subject of this book, is a composite science. For an understanding of the subject it will be necessary to draw upon the accumulated knowledge of endocrinology, histology, embryology, anatomy, physiology, and genetics. The perpetuation of the species, which is the ultimate aim if not the reason for being of all organisms, involves reproductive processes that may vary in their complexity and in the mechanisms employed. Because this discussion deals with mammals and birds, we shall be mostly concerned with sexual reproduction of the dioecious type. Even in these higher vertebrates, however, asexual reproduction, in the general sense of the word, occurs; for all processes of growth are basically due to the asexual fission of somatic cells.

The two sexes involved in dioecious reproduction are highly specialized. The degree of specialization is the result of the complex synchronization of reproductive events, which, as a rule, follow predictable, well-regulated patterns. The details of the reproductive patterns differ in various species. Reproductive events are regulated by a complex of interlocking hormone systems, which are themselves locked into a neural control system. This neurohormonal control system will be discussed in detail, because it provides a maximum of checks that ensure a normal and well-balanced functioning of the end organs affected by hormones, which in turn results in synchronization of the function of the sex mechanism. The neuroendocrine systems and the comparative anatomy and physiology of the sex mechanisms, both largely controlled by these systems, are the main subjects of this book.

The processes of reproduction occasionally decline in efficiency because one of the hormonal, neural, or humoral links becomes impaired, or they function out of phase, disrupting the sensitive mechanism of synchronization that underlies most reproductive events. When this happens, partial or complete sterility results. Sterility, because of its importance in domestic animals as well as in human beings, will form part of the discussion. First, however, we shall consider some of the basic concepts of sex, the anatomy of the reproductive system, and the hormonal and other signaling systems that have evolved in the different species. The problems faced by the rat, the elephant, and the chicken, in reproducing the species, are basically the same. Eggs must be matured and shed, and a signal must be given to the male that the latter event is about to happen in order to ensure the presence of viable sperm. These and subsequent events, such as pregnancy, parturition, and lactation, or the incubation of eggs by birds, depend on humoral and neural feedback mechanisms that form chains of events. It is essential to remember that no reproductive event ever stands alone, and that any one event is only one link in a chain. Thinking of chains of events appears to be difficult for the beginner, but he must learn to think in that way if he wishes to understand reproductive phenomena.

chapter 1

The Biology of Sex

The word "sex" comes from the Latin word *sexus,* which means division and is derived from *secare,* which means to cut or to separate. Biologically, sex is not an entity but "the sum of the peculiarities of structure and function that distinguish a male from a female" (*Webster's New International Dictionary,* Second Edition). The male and female components of a population can not always be separated into two distinct groups, especially if one uses only one or two external sex characters as the basis of separation. All populations are actually dichotomies composed of males and females, differing—to a greater or lesser degree—in the *sum total* of their peculiarities of structure and function. In some instances the sexes overlap completely, making it impossible to distinguish them externally. For a clearer understanding of the continuous variation between the sexes, it may be well to think in terms of a *genotypic* and a *phenotypic* sex.

Genotypic Sex

Genotypic sex is determined by the type of sex chromosomes an individual receives from the parents (Table 1-1).

Table 1-1. "Avian" and "Drosphila" types of sex determination typical of birds and mammals

CATEGORY	TYPES OF SEX CHROMOSOMES IN GERM CELLS	TYPES AND PROPORTIONS OF GAMETES PRODUCED
Female mammal	X only	All eggs carry X
Male mammal	X and Y	50% of sperm carry X 50% of sperm carry Y
Female bird	X and Y	50% of eggs carry X 50% of eggs carry Y
Male bird	X only	All sperm carry X

To some extent the genotypic character "sex" resembles a genetic character that is controlled by a single gene. In both cases we are dealing with an all-or-none character; in the case of sexuality the "sum total of peculiarities of structure and function" is either male or female. This implies, and to some extent correctly, that the characteristics of "maleness" or of "femaleness" are fixed unalterably when the sperm fertilizes the egg and that they are not subject to environmental modification, just as the whiteness of an albino animal, once it has been fixed by the proper combination of genes, is not subject to environmental modification. Actually, the expression of degrees of sexuality is as variable as the somatic characters that are determined by multiple genes. This variability expresses itself in the different degrees of masculinity or of femininity that are normally seen in a population. It is this degree of the expression of one sex or the other that we find it convenient to call phenotypic sex.

In man much work has been done recently on the chromosomal sex of individuals who show endocrine (including reproductive) and mental disorders. In individuals showing the Klinefelter syndrome, which is characterized by gonadal hypofunction, the genotype is usually XXY (instead of XY), but in those showing Turner's syndrome, which is characterized by gonadal agenesis or aplasia, the genotype is frequently XO rather than XY or XX.

These unusual genotypes of the sex chromosome complex are called aneuploidy; they are ascribed to errors in chromosome division occurring during meiosis. If, as the result of nondisjunction, both X chromosomes go to the ovum, fertilization by a sperm will lead to the formation of either an XXX or an XXY zygote (maternal nondisjunction). In paternal nondisjunction, some sperm will be of the genotype XY, and others will have no sex chromosome (O). Fertilization of eggs of a normal genotype will result in zygotes of either the XXY or XO genotypes. As already noted, such aneuploid individuals very frequently show gonadal or endocrine defects.

Similar studies in other animals are lacking and it is not known how frequently aneuploidy of sex chromosomes occurs in them. It appears possible that cases of gonadal disfunction or gonadal aplasia seen in domestic animals may be due to aneuploidy unless the profit motive in animal breeding (inapplicable in human matings) has resulted in the elimination from the breeding population of families prone to show aneuploidy. Research along these lines would be of great theoretical and perhaps practical significance and might explain why intersexuality is so frequently seen in some species (goats and pigs), although it is rare in others.

Phenotypic Sex

To explain how an all-or-none character such as sex can be subject to variability, Bridges advanced the *genic balance* theory of sex determination. This theory accepts the basic assumption that sex is determined at the time of fertilization by the proper combination of the sex chromosomes. In addition to this, the theory assumes that the autosomes carry genes for maleness and the sex chromosomes carry genes for femaleness. If the number of genes for maleness on the autosomes is large, then, in the case of an XY male, these genes overbalance the genes for femaleness carried on the sex chromosomes. Such a male may be phenotypically more masculine than a male that has received fewer maleness genes on its autosomes. It is postulated that, though the XY type of sex determination is permanently fixed and is not subject to genetic variability, the presence of maleness genes on the autosomes makes divergence in the phenotypic expression of degrees of sexuality possible. The sex chromosomes establish the blueprint for genotypic sex; autosomal genes cannot alter this blueprint drastically in most higher vertebrates, but they may be responsible for the variations in the expression of phenotypic sexuality that are observed in most higher animals, including man.

It is not known how the autosomal sex genes accomplish phenotypic sex modification. They may act by controlling the glandular mechanisms of both sexes and by governing the rates at which sex hormones —which are responsible for the phenotypic, or external, expression of sex traits—are secreted. It may be that large amounts of one or the other of the sex hormones produce a "masculine" male or female, smaller amounts produce an "average" male or female, and still smaller quantities result in "effeminate" individuals.

Sex Ratios

In view of the preceding discussion it may be assumed that the combination of sex chromosomes effectively determines the proportion of the sexes in a population and holds it near equality. A casual inspection of available statistics dealing with sex ratios bears out this assumption, but sex ratios sometimes deviate very significantly from the expected equality. These exceptions deserve closer scrutiny, but, before we take them up, a few general statements concerning terminology and the factors affecting sex ratios will be useful.

It is conventional to express sex ratios as the number of males per 100 females. If we say that the sex ratio of a certain population is 108, we mean that there are 108 males per 100 females at the time the count was made. Occasionally, for greater ease of statistical manipulation, it becomes desirable to express sex ratios as percentage of males (as in Table 1-2). Three different figures expressing sex ratios are generally found in the literature: the primary, secondary, and tertiary sex ratios.

The primary sex ratio is the proportion of males to females at the time of fertilization or conception. This is only a theoretical concept, for it is virtually impossible to determine the sex of the zygote or of the very early embryo. The concept is useful, however, and we shall return to its meaning later. If a way were found to ascertain, in a routine manner, the sex of zygotes or very early embryos, significant contributions to this interesting area of study could be made.

The secondary sex ratio expresses the proportion of the sexes at the time of birth. Strictly speaking, this term is used properly only with reference to the sex of the young at birth, but frequently it is made to include the proportion of the sexes during intrauterine development, from the time the sex can first be known to the time of birth. For reasons that will become obvious shortly, this use should be avoided.

The tertiary sex ratio is of no great concern for the present discussion, although it is important in vital statistics, where it is used to express the proportion of the sexes when they reach procreative age.

We have agreed that, if the theory of the chromosomal type of sex determination is correct, we should find the two sexes about equal in the primary and secondary ratios. Table 1-2 summarizes the sex ratios at birth of a variety of mammals and birds, as recorded by a number of investigators. Large numbers of observations are involved in most of the cases tabulated.

One is struck by the great variation in the sex ratios of the animals listed and particularly by the deviations from equality even within the same species. Before we attempt to interpret these observations, let us see what factors have been found to modify sex ratios experimentally. In a classical study Helen Dean King found that sex ratios may be modified by genetic selection. She started with a strain of rats that had a secondary sex ratio of about 110. By combining inbreeding with

Table 1-2. Secondary sex ratios commonly observed in some birds and mammals

SPECIES	NUMBER OBSERVED	PERCENT MALES (HIGH RATIO)	NUMBER OBSERVED	PERCENT MALES (LOW RATIO)
Canary	68	77.9	200	43.5
Dog	1,400	55.4	6,878	52.4
Pig	2,357	52.8	16,233	48.8
Mouse	2,903	52.6	1,464	44.4
Rat	1,001	51.9	1,862	46.2
Cattle	4,900	51.8	982	48.6
Guinea pig	7,989	51.7	2,014	49.4
Horse	25,560	49.9	135,826	49.1
Sheep	50,685	49.5	8,965	49.2
Domestic chicken	20,037	48.6	2,501	46.8

SOURCE: Data modified from various sources, especially from Lawrence. 1941. *Quart. Rev. Biol.*, 16:35.

selection, she was able to split this strain into two substrains, which differed significantly in their sex ratios. By the twenty-fifth generation of inbreeding and selection, the sex ratio of the high strain had risen to 124 and that of the low strain had dropped to 82. This and other experiments show that the sex ratios of animals can be modified by genetic selection. The mechanism through which this is accomplished remains unknown. It is improbable that genetic selection modifies the role of the entire sex chromosome in sex determination. It is more likely that the effect is produced by selection for a greater or lesser number of the sex genes postulated by Bridges as carried on the autosomes and the X chromosomes. By selection for a larger number of sex genes for maleness on the autosomes, the sex ratio may shift in the direction of an increasing proportion of males; selection for fewer maleness genes would cause the ratio to go in the direction of a preponderance of females.

The frequency of ejaculations by the male also seems to have an effect on the secondary ratio. Stallions that were used frequently for mating produced a high sex ratio of 101, whereas those used one-third as often produced a ratio of 97. Seasonal factors seem to influence the ratio in mice. In this species Parkes found a sex ratio of 98.9 during the months from March to June, of 133.2 during the months from July to October. Johansson, making a similar comparison in dairy cattle, found no such difference.

The ratio may change with increasing parity of the female. The ratio in rats drops from 122 for the first litter to 103.1 for the fourth. However, Parkes found the opposite effect in mice: the first birth had a sex ratio of 124.3 but subsequent births rose to 150.0.

These findings suggest strongly that both genetic and environmental (internal and external) factors are capable of modifying the secondary sex ratio. It is reasonable to suspect that the so-called "normal" sex ratios (Table 1-2) were subjected to modifying influences of one kind or another and that therein may lie the explanation for the great variability in ratios found both between and within species. In studying the sex ratios of a population, one should find the "normal" sex ratios that are typical of the population, rather than assume that they should be near equality and should agree with the ratios found by other investigators. One should also remember that some species have high "normal" ratios (dog: 110–124), others low "normal" ratios (horse, sheep, and chicken all have ratios of less than 100).

One disturbing finding has yet to be explained satisfactorily. It has been found repeatedly in human beings that the sex ratio of abortions is extremely high and that at certain stages of pregnancy three or four times as many male as female fetuses may be aborted. Studies of fetal ratios in domestic animals have shown that during the early stages of gestation there are significantly more males than females among the conceptuses. A Wisconsin study, for instance, showed that the ratio of fetal calves 5–10 centimeters in length was 193, or 66 percent males. It decreased to about 100 near term. Similar observations have been made on the ratios of sheep and pigs. There are two plausible explanations for the excess of males in human abortions and the preponderance of males during early phases of gestation in domestic animals. It is possible that the primary sex ratio is not equality, and that more males than females are conceived. If the intrauterine mortality is primarily at the expense of the male, the excess of males is eliminated and the sex ratio approaches equality by the time of parturition. If this assumption is made, it does not invalidate the chromosome theory of sex determination, but it calls for the further assumption that in mammals the two types of sperm are not produced in equal numbers, or that, if they are produced in equal numbers, the Y-bearing sperm has a much greater change of fertilizing the egg than the X-bearing sperm. Although either or both of these suppositions are possible, there is no experimental evidence for them.

The second explanation, which fits the facts of the case and which seems probable, assumes that the primary ratio is equality but that during the early embryonal stages, during which the sex of the conceptuses cannot be readily determined, embryonal mortality is primarily at the expense of the female. By the time the sex can be determined, the ratio is in favor of the male. From then on until parturition, fetal mortality occurs mostly at the expense of the male; so, by the time of birth, equality has been re-established. There is need for much additional work on this interesting subject, but what is needed most is a method that would permit the routine determination of the primary sex ratio.

Many attempts have been made to control sex. None of the attempts —electrophoretic, mechanical, or chemical separation of the X- and Y-bearing sperm—has succeeded. A solution of this problem would have an enormous significance to the field of animal breeding, for in many branches of livestock production males are unwanted. A fortune awaits the scientist who finds a practical method of regulating the proportion of the sexes without resorting to the introduction of lethal genes and thus reducing the productivity of the mother. It should be remembered that any method that succeeds in domestic animals will also work in man. Whether ethically, morally, and politically we are sufficiently advanced to use such a method wisely, if it is made available, remains to be seen.

Sex Chromatin

We have said that the primary sex ratio is only a theoretical concept since it is virtually impossible to diagnose the sex at the time of conception. This statement is essentially correct, but it has to be modified to some extent, for it has recently become possible to determine the genetic sex of very young embryos by use of the "sex chromatin." This mass of chromatin is present in the somatic nuclei of all the mammals studied with the possible exception of rodents. The sex chromatin is about 1 micron in diameter, is feulgen-positive, and is usually found lying against the inner surface of the nuclear membrane, although in nerve cells it may lie adjacent to the nucleolus (Fig. 1-1). The sex chromatin is present only in genetic females and is thought to be derived from the fused heteropyknotic portions of the two X-chromosomes.

The sex chromatin can be used for diagnostic purposes in a variety of ways. The genetic sex of embryos as small as one millimeter in length can be determined before sexual differentiation and long before the gonads have differentiated to the point where sexing can be done histologically. The sex chromatin is even present in primordial germ

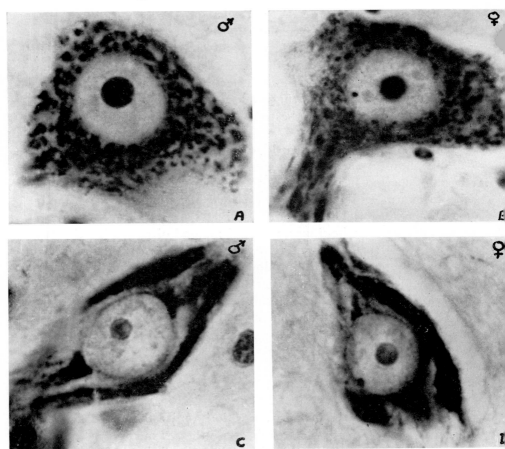

Figure 1-1. *Sex chromatin is present in all the cells of females and absent from those of males. (Reproduced by permission from Moore and others, 1957, J. Exp. Zool., 135: 101, and Prince and others, 1955, Anat. Rec., 122: 153.)*

A. A cell from the spinal cord of a normal bull calf.

B. A similar cell from a heifer calf; note the chromatin mass at nine o'clock.

C. A nerve cell from a male monkey.

D. A nerve cell from a female monkey; the sex chromatin lies against the cell membrane.

cells before they have arrived at the genital ridge. It has recently become possible to predict the sex of human babies from biopsy specimens of embryonal tissue without obvious damage to the fetus or to the normal course of gestation.

In adult human intersexes, in whom both sexes, phenotypically, may be equally well developed, it is possible to determine the genetic sex from skin biopsies and from oral or nasal smears and to decide accordingly whether hormonal or surgical therapy should be in the direction of maleness or femaleness.

The discovery of the sex chromatin is too new to permit an evaluation of the contributions that such studies can make to our understanding of early sex differentiations. Probably most important is that the sex chromatin, as a diagnostic criterion of genetic sex, permits much greater assurance of accuracy of sexing in studies concerned with the embryology of sex. Only additional studies will show whether the sex chromatin is unalterably fixed at the time of conception or can be modified by the action of sex hormones. Apparently, as in freemartins, the sex chromatin is not modified because genetic females are exposed to the prolonged action of male sex hormone. Similar studies in human intersexes are now in progress. The sex chromatin now appears to be a useful tool for the study of sex embryology, sex differentiation, primary sex ratios, and intersexuality.

SUMMARY

This chapter briefly summarizes present thinking on the subject of sex ratios. (Students interested in details should consult the works of Lawrence and Crew, in that order.) Sex ratios deviate from equality frequently and significantly; this deviation may be caused by a variety of factors, such as genetic selection, season, age of dam, parity of dam, and frequency of ejaculation by the male. Because the internal and external environment influences sex ratios, it is incorrect to assume that the "normal" sex ratio must be 50/50. The sex ratios of dogs, pigs, cattle, and rodents are normally high; those of horses, sheep, and chickens are normally low. The origin of sex chromosome aneuploidy is discussed and it is pointed out that in both men and women individuals with the genotypes XXY or XO, reproductive or endocrine disorders are very common. Whether sex chromosome aneuploidy occurs in other animals as frequently as in man is not known. The sex chromatin serves as a diagnostic feature of the genetic sex of embryos before sex differentiation as well as of normal and intersexual adult mammals.

REFERENCES

C. B. Bridges. 1939. "The genetics of sex in drosophila" in *Sex and Internal Secretions,* 2nd ed. Williams & Wilkins (Baltimore).

F. A. E. Crew. 1952. "The factors which determine sex" in Marshall's *Physiology of Reproduction,* Vol. II. Longmans (New York).

P. S. Lawrence. 1941. "The sex ratio, fertility and ancestral longevity." *Quart. Rev. Biol.,* **16**:35.

B. Lennox. 1956. "Nuclear sexing: A review incorporating some personal observations." *Scottish Med. J.,* 1:97.

H. Nowakowski and W. Lenz. 1961. "Genetic aspects of male hypogonadism" in *Recent Progress in Hormone Research.* Vol. XVII. Academic Press, New York and London.

R. Pearl. 1939. *The Natural History of Populations.* Oxford (London).

C. Tietze 1948. "A note on the sex ratio of abortions." *Human Biol.,* 20:156.

chapter 2

The Structure of Male
and Female Reproductive Systems

The Indifferent Stage

Though the genotypic sex of an individual is fixed at the time of fertilization, the reproductive systems of both sexes go through a stage of embryonal development during which it is difficult, if not impossible, to tell the sexes apart by either gross or microscopic examination. This period is known as the indifferent stage. In this stage all *Anlagen* for subsequent differentiation into complete male and female systems are present in a rudimentary form; the blueprint, as it were, is finished. All the materials for the later elaboration of the fittings and furnishings of the structures are present, but no attempt is made to arrange the internal furnishings permanently until final orders are received for the emphasis of either male or female aspects of the different structures. This state of affairs makes it possible to discuss the early development of the reproductive systems of both sexes together without distinguishing between them.

The question whether hormones secreted by embryonal glands cause differentiation of sex during embryonal development is of great interest, but cannot be answered with any finality at the present time. It has been shown that embryonal testes of both bulls and rats contain the male sex hormone, androgen; but no androgen is present in the urine of postnatal calves. The thyroid gland of larval amphibians, if macerated *in situ*, will induce metamorphosis of the larva into an adult animal. If the gland is left undisturbed, it does not cause metamorphosis until a considerably later time in the life of the larva. These and other facts argue for the assumption that embryonal glands are capable of producing their specific hormones, but that these hormones are not released into the circulation of the embryo, or at least that they are not released in sufficient quantities to have any discernible effect on their specific target organs.

Other experiments have shown that tissues that depend on hormones in the adult animal, for maintenance and normal function, may differentiate in the embryo without the aid of hormones. This is suggested by experiments carried out by C. R. Moore, in which pouch young of the opossum were castrated. The accessory glands and structures developed and differentiated normally in spite of the absence of the gonads and hence of androgen. This led Moore to the idea that during the early stages of differentiation the sex apparatus does not depend on hormonal stimulation, but grows under the impetus of the "genetic potential" (whatever that may mean). Jost's objection to this interpretation is that embryonal hormones may initiate differentiation but may not be necessary to its maintenance once it has begun.

In general, maternal steroid hormones cross the placental barrier

Figure 2-1.   *The role of genetic and endocrine factors in sexual differentiation. The development from the indifferent stage through the proliferative stage apparently occurs without hormonal stimulation. Hormones begin to control the differentiation of the gonads and of the gonad-dependent structures shortly after birth.*

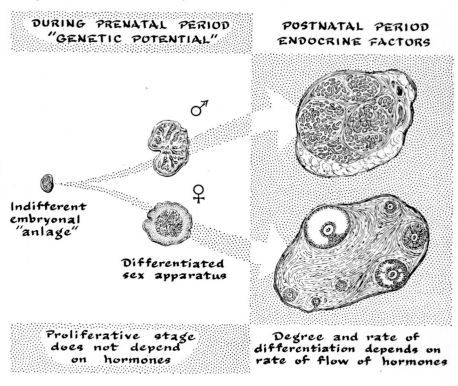

quite easily while the protein and polypeptide hormones do not. (One exception to this rule, to be noted later, is the pregnant mare serum which is produced in the endometrial cups of the uterus and which drastically affects the genitalia of the fetus.) The interesting work of Jost and his collaborators has shown that the glands of the fetal rat and rabbit do depend on hypophyseal trophic substances of fetal origin. Thus, the fetal thyroids and adrenals both atrophy after *in utero* decapitation (that is, "hypophysectomy") of the fetus. These experiments show that the fetal hypophysis does produce trophic hormones which stimulate their respective end organs and that the appropriate trophic hormones of maternal origin are either unable to cross the placental barrier or are of the wrong configuration—so far as the fetus is concerned—to be stimulatory. The latter possibility is partly ruled out because Jost's group established that the glycogen content of the liver increases spectacularly during the last third of pregnancy in rats and rabbit fetuses. In decapitated fetuses this increase in liver glycogen is absent but it can be caused to occur if the decapitated young are injected *in utero* with a combination of adrenal steroid hormones and growth hormone. (Prolactin can be substituted for growth hormone, but much larger quantities of it than of growth hormone are required and it remains unclear whether its ability to cause glycogenesis can be explained on the basis of its possible contamination with growth hormone or whether it is due to its conjectured similarity in physiologic action to somatotrophin.) These findings show that not only does the fetal hypophysis secrete and release trophic hormones but that the fetal end organs are capable of responding.

A graphic summary of the genetic and endocrine factors that may enter into the prenatal and postnatal differentiation of the reproductive systems is shown in Figure 2-1.

Let us now consider the indifferent reproductive system and its subsequent development.

Differentiation of the Systems

Origin of Germ Cells

It is now well established that germ cells originate extragonadally in the yolk-sac endoderm and that they migrate from there by ameboid movements (in mammals) or via the circulatory system (in the chick)

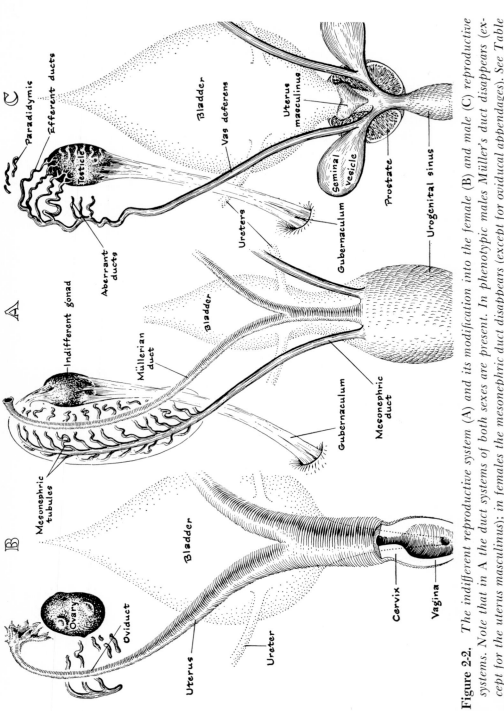

Figure 2-2. The indifferent reproductive system (A) and its modification into the female (B) and male (C) reproductive systems. Note that in A the duct systems of both sexes are present. In phenotypic males Müller's duct disappears (except for the uterus masculinus); in females the mesonephric duct disappears (except for oviducal appendages). See Table 2-1 for details. (Modified and redrawn from Blom and Christensen, 1947, Skandinavisk Veterinaztidskrift.)

Table 2-1. Homologies of male and female reproductive systems

INDIFFERENT	MALE	FEMALE
	INTERNAL GENITALIA	
Gonad	Testis Rete testis	Ovary Rete ovarii*
Mesonephric tubules	Vas efferens Paradidymis* Vas aberrans*	Epoophoron* Paroophoron*
Mesonephric duct	Epididymis Vas deferens Ejaculatory duct	Duct part of epoophoron* (Gartner's duct)
	Seminale vesicle Appendix of the epididymis*	
Müllerian duct	Appendage of testis*	Appendage of the ovary* (hydatid) Fimbria of oviduct Oviduct
	Prostatic utricle* (uterus masculinus)	Uterus Vagina [all or part?]
Urogenital sinus	Prostatic, membranous, and cavernous urethra	Urethra Vestibule Vagina [in part?]
	Bulbo-urethral glands (Cowper's glands) Prostate	Vestibular glands (Bartholin's glands) Para-urethral glands*
	EXTERNAL GENITALIA	
Genital tubercle	Glans penis Corpus penis	Glans clitoris Corpus clitoridis
Urethral folds	Raphe of scrotum and penis	Labia minora
Labioscrotal swellings	Scrotum	Labia majora

* Rudimentary.

to the genital ridge, where the first microscopically demonstrable aggregation of germ cells occurs. Embryological analysis of several species shows quite clearly that the formation of a gonad depends on the arrival of germ cells and that the genital ridge alone is incapable of developing into anything resembling a gonad. If the germ cells are prevented from migrating to the genital ridge, either experimentally or by accidents of development, the afflicted animal will be born without one or both of the gonads. Unilateral and bilateral agonadism are not rare and have been seen in several species (for one such case in the female pig see Fig. 12-1E, p. 289).

Primordial germs cells are able to cause endodermal and mesodermal cells to enclose them. This ability is of interest because it permits germ cells, after they arrive at the genital ridge, to form follicle cells. The genital ridge itself consists of a mesenchymal thickening covered by mesothelium. The latter gradually thickens and becomes the germinal epithelium. The cells within this epithelium differentiate, the larger ones becoming the primordia of the gonads. If a gonad is to become a testis, the cells in the germinal epithelium grow into the underlying mesenchymal tissue and form there chordlike masses, which eventually become the seminiferous tubules of the testis. If a gonad is to become an ovary, the primordial germ cells grow into the mesenchyme, where they become differentiated into ovarian follicles containing ova.

Origin of the Duct System

It is significant that the genital ridge lies close to the mesonephric kidney, which, at this stage of embryonal development, is still the functional kidney. The significance of this proximity is that the differentiating gonad utilizes parts of the duct system of the embryonal kidney for its own excurrent ducts. The mesonephric tubules and the mesonephric ducts are used very extensively by the male, in fact, for its permanent duct system; in the female, however, all these ducts are seen only as rudiments. Because the structures of the reproductive systems of the two sexes arise from indifferent rudiments in the embryo, we speak of them as being homologous in the two sexes. It would lead us into too much detail to discuss the development of the male and female duct systems from the indifferent to the differentiated state. The origins of the various systems are summarized in the table of homologues (Table 2-1) and in Figure 2-2.

Origin of the External Genitalia

Like the gonads, the external genitalia develop from a stage in which the indifferent homologue possesses all the rudimentary anatomic features of both sexes. As development progresses, some of these features become accentuated while others remain undeveloped, according to the sex-genetic destiny of the embryo. The earliest sign is the genital swelling, which later differentiates into the genital tubercle and the genital folds. If the embryo is genetically destined to become a male, the genital tubercle greatly elongates to become the penis. The penis is partly enclosed by the prepuce, which develops from the genital folds. The genital swellings enlarge to form the scrotal pouches. If the embryo is destined to become a female, the genital tubercle becomes the clitoris, which is the homologue of the penis. The genital folds turn into the labia minora and the genital swellings into the labia majora. The opening of the urogenital sinus in the embryo does not undergo any changes in the female (in contrast to the male), but persists almost in its original position. The prepuce is rudimentary in females.

Aside from illustrating the opportunism of organisms in utilizing parts of embryonal organ systems for subsequent use in postnatal life, this discussion should serve as a reminder that both sexes develop from an indifferent stage and that each sex carries, as rudiments, the organ systems of the opposite sex. As a rule, these rudiments remain such and do not impede the normal function of the prevalent organ system, which is typical of the genotypic sex of the individual. Occasionally, however, mistakes do happen; the system that is intended to be rudimentary differentiates and, under the influence of hormones, gains considerable prominence. This may lead to aberrations or obstructions of the duct system or, if the gonads are involved, to intersexuality, which is not rare in animals. These aberrations may be slight and therefore harmless, but they may become great enough to lead to complete sterility. To this problem we shall return later in greater detail.

The Female Reproductive System

The reproductive system of the female consists of the ovaries and the duct system. The latter not only receives the eggs ovulated by the ovary and conveys them to the site of ultimate implantation, the uterus, but also receives the sperm and conveys it to the site of fertilization, the oviduct. The duct system of birds differs in all essentials from that of mammals and will be discussed separately.

In mammals the ovaries and the duct portion of the reproductive system are connected with each other, and are attached to the body wall, by a series of ligaments. The ovary receives its blood and nerve supply through the hilus, which is also attached to the uterus. The oviduct lies in a fold of the mesosalpinx, which in turn is attached to the mesovarian ligament. This ligament is continuous with the inguinal ligament, which is a homologue of the gubernaculum of the testes. Another part of this ligament forms the round ligament of the uterus, which extends from the uterus to the inguinal region.

Mammalian Ovaries

In all mammals the ovaries are paired. They remain near the kidneys, where they first differentiate, and they do not undergo the elaborate descent that is typical of the testes. The free surface of the ovary (which is not taken up by the hilus or the mesovarium) bulges into the body cavity.

The size of the ovary depends largely on the age and reproductive state of the female. Because the growth of the ovary and the development of its histological components are controlled by hormones from the pituitary gland, much can be learned about the quality and quantity of the hormones acting on the ovary from its size and histological appearance. For larger animals, microscopic and macroscopic examination of the ovaries is especially useful in diagnosis of abnormalities of the ovary-pituitary relationship. In laboratory animals this relation is the key to the bioassay of pituitary hormones.

The shape of the ovary varies greatly with the species and depends largely on whether the females are habitually litter-bearing (polytocous) or single-bearing (monotocous). In the former the ovary is usually berry-shaped; in the latter it is ovoid. In the mare the ovary is kidney-shaped, with a distinct depression (the ovulation fossa) on one surface. It was once thought that all ovulations occurred from this depression (hence the name), but now it is known that ovulations may occur in other areas as well.

Histology of the Mammalian Ovary.   For the purposes of this discussion a brief summary of the histology of the ovary will suffice. The two most important components of the ovary are the follicle and the corpus luteum.

THE OVARIAN FOLLICLE.   Ovarian follicles go through three stages of growth. In the embryo, as well as in the postnatal female, the great majority of them are primary follicles. They form a thick layer under the tunica albuginea and are distinguished by the fact that the ova contained in them have no vitelline membrane. The ova are surrounded by many layers of follicular cells, which form the granulosa layer of the more mature follicle. When an ovum acquires a membrane (the zona pellucida) and when the follicle has grown, it becomes a secondary follicle. At this stage the follicle has also assumed a more oval shape and has moved away from the cortex toward the medullary portion of the ovary. Eventually a clear, fluid-filled space (the antrum) forms around the ovum and the granulosa cell layers surrounding it. The fluid is called follicular fluid or liquor folliculi. Follicles with antra are called tertiary follicles, the major difference between them and mature Graafian follicles being in size. As a follicle grows, the antrum enlarges until it extends through the whole thickness of the ovarian cortex. The mature follicle, distended by accumulated follicular fluid, protrudes like a blister above the free surface of the ovary (Fig. 2-3A).

At this stage the egg is embedded in a solid mass of follicular cells forming the cumulus oopherus (or discus proligerus), which protrudes into the fluid-filled antrum. In most follicles the cumulus is located on the surface opposite the side that will rupture at ovulation. Occasionally, however, in histological preparations, one finds a cumulus on the side that will rupture. Whether such follicles ovulate normally is not known.

The other important cellular components of the follicle are the granulosa cells, which line the antrum and form the cumulus oophorus, and the corona radiata immediately around the egg (Fig. 2-3B). In some animals the corona cells remain attached to the ovum after ovulation; in others the eggs are ovulated naked. The significance of this distinction is not known. The granulosa cell layer is separated from the theca folliculi (which consists of the theca interna and the theca externa) by the basement membrane and connective tissue cells. The granulosa cells and theca cells play an important role in the formation of the corpus luteum, and we shall return to them in that connection.

In addition to the normally developing follicles, an ovary always has a certain number of degenerating follicles and follicles undergoing atresia. Follicular atresia normally accompanies the formation and maturation of follicles; it becomes abnormal only when large numbers of follicles become atretic. The endocrine causes and the significance of atresia will be discussed later. We simply note here that it always begins with the ovum. In an otherwise normal-appearing follicle, impending atresia is signaled by the staining reaction of the membrane around the eggs. The membrane takes on a deep blue or purple stain and stands

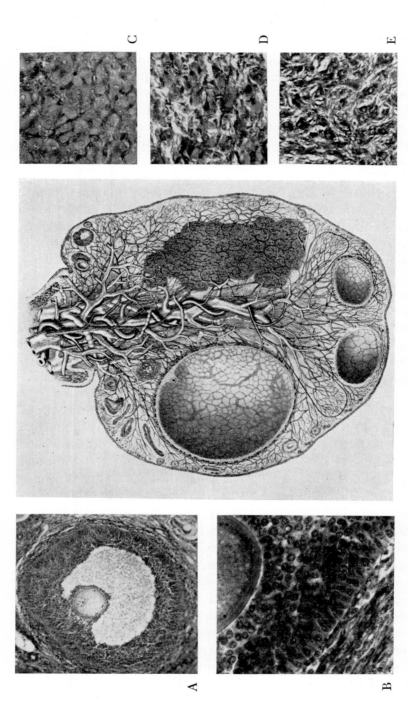

Figure 2-3. *General architecture of a mammalian ovary. (Picture of ovary by permission of Dr. Eugen Seiferle.)*

A. Tertiary follicle.   B. Ovum, granulosa layer, and thea folliculi layer.

C, D, E. Three stages in the life of a corpus luteum: C, height of activity of a corpus luteum of a ewe 8 days afterovulation; D, 12 days after ovulation; E, 16 days old (a corpus albicans). Note that with increasing age the luteal cells disappear and become replaced by connective tissue.

out very prominently in the otherwise normally staining follicle. In later stages of atresia, other histological symptoms of disintegration appear: accumulation of fat droplets and of coarse granules inside the egg; shrinkage or collapse of the egg itself; detachment of the ovum from the surrounding granulosa cells; and eventual degeneration of the granulosa cells. Atresia may affect follicles in all three stages of development, but in domestic animals it is most commonly seen in tertiary follicles.

CORPORA LUTEA AND ALBICANTIA.   After ovulation the follicular cavity is filled with blood and lymph. In some species (swine) these fluids distend the ovulated follicle so much that for from five to seven days after rupture it is larger than at any time before. In other species (usually in sheep and cattle) the accumulation of fluids is insignificant, and the follicle is smaller than it was before ovulation. Gradually the blood clot is resorbed as luteinization progresses, and eventually the space is filled by the corpus luteum. Histologically, the corpus luteum is composed mostly of granulosa cells, but theca cells also may contribute to its formation. The increase in the size of the corpus luteum occurs because of the hypertrophy and hyperplasia of the granulosa and theca cells. Except in women, these two cell types generally lose their identity in the formed corpus luteum.

As a corpus luteum passes the peak of its functional activity, more and more connective tissue, fat, and hyaline-like substances appear among the luteal cells. The whole corpus luteum gradually decreases in size, eventually becoming a barely visible scar on the surface of the ovary. It also loses its initial red-brown color and becomes white or pale brown. It is then called the corpus albicans (Fig. 2-3E).

OTHER STRUCTURES.   Occasionally, in the ovaries of pigs, sheep, cattle, and human beings, one sees a more or less elaborate duct system, which is usually confined to the medulla of the ovary. This system was traced out in the ovaries from a sheep and a pig and was found to end blindly. The ducts are remnants of the epoopheron, which may be lined by either tall-columnar or cuboidal epithelia. They do not interfere with normal reproduction.

In the granulosa layers of the follicles of many species one often sees small, dark-staining granules that form the center of a stellate arrangement of granulosa cells. These granules (the Call-Exner bodies) may be very numerous in the ovaries of some females and completely absent from other females of the same species. Their significance is unknown.

In female swine, in which an intensive study of them was made, there is no apparent correlation between their presence and reproductive performance.

Avian Ovaries

The Rudimentary Right Ovary. In the great majority of Aves only the left ovary is functional. The right ovary is present in embryos and persists macroscopically visible for a few days after hatching. In adult females it persists only as a microscopic vestige. If the functional ovary is removed surgically or, as frequently happens, is destroyed by disease, the right rudiment enlarges and becomes functional. The age at which the removal of the functional ovary occurs determines the future development of the rudiment. If the ovary is removed from chickens less than twenty days old, the rudiment hypertrophies into a structure resembling a testis (Fig. 2-4A) and capable of spermatogenesis. However, because the Wolffian duct system does not develop in genetic females, there is no duct connection between the testis and the copulatory organ in the cloaca. The often-cited case of the celebrated hen that laid eggs and became the mother of chicks, then lost her ovary, differentiated the rudiment into a testis, and fathered a brood of chicks, is probably a canard. Theoretically, such versatility is, of course, possible; but it is highly improbable.

If the ovary is removed at a greater age, the rudiment develops into a functional ovary (Fig. 2-4B), complete with ova that are capable of being ovulated. Since, in the female, the Müllerian duct system is developed unilaterally, such females do not have an oviduct on the side of the rudimentary gonad, and there is no way to conduct the ovulated eggs to the outside. Operations at intermediate ages (as well as in a certain proportion at the other two ages) cause the rudiment to form an ovotestis in which the germ cells of both sexes are present but usually in an undifferentiated condition (Fig. 2-4C). If either a testis or an ovotestis is formed after the loss of the functional ovary, the genetic female develops all the sex characteristics of the male, including a large red comb, male plumage, crowing, and male copulatory behavior toward the normal female.

This ambisexual versatility of birds (it is not restricted to the Gallinaceae but has been recorded in ducks, songbirds, and many other kinds) has excited the imaginations of naturalists and folklorists for many centuries. Birds that had changed sex were described and specu-

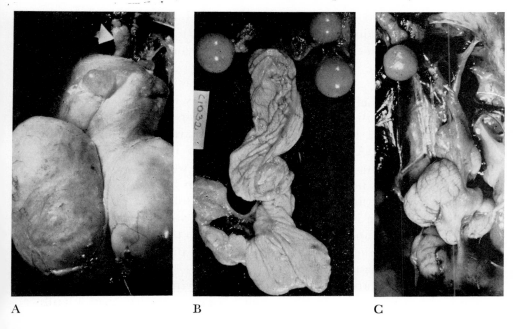

A   B   C

Figure 2-4. *Rudimentary gonads in sinestrally ovariectomized chickens. (From W. Kornfeld, Ph.D. Thesis, University of Ilinois, 1953.)*

   A. Testis (arrow). The oviduct is filled with coagulated albumen. (The large blister below the testicle is not a follicle but a cyst of the oviduct.)

   B. Ovary on right side (left side of picture) and regenerated normal ovary on left side, both containing mature follicles. In addition to a normal (large) oviduct, there is a small rudimentary oviduct on the right side.

   C. Ovotestis on right side (testis on top, follicle below).

lated on by Aristotle and had also been noted before his time. Until as late as the eighteenth century "hens that crow" and "cocks that lay eggs" have always been associated with the supernatural, either as indispensable appurtenances of sorcery and witchcraft or as portents of evil. The cockatrice, a basilisk whose breath or look was said to be fatal to men, was a serpent or lizard that was thought to have hatched from cock's eggs.

A wealth of biologically interesting secrets remains hidden in these sex changelings. It is not known why the age at operation plays a role in determining the fate of the rudimentary gonad. Neither is the chromosome constitution of the differentiated gonad of these genetically female intersexes known. Recently it has been found that, in the normal female with a functional ovary, the rudiment is prevented from developing by the estrogen secreted by the ovary. Immature females, even shortly after hatching, secrete enough estrogen to suppress the development of the rudiment. This is why the right gonad remains rudimentary as long as the ovary functions.

The Functional Left Ovary.   Morphologically the avian ovary differs from the mammalian ovary in that it consists of two major lobes. Within each lobe, large numbers of follicles are carried on follicular stalks (Fig. 2-5A). A more important difference is that the avian ovum contains a large quantity of yolk, compared to which the germinal portion of the egg is negligible in size. The avian follicle has no antrum and no follicular fluid, the ovum filling the follicular sac competely. The avian follicle is lined by granulosa cells, and the arrangement of the theca interna and externa is very similar to the arrangement found in mammals. In their histological appearance these cells are also very similar to their mammalian counterparts.

Avian follicles are probably the fastest-growing structures found in the higher vertebrates. Starting from a diameter of less than 1 millimeter and a weight of less than 100 milligrams, the ovum reaches a mature size and a weight of 18–20 grams in nine days. To accomplish this prodigious task of transportation and deposition of yolk material into the ovum, a very complex circulatory system has been developed. The main feature of this system is an enormous development of the venous supply, which is arranged in three concentric layers around the follicle, and which terminates in an extremely fine venous capillary network enveloping the growing ovum. In contrast, the arterial supply is poorly developed, the system apparently depending on getting the blood into the venous network, where it stays long enough to permit transfer of the yolk antecedents to the ovum (Fig. 2-5B). The mechanics of the transfer of lipoproteins through the membranes of the capillaries, the cells lining the follicle, and the vitelline membrane of the ovum have not been throughly investigated. It has been possible, with vital stain techniques, to demonstrate yolk precursors in the follicular circulatory system, in the granulosa cells, and, of course, inside the ovum. How these relatively enormous globules pass, apparently intact, from the capillaries into the granulosa cells and then through the vitelline membrane into the ovum, remains a mystery.

The intricate follicular circulatory system described serves primarily one of the larger follicles, but it is also utilized by smaller follicles, which grow in large numbers on the same follicular stalk on which the large follicle is growing. When the largest follicle ovulates, spiral

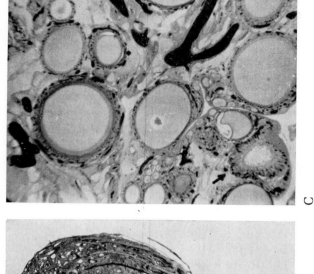

A

B

C

Figure 2-5. *Chicken ovaries.* (*From Nalbandov and James, 1949, Am. J. Anat., 85: 347.*)

A. The ovarian vein was injected with ink to show the vascular system. Typical complement of follicles, which are destined to ovulate in order of size. The largest follicle is ischemic, possibly because it would have ovulated within a few minutes if the hen had lived (see p. 138).

B. Resin cast of a large follicle to show the basket of veins enclosing the ovum; arteries are shown in black.

C. Histological detail of chicken ovary. The arrow (top right) points to an atretic follicle (frequently mistaken for an "avian corpus luteum." The ovary was injected with India ink to show the circulatory system.

arteries in its wall become constricted, largely because of the release of tension in the collapsed follicle wall. Thus the blood flow to the now emptly follicular sac is greatly reduced. This may be one reason why there is rarely if ever any bleeding into the lumen of the ovulated follicle, or even in the torn stigma through which the follicle is ovulated. The stigma itself is less vascular than the adjacent follicle wall but is by no means devoid of blood vessels. In spite of the reduced blood flow to the ovulated follicle sac, vascularization remains sufficient to permit rapid growth of the smaller follicles clustered along the follicle stalk. One of these is destined to enlarge more rapidly than the rest; as it enlarges, its blood system rapidly increases in complexity until it reaches ovulatory size and ruptures; then the whole process is repeated. Thus the major part of the intricate vascular system is used for a succession of follicles, which are growing on the follicular stalk and awaiting their turn until the circulatory system becomes available for their own rapid growth.

After ovulation an empty follicle shrinks but remains visible for a considerable time. No structure comparable to the mammalian corpus luteum is formed in birds, but the empty follicle seems to play a role in the reproductive cycle of chickens. More will be said about this in connection with the endocrinology of the chicken ovary. In at least two species of wild birds, the mallard and the pheasant, ovulated follicles persist in microscopically and macroscopically recognizable form for as long as ninety days after ovulation. One can therefore roughly estimate the seasonal egg production of these species by counting the number of ovulated follicles present in the ovary.

In chicken ovaries, large, clear interstitial cells are found in clusters close to the theca. Similar cells are found in the three types of rudimentary gonads. These cells degenerate after hypophysectomy. Because the hen secretes considerable amounts of androgen, there is the temptation to ascribe androgen secretion to these cells, but experimental data on this point are lacking, and it is equally plausible to assume that these clear cells secrete progesterone, which has been found in the blood of chickens; the possibility also remains that the clear cells have no secretory function at all.

The Duct System

The Mammalian Duct System.   The duct system in female mammals consists of the following parts: the oviducts, or Fallopian tubes; the uterus, including the uterine horns and the uterine body; the cervix; the vagina and the external genitalia (Fig. 2-6).

OVIDUCTS.   These paired tubes, the connecting tubes between ovaries and uterus, are long and convoluted derivatives of the Müllerian ducts. The ovarian end of an oviduct is flared out into a fimbria, or funnel, with fringed edges. In their natural position the fimbriae either envelop the ovaries or are very close to them. At the time of ovulation the fimbriated ends of the oviducts show great motility, which probably helps the egg to find its way into the oviduct. While the fimbria may not actually "massage" the ovary to aid the process of ovulation, as has been stated by some of the older anatomists describing the process, they can pick up eggs that have been lost in the body cavity or that have been ovulated from the opposite ovary. This has been demonstrated experimentally by unilateral castration of females and occlusion of the oviduct on the opposite side. Animals prepared in this way showed some fertility, thus indicating that the patent oviduct has the ability to pick up eggs ovulated by the contralateral ovary.

In some species the ovarian end of the oviduct forms a complete capsule, which encloses the ovary as in a sac. This sac (as opposed to the open, funnel-shaped fimbria) is called the bursa ovarii. In the rat and in the mouse the bursa is complete except for a small perforation in one wall. In the dog, the fox, and the mink, the bursa has a slit that is big enough to permit the ovary to pass through with ease. Some litter-bearing animals, such as those named above, have a bursa, but others, such as the pig and the rabbit, do not. The bursa undoubtedly improves an egg's chance of arriving in the uterus; but most animals have no bursa, and the reproductive waste due to loss of eggs between the ovary and the uterus is no greater among such animals than among animals that have a bursa.

Histology of the oviduct.   The lumen of the oviduct is lined by a much-folded mucous membrane (Fig. 2-6A). The epithelium lining the lumen is simple-columnar and ciliated. The cilia beat away from the ovary, creating a current within the oviduct toward the uterus. Some of the nonciliated cells are transformed into goblet cells, and there are no other glands in the oviduct. In rabbits, eggs acquire a layer of secretions during the trip through the oviduct. This layer was once thought to be albuminous but is now known to be a polysaccharide. The eggs of most other common mammals remain uncoated.

The musculature of the oviduct consists of the inner circular layer and the outer longitudinal layer. Both peristalsis and antiperistalsis

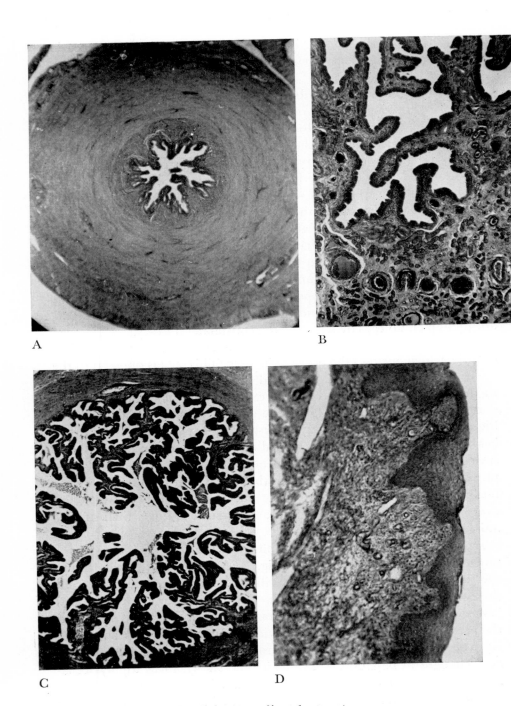

Figure 2-6. *Structure of the mammalian duct system.*

A. Oviduct. B. Uterus. C. Cervix. D. Vagina.

take place; the latter occurs less commonly and may be an artifact. Eggs spend most of the time required for their passage through the oviduct in the ovarian half of the duct, and it is there that fertilization takes place. Fertilization does not take place in the uterus, as is sometimes assumed.

UTERUS. The uterus usually consists of two horns and a body. The whole organ is attached to the pelvic and abdominal walls by the broad ligament of the uterus. Through this ligament the uterus receives its blood and nerve supplies. The outer layer of the broad ligament forms the round ligament of the uterus.

Variations in uterine anatomy. In the Didelphia the two halves of the duct system have separate external openings (two vaginae, hence the name "didelphia'), two cervices, and two separate and unconnected uterine horns. This arrangement is found in all pouch-bearing animals, such as the platypus and the opossum. Adapting itself to this peculiarity of the female, the male has a forked penis, which is capable of entering the two vaginae simultaneously, giving rise to the well-known superstition that copulation in the opossum is accomplished through the nostrils.

None of the common laboratory and domestic animals has two vaginae, but there is a great variety of peculiarities in the uterine anatomy of these mammals. The types most commonly encountered are compared and described in Figure 2-7.

Abnormalities in uterine anatomy are common, and reversions of complex types to the simpler and more primitive conditions from which they evolved have been recorded in all species. In primates, for example, bipartite, bicornuate, and even duplex uteri occur occasionally; women with two cervices and duplex uteri have been known to conceive in the two horns separately to ovulations in two different intermenstrual periods twenty-eight days apart. Cows, sheep, and pigs with two cervices and two completely separate horns are also occasionally encountered. These reversions to the more primitive types of duct systems do not seem to interfere with fertility.

Histology of the uterus. The uterine wall consists of the following layers: (1) the serous membrane, which covers the hole viscus; (2) the myometrium, which itself consists of three layers—the internal circular muscle, the external longitudinal muscle, and, separating the muscle layers, the vascular layer; (3) the endometrium, which consists of the epithelial lining of the lumen, the glandular layer, and the connective tissue.

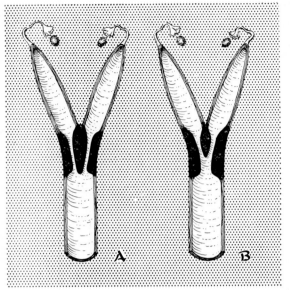 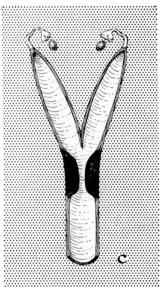

Duplex uterus: two cervixes, no uterine body, horns completely separated.

A. Rat, mouse, rabbit.

B. Guinea pig.

Bicornuate uterus: one cervix, uterine body very small.

C. Pig, insectivores.

Figure 2-7. *Comparison of the anatomy of the four basic types of uterus.*

The myometrium is usually the thickest of the three layers. Its vascular layer carries the extremely important blood vessels supplying the uterus. The smooth muscle cells in the myometrium are capable of increasing greatly in length during pregnancy; they are also responsive to hormones, which, at parturition and occasionally at other times, cause uterine contractions.

The epithelium lining the lumen of the uterus is simple-columnar. In women some patches of the epithelium may bear cilia, which are said to beat toward the cervix, but no cilia have been seen in the uteri of other mammals.

The uterine glands are the most important component of the endometrium. The glands are tubular invaginations of the epithelium, and they too are lined with simple-columnar epithelium. The distal ends of the glands may be either straight or convoluted, depending on the stage of the estrous cycle at which they are observed. The changes occurring in the glands and their function will be discussed in detail in

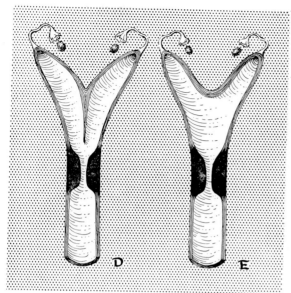

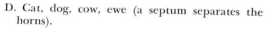

Bipartite uterus: one cervix, uterine body prominent.

D. Cat, dog, cow, ewe (a septum separates the horns).

E. Mare (uterine body especially prominent).

Simplex uterus: one cervix, body very prominent, horns absent.

F. Primates.

Chapter 4. In ruminants special areas of the uterine surface are for the future attachment of the placenta. These are called the cotyledonary areas; no glands are found underneath the cotyledons.

CERVIX.   The cervix is a sphincter muscle that lies between the uterus and the vagina. The anatomy of the cervix varies in different mammals, but in most of them the lumen is interrupted by transverse interlocking ridges called annular rings, which are developed to different degrees of prominence. Annular rings are very prominent in the cow, less so in the pig, and least so in the mare.

Histology of the cervix.   The lumen of the cervix is lined by tall-columnar epithelium. Goblet cells are present in the mucosa, which is so intricately folded and branched that it has an enormous secretory surface. The secretion is a mucus, which changes in amount and viscosity with the stages of the cycle. The intricate folds look like a fern leaf and give the cervix the characteristic appearance seen under the microscope. The myometrium of the cervix is very rich in dense fibrous tissue, has a large number of smooth muscle cells, and includes much collagenous and elastic tissue.

Function of the cervix. The main function of the cervix is to close the uterine lumen against microscopic and macroscopic intruders. The cervical canal is closed at all times except during parturition. In pigs, castration and progesterone cause considerable relaxation of the cervix, whereas estrogen causes the greatest contraction of the sphincter muscle and thus a tightening of the cervical lumen (Fig. 2-8). In pregnant animals the cervical mucus hardens and seals off the canal by forming the cervical plug. Immediately before parturition this plug liquefies, probably under hormonal influence, and shortly thereafter the cervix as a whole relaxes (for the hormonal control of this effect see Chapter 10). Breaking the cervical seal in pregnant cows usually leads to abortion or mummification of the fetus. Apparently this effect is due to bacterial invasion of the uterine lumen, for it can be prevented by

Figure 2-8. *Degree of opening of the cervical canal of pigs during the estrous cycle as measured by the diameter of the rod that can be inserted into the lumen. The dotted line shows that injection of estrogen (E 1, 2, and 3 mg daily) hastens closure of the lumen somewhat. (From J. C. Smith, M.S. Thesis, University of Illinois, 1955.)*

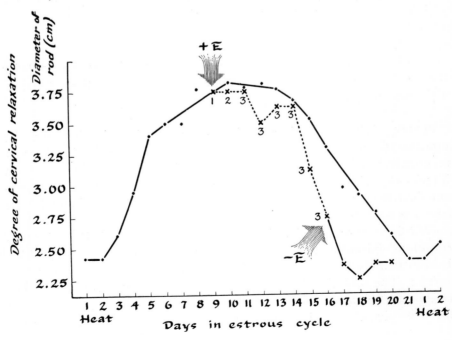

antibiotics given when the cervical seal is broken. It is important to remember, nevertheless, that intrauterine artificial insemination of cows that show heat after conception may lead to interruption of pregnancy.

VAGINA AND EXTERNAL GENITALIA. The vagina can be divided into two parts: the vestibule (the outermost part of the vagina) and the posterior vagina (extending from the urethral opening to the cervix). The muscular coat is less well developed in the vagina than in the other portions of the duct system. It consists of a thin layer of longitudinal fibers and a thicker layer of circular fibers. Much loose and dense connective tissue, well supplied with venous plexus, nerve bundles, and small groups of nerve cells, is characteristic of the vagina.

In normally cycling females the epithelial lining of the vagina undergoes periodic changes, which are controlled by hormones secreted by the ovaries. The epithelium may be low-cuboidal or stratified-squamous, depending on the stage of the cycle at which it is examined. The histology of the vagina in most mammals, especially in those with short estrous cycles, has been found to reflect quite faithfully the events that take place in the ovaries. This important relationship—between ovarian cycles and changes in vaginal histology—will be discussed in greater detail in Chapter 4.

There are no glands in the vagina. The mucus normally found in its lumen, which becomes especially copious in females in heat, originates largely in the cervix, whence it flows into the vaginal lumen.

In virginal females there is a transverse fold, the hymen, which forms the border between the anterior part of the vagina and the vestibule. The hymen has a core of thin connective tissue, which is covered with stratified-squamous epithelium. Normally it is torn and disappears by the time reproductive age is reached, but occasionally it may persist in mature females because of unusual toughness and may prevent normal copulation. In such cases it can be cut.

The external genitalia comprise the clitoris, the labia majora and minora, and certain glands that open into the vaginal vestibule. The clitoris is the embryological homologue of the penis (Table 2-1) and consists of two small erectile cavernous bodies ending in the rudimentary glans clitoris. The paired glands of Bartholin, the vestibular glands, open on the inner surface of the labia minora. They are tubo-alveolar glands and closely resemble the bulbo-urethral glands of the male. They secrete a lubricating mucus.

The labia minora have a core of spongy connective tissue and are covered with stratified-squamous epithelium. Many large sebaceous glands are found on their surface. The labia minora are most prominent in human females, are quite small in domestic animals, and are almost completely missing in laboratory mammals.

The labia majora are folds of skin with a large amount of fatty tissue and a thin layer of smooth muscle. The outer surface is covered with hair, and the inner surface is smooth and hairless. On both surfaces there are many sweat and sebaceous glands. The outer genitalia are well supplied with sensory nerve endings, which play an important role during sexual excitation of the female. The clitoris is capable of limited erection during the sex act, and the labia, because of an increased flow of blood, become extremely turgid.

The Avian Duct System.   As we have seen, the mammalian duct system consists of several morphologically separate parts, which differ in circumference and in external and internal architecture. In contrast, the duct system of birds is a tube of almost uniform diameter with a single unilateral distention near the cloaca (Fig. 2-9). Furthermore, whereas in mammals the duct system is paired, in the great majority of birds only the left half of the Müllerian duct system persists; the right half degenerates completely or persists only in rudimentary, usually nonpatent form. There are, however, exceptions to this rule; in certain Raptores both sides of the duct system persist. In chickens and in other birds one finds occasional individuals (or even genetic strains of chickens) in which both sides of the duct system are developed and capable of normal physiological function.

ANATOMY OF THE AVIAN OVIDUCT.   On the basis of the physiological function and the microscopic anatomy of the Müllerian duct, which in birds is usually called the oviduct, it is possible to distinguish the following parts: infundibulum, magnum, isthmus, shell gland, and vagina.

Infundibulum.   This consists of the funnel, or fimbria, which receives the ovulated ovum, and the chalaziferous region, in which the chalazae—two coiled, springlike cords that extend from the yolk to the poles of the egg—are formed. Though speculations concerning their function began in antiquity, their true reason for being still remains unknown.

Magnum.   The infundibular region merges, externally imperceptibly, into the magnum, which is the longest portion of the oviduct. The magnum is also called the albumen-secreting region, because here

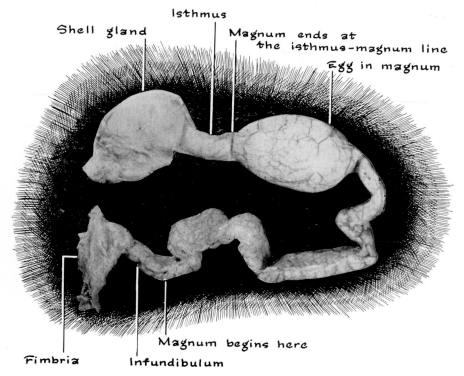

Isthmus

Shell gland

Magnum ends at
the isthmus-magnum line

Egg in magnum

Magnum begins here

Fimbria   Infundibulum

Figure 2-9. *Avian oviduct.*

the white of the egg is deposited round the yolk as it passes through.

Isthmus.   Between the magnum and the next region, the isthmus, there is a distinct, externally visible line of demarcation, which girdles the whole duct (Fig. 2-9). This is called the magnum-isthmus junction. The yolk reaches the isthmus already surrounded by albumen and acquires the soft shell membranes in this part of the oviduct.

Shell gland (or uterus).   From the isthmus the egg passes into the expanded caudal portion of the oviduct, the shell gland, where it acquires the hard calciferous shell. The term "shell gland" rather than "uterus" is clearly preferred, for this region of the oviduct is in no sense comparable or homologous to the mammalian uterus.

Vagina.   After formation of the egg is completed in the shell gland, the egg is expelled through the rather short vagina, in which it remains only a short time and in which it becomes coated with mucus (the "bloom" of the egg), which seals the shell pores; presumably, this hinders bacterial invasion.

The oviduct needs little time to perform its various tasks. The times spent by the egg in the different parts of the duct, in relation to their length, are summarized in Table 2-2. Note that each 5 centimeters of

Table 2-2. Average lengths of parts of oviduct of hens, their contribution to egg, and time spent by egg in each

SECTION OF OVIDUCT	AVERAGE LENGTH (centimeters)	KIND	CONTRIBUTION		TIME SPENT BY EGG IN (hours)
			TOTAL AMOUNT (grams)	PERCENT SOLIDS	
Infundibulum	11.0	Chalaza	. . .	. . .	0.25
Magnum	33.6	Albumen	32.9	12.2	3
Isthmus	10.6	Shell membrane	0.3	80.0	1.25
Shell gland	10.1	Calciferous shell	6.1	98.4	18–22
Vagina	6.9	Mucus	0.1	. . .	1/60

the magnum secrete 5–6 grams of albumen in the thirty minutes that it takes the egg to move through that distance. This is a truly prodigious accomplishment even though most (88 percent) of that secretion is water. The egg spends the longest time in the shell gland, where the secretion is least in weight but where 98 percent of the secretions are solids. The calcium carbonate and traces of other minerals are deposited at the rate of 0.3 gram per hour.

HISTOLOGY OF THE AVIAN OVIDUCT.   To accomplish the phenomenal task of transporting and secreting about 40 grams of material, consisting of 10 grams of solids and 30 grams of water, in about twenty-six hours, the chicken oviduct must be complex. Only an abridged account of its histology can be given here. Those interested in details should consult the unsurpassed monograph by Richardson (1935).

The gross histological structure of the oviduct consists of the external peritoneal coat (serosa), the outer longitudinal and inner circular muscle coats, the connective tissue layer carrying the blood vessels and nerves, and, finally, the mucosa lining the whole duct. In the young chick, the mucosa is a simple, ungrooved, and unfolded lining. As sexual maturity approaches, and as the oviduct begins to be stimulated by estrogen and progesterone, the mucosa become intricately grooved and folded into primary, secondary, and tertiary folds. Numerous glands are found throughout the length of the whole duct. At the height of secretory activity the cells vary in type from simple tall-columnar cells to transitional columnar cells, the great majority being ciliated. The glands secrete the substances peculiar to the region of the duct in which they are found, albumen aggregating in large coarse globules that fill the cells and the gland lumina. The endocrinology of the secretion of these substances is known (see p. 149), but the mechanism by which they are excreted to the surface of the duct, where they are deposited round the forming egg, remains unknown. Avian oviducts can not distinguish between an ovum and any other foreign body, and they secrete albumen, soft membranes, and a hard shell round any oviducal inclusion. Nothing is known about the nature of the physical forces that are responsible for the shape of the egg (sharper end posterior); it is apparent long before the egg acquires the rigidity imparted to it by the hard shell, and is easily discernible, in fact, in the upper portions of the magnum, where only a very thin layer of albumen has been deposited round the yolk.

The Male Reproductive System

The reproductive system of the male consists of paired testes, paired accessory glands, and the duct system, including the copulatory organ.

The Testes

The indifferent gonads of early embryos differentiate in females into ovaries and in males into testes. In all species the testes develop in the vicinity of the kidneys, in the region of the primitive ridge. In mammals the testes undergo an elaborate descent, ending, for most species, in the scrotum. In birds the testes do not descend but remain approximately in the position in which they originate. The function of testes is twofold: they produce the male sex hormone, androgen, and they form the male gametes, the sperm.

The sperm are produced in the seminiferous tubules, which make up over 90 percent of the testicular mass. The tubules are extremely convoluted; each testis contains tubules that would be several miles long if they were straightened out. The histology of the tubules changes progressively with age. In young males the tubules are simple, the germinal epithelium consisting only of spermatogonia and Sertoli cells. In older males the spermatogonia give rise to primary spermatocytes, which, after the first miotic division, give rise to the haploid secondary spermatocytes. These, in turn, become spermatids, which, after a series of transformations called spermiogenesis, give rise to sperm cells consisting of a head, a middle piece, and a tail. The Sertoli cells, which are found along the basement membrane of the tubules, are called "sperm mother cells" because it is thought that the sperm heads, which become embedded in these cells, undergo a ripening process in them. The processes of spermatogenesis and spermiogenesis, which are controlled by hormones, will be discussed in another section. These processes are fairly uniform in all animals studied; the major differences arise from the seasonal spermatogenesis of many species, the testes being completely inactive (juvenile) during the nonbreeding season and recrudescing during the breeding season or shortly before its onset. Testicular regression and recrudescence are both caused by the ebb and flow of pituitary hormones.

The other major function of the testes is the secretion of the male sex hormone. The best available evidence indicates that only the Leydig cells of the interstitial tissue secrete androgen, but it has not been possible to rule out completely the slight possibility that components of the seminiferous tubules may participate in this function. There is considerable difference between species in the degree of development of the Leydig cells. In young cocks the Leydig cells are much more numerous than in older birds; it is difficult, in fact, to find Leydig cells in the interstitial tissue of mature cocks. But there is no evidence that adult cocks secrete less androgen than growing males, and the assumption is valid that the few Leydig cells found in adults produce androgen as efficiently as the more numerous cells of younger birds. Leydig cells can be seen in all mammals at all ages when the males are in breeding condition, but here again there are differences among the species in the number of Leydig cells present. In boars and rats the interstitial tissue is very well developed, and large aggregates of Leydig cells occupy a good share of the total testicular volume. In men and bulls Leydig cells are much less prominent and do not form large nests as they do in the other species (Fig. 2-10AB). Secretion of androgen by Leydig cells is controlled by pituitary hormones, and the rate of the secretion depends on the rate of the pituitary function.

Functions of the Scrotum and the Pampiniform Plexus.   In all mammals, except those living in the sea and the pachyderms, the testes descend into the scrotum. In continuously breeding species they remain in the scrotum; in seasonally breeding species they ascend through the inguinal canal and remain in the body cavity during the nonbreeding season. In birds the testes do not descend but remain in the vicinity of the kidneys. The scrotal pouch is formed as the result of the

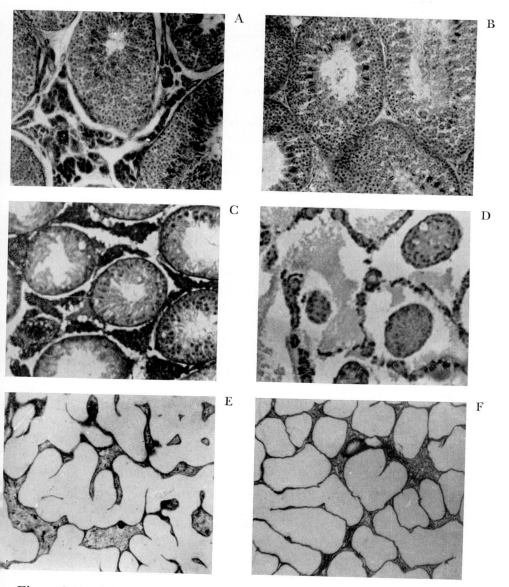

Figure 2-10. *Histology of normal and abnormal testes.*

A. Normal testis of a boar; note the massive development of interstitial tissue.

B. Normal testis of a bull. Note the scant intertubular tissue.

C. What happens to testes confined to the body cavity for 20 days. Note that here, as also in D and E, the interstitial tissue is nearly intact while the tubules show progressive degeneration.

D. What happens to testes confined to the body cavity for 80 days.

E. Testis from a spontaneous bilateral cryptorchid goat that was probably two years old.

F. Testis of a rat injected with massive doses of desoxycorticosterone. The same degree of destruction is noted in males on diets deficient in vitamin E.

double action of the physical pressure exerted by the testes and the stimulatory effect of androgen. Neither of these factors alone is sufficient to induce the formation of the scrotum. The main function of the scrotum is to provide for the testes an environment that is 1–8°F cooler than the body cavity.

Though the mere presence of the testes in the scrotum assures them of an environment cooler than the body cavity, the scrotum is capable of further regulating their temperature. It accomplishes this by a double muscle system that draws the testes close to the body wall for warmth or lets them fall away from the body wall for cooling. The two muscles involved are the external cremaster and the tunica dartos. The former passes through the inguinal canal and is attached to the tunica vaginalis enveloping each testis; when it contracts, it raises the tunica vaginalis and with it the testis. The tunica dartos adheres to the scrotal skin very closely and forms the septum that separates the scrotum into the two pouches. Exposure to cold makes the dartos contract, thus causing the scrotal skin to pucker and forcing the testes closer to the body wall. Both muscles atrophy and lose their ability to contract after castration, but they regain it after treatment with androgen.

There is a second mechanism, originally suggested by R. G. Harrison, which is equal in importance to the scrotum in providing the temperature regulation (cooling) which is so vital for the normal physiological function of the testes. This mechanism involves the so-called pampiniform plexus, which is the intricately and prodigiously looped system of veins and arteries that lies on the surface of the epididymis and which, gradually becoming less looped, follows the spermatic cord into the inguinal canal (Fig. 2-11). The arterial branch of this plexus is supplied by the spermatic artery and the venous part empties into the spermatic vein. By actual measurements in rams it has been established that the blood enters the plexus at a temperature of 39.0°C and that by the time it enters the testicle it is at or near the temperature (34.8°C) typical of that organ. Similarly, the cool venous blood leaving the testicle and entering the pampiniform plexus becomes gradually warmer as it approaches and joins the main peripheral circulation. The cellular and biochemical mechanisms by which the descending blood loses heat are completely unknown. It is probable that in males such as stallions, boars, rats, and others that possess a scrotum which is tight and not pendulous, as it is in men, rams, or bulls (see Fig. 2-12), the pampiniform plexus plays a major role in cooling the testes.

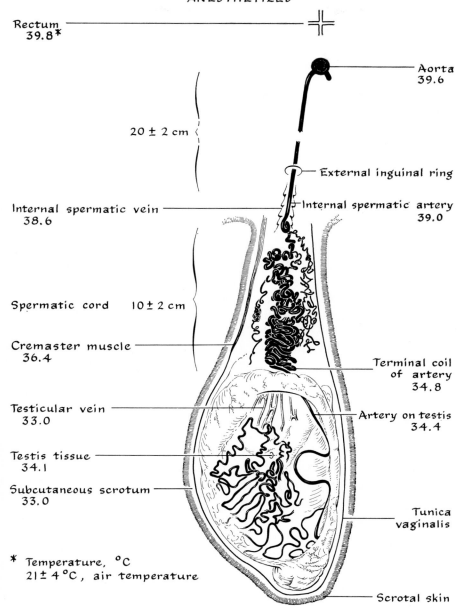

ANESTHETIZED

Rectum
39.8*

Aorta
39.6

20 ± 2 cm

External inguinal ring

Internal spermatic vein
38.6

Internal spermatic artery
39.0

Spermatic cord   10 ± 2 cm

Cremaster muscle
36.4

Terminal coil
of artery
34.8

Testicular vein
33.0

Artery on testis
34.4

Testis tissue
34.1

Subcutaneous scrotum
33.0

Tunica
vaginalis

* Temperature, °C
21 ± 4 °C, air temperature

Scrotal skin

Figure 2-11. *The effect of the pampiniform plexus on the modification of temperature of blood entering and leaving the scrotum and testes of rams. (From Waites and Moule 1961, J. Reprod. Fertil. 2:213–224).*

Recent work has provided evidence that the subcutaneous injection of minute amounts of cadmium—for instance, in the neck region of a male rat—rapidly causes sterility, owing to a complete eventual destruction of the seminiferous tubules and, to a lesser extent, of the interstitial tissue. It is interesting to note that cadmium exerts its initial effects on the lining of the blood vessels of the pampiniform plexus. The ultimate destruction of the tubules is due to the inability of the impaired plexus to cool the arterial blood. The female, which has no such plexus, is not affected by cadmium. It is not known what it is about the blood vessels of the pampiniform plexus that makes only them vulnerable to the cadmium effect, since none of the other vessels show detectable damage (Parenthetically, it may be mentioned that if rats are pretreated with zinc, or if zinc is given simultaneously with cadmium, the animals are completely protected against the deleterious effects of the latter.)

No work has been done on cadmium injection in domestic animals. If the cadmium were as effective in rendering them sterile as in rats (permanently so), this method would be easier to apply than surgical castration, especially since it could also be used in fully grown males.

Sheepherders learned long ago that it is possible to cause temporary sterility in rams by tying the testes close to the body wall, thus preventing them from cooling off when the environmental temperature rises. It has also been known for a long time that cryptorchids—animals whose testes remain inside the body cavity instead of descending into the scrotum—are sterile. Cryptorchism occurs spontaneously in practically all mammalian species. It is common in man and most domestic animals, and in pigs and goats it is frequently hereditary. It may be caused by hormonal deficiencies and may then be alleviated by the injection of androgen, which causes testicular descent when it is given in proper doses. If cryptorchism is caused by an anatomical obstruction of the inguinal canal that prevents the testes from entering the scrotum, hormonal therapy is useless, but testicular descent may be brought about by surgical correction of the obstruction.

In most mammals, especially in laboratory mammals, it is easy to produce experimental cryptorchism by pushing the testes through the inguinal canal into the body cavity and preventing their descent by surgical closure of the canal. Such cryptorchids continue to mate, but the semen they produce contains increasing amounts of abnormal sperm. Eventually spermatogenesis stops completely. The seminiferous tubules become more and more disorganized; the germinal epithelium

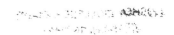

sloughs off, its debris filling the lumen of the tubules. After prolonged confinement to the body cavity the germinal epithelium disappears more or less completely, the spermatogonia being affected last. If the testes are returned to the scrotum at this stage, complete recovery may occur and spermatogenesis may be resumed, but after prolonged exposure to body temperature the damage becomes irreversible. The testes of natural and experimental cryptorchids are smaller than normal testes, the seminiferous tubules having shrunk considerably and the intertubular spaces having become proportionately larger than in normal testes (Fig. 2-10CD).

The effect of body temperature on the ability of testes to secrete androgen is not quite clear. There is probably no effect on the Leydig cells and on androgen secretion when the testes of adult males are confined to the body cavity, but cryptorchism in young males seems to reduce the rate of androgen secretion somewhat. There is probably considerable difference among the species in this respect. Unilaterally cryptorchid stallions (called ridglings) are said to be sexually more vigorous and aggressive than normal males.

Even in males whose testes have descended, the scrotum cannot always compensate for the effect of high temperatures on spermatogenesis. Notable examples of this are man, who may become temporarily or permanently sterile after prolonged fever, and rams, which are subject to the so-called summer sterility. In rams the higher temperature of summer causes the production of increasing numbers of defective spermatozoa and eventually brings about impaired fertility or complete sterility for the duration of hot weather. That these deleterious effects are due to heat can be inferred from the facts that the onset of lower fall temperatures alleviates summer sterility and that rams placed in cool environments are significantly more fertile than those exposed to normal summer temperature. Finally, when the scrotum and the body of rams are sheared (thus lowering body temperature and scrotal temperature), the fertility of the rams remains high in spite of higher environmental temperatures.

Why high temperatures are injurious to spermatogenesis is not known. According to some reports, summer sterility in rams can be overcome by treatment with thyroid preparations if the treatment is begun before spermatogenesis begins to deteriorate; the feeding of androgen to rams does prevent summer sterility, but the results obtained from these treatments vary considerably in different experiments.

The Duct System and Accessory Glands

The duct system of the male is derived, to a large extent, from the Wolffian duct system of the mesonephric kidney (Fig. 2-2). A part of the Müllerian system, which the female utilizes for most of its ducts, persists in the male as a rudiment in the prostate, where it forms the prostatic utricle (uterus masculinus). This structure retains its ability to respond to female sex hormones and is frequently responsible for the prostatic enlargement commonly occurring in men and dogs past the prime of life.

The mesonephric tubules give rise to the vas efferens, the mesonephric duct to the epididymis, the vas deferens, and the seminal vesicles, the last being formed from evaginations of the duct. The remainder of the duct system (the prostatic, membranous, and cavernous urethra) comes from the urogenital sinus, as do the other two male accessory glands—the prostate and Cowper's glands (bulbo-urethral glands) (Table 2-1). The accessory glands are developed to different degrees in different mammals (Fig. 2-12). Seminal vesicles are absent from the dog, the fox, and the wolf. The boar's preputial pouch, near the tip of the penis (Fig. 2-12), cannot be properly classified as an accessory gland, but it regresses in size very significantly after castration. Its function is not known. Urine accumulates in this pouch and is responsible for the strong male sex odor of boars, which permeates even their meat and accounts for its disagreeable taste.

The ductuli efferentia become convoluted where they originate from the rete testes. These ducts are lined by alternate clusters of tall and low epithelial cells, which bear presumably nonmotile cilia. They gradually fuse into the single duct of the epididymis. This duct, intricately convoluted, forms the head, body, and tail of the epididymis, which is lined by tall, pseudostratified epithelial cells bearing non-motile stereocilia. Gradually becoming less convoluted, the duct acquires a bigger lumen and a thicker wall; when it leaves the tail of the epididymis, it becomes the vas deferens. Here the pseudostratified, stereociliated epithelium is lower than in the epididymis. The vas is surrounded by well-developed muscle layers, an inner and an outer longitudinal layer and a circular layer between them. It is probably the contraction of these muscle layers that is responsible for the movement of the sperm through the duct system.

The two vasa deferentia lie side by side without fusing internally in the region of the bladder and form the ampulla of the vasa deferentia.

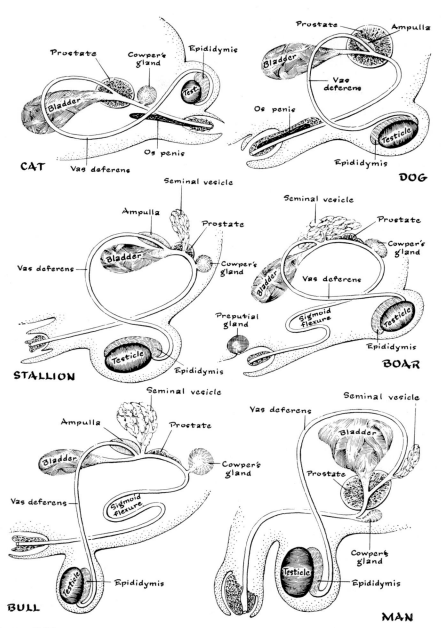

Figure 2-12. *Reproductive systems of the male cat, the dog, the stallion, the boar, the bull, and man. Compare the relative sizes of the various accessory glands, and note that all these species have the prostate; that the dog and the cat have no seminal vesicles; that the dog has no Cowper's gland; that the cat, the boar, and man have no ampullar swelling; that the bull and the boar have the sigmoid flexure of the penis; that the dog and the cat have the os penis; that only the boar has the preputial pouch.*

In most species there is a thickening of the wall but very little increase in the lumen in the region of the ampulla. Here the urethra, the ducts from the paired seminal vesicles, and the multiple prostatic ducts empty into the now common duct system. A short distance further the multiple ducts from the bulbo-urethral (Cowper's) glands also empty into the duct, which is now called the prostatic urethra. The epithelium in this area is simple, pseudostratified, and columnar. (For further details of the gross and microscopic anatomy of the male urethra consult any textbook of histology.)

The Penis

In some mammals, especially in the bull and the boar, the male urethra forms a loop called the sigmoid flexure. In other mammals the flexure is very slight (man) or completely missing. In man the penis consists of three—and in all domestic and laboratory mammals of two —cylindrical bodies called the corpora cavernosa penis. The cavernous spaces of the corpora cavernosa become filled with blood during sexual excitation; escape of the blood is partly and eventually completely blocked as the penis becomes more turgid and erect and is pulled against the bony rim of the pelvis. Erection is thus largely due to inability of the blood to drain from the cavernous spaces of the penis.

Many species have in the penis a bony structure that is formed by ossification of a corpus cavernosum. This bony structure, called the os penis (or the baculum), is found in all Canidae, sea lions, Mustellidae, and a variety of other animals.

The end of the penis, capping the corpora cavernosa, is called the glans penis. In man it is mushroom-shaped; in other mammals it assumes a variety of other shapes. In the opossum it is forked, the fork including the terminal 2 centimeters of the penis. In the boar it is corkscrew-shaped, and in the bull there is a less pronounced twist along the longitudinal axis. In the goat and the ram a thin projection extends 3–4 centimeters beyond the tip of the glans. This is called the urethral process or the vermiform process, the latter being a very apt descriptive term.

The Male Accessory Glands

These glands include the paired seminal vesicles, the prostate (which in rats consists of three lobes, in other mammals of one single structure), and the paired bulbo-urethral, or Cowper's, glands. There is considerable variation in the relative size and anatomy of the glands in different species. In the cat and dog the seminal vesicles are absent, and the prostate is relatively much better developed than it is in other mammals. In the bull, and especially in the boar, the seminal vesicles are greatly enlarged, but the prostate is relatively small and poorly developed (Fig. 2-11). The anatomic structure is also extremely divergent. In man the seminal vesicles are hollow sacs with numerous outpocketings; in rats they are frond-shaped and elongated and consist of many compartments. The lumina of all three of these glands are lined with tall-columnar epithelium.

Function of the Male Accessory Glands.   Sperm cells contained in the lumina of the seminiferous tubules and the proximal excurrent ducts are nonmotile. They become motile and presumably metabolically active when they come in contact with the so-called seminal plasma. There is considerable variation among the species in the amount of seminal fluid contributed by the various accessory glands and the testes. In man the prostate contributes 15–30 percent and the seminal vesicles 40–80 percent of the total ejaculate. In the boar 15–20 percent of the semen plasma is derived from the seminal vesicles, 2–5 percent from the testes and the epididymis, 10–25 percent from Cowper's glands, and the remainder from the urethral glands. In any species, not more than 2–5 percent of the total ejaculate is made up of the secretion of the testes and the epididymis. The seminal plasma is added to the sperm during ejaculation. In some animals (boars and man), in which the process of ejaculation lasts a considerable time, it is possible, by use of the fractional-ejaculate method, to determine the sequence in which the different accessory glands make their contribution to the total ejaculate. It is probable that in all animals (but certainly in boars and man) the urethrae are first "flushed" by a sperm-free ejaculate, probably originating from the urethral glands and the bulbo-urethral glands. This is followed by a second ejaculate, rich in sperm, which contains contributions from the seminal vesicles and the prostate. This sperm-rich fraction is followed by a sperm-free ejaculate, which is probably predominantly of vesicular origin.

The seminal plasma has two main functions: it serves as a suspending and activating medium for the previously nonmotile sperm cells, and it furnishes the cells with a substrate that is rich in electrolytes (sodium and potassium chloride), nitrogen, citric acid, fructose, ascorbic acid, inositol, phosphatase, and ergothionene, and contains traces of vitamins and enzymes. Neither of these functions is essential to sperm fertility, for sperm become motile in any physiological liquid, and epididymal and even testicular sperm are capable of fertilizing eggs (though their fertilizing ability is less than that of more mature sperm). We have seen that cats and dogs have no seminal vesicles, and one can remove the seminal vesicles and the prostate from boars and rats without impairing their fertility. Nevertheless, the secretions of the male accessory glands should be considered an essential and integral part of semen, without which sperm cells could not attain their greatest fertilizing ability.

The semen of several species coagulates upon ejaculation. The semen of men coagulates shortly after ejaculation but liquefies again, presumably under the action of proteolytic enzymes contributed by the prostate. The semen of rats coagulates because of the action of the secretion of the coagulating gland of the prostate on the seminal fluid. The resulting coagulum forms the vaginal plug in the vagina of the female. It was earlier thought that the formation of the vaginal plug was essential to the maximal fertility of the rat, but most recent evidence shows that removal of the plug immediately after copulation does not reduce fertility; in fact, the plug (which can be used as an indication that a female has mated) very frequently drops out shortly after mating. The semen of guinea pigs also forms a jellylike vaginal plug, the coagulation being due to a substance contributed by a portion of the prostate gland. A vaginal plug is also formed in baboons and squirrels, but not in other animals.

The pH of fresh semen is frequently about 7.0; in some animals (bull, dog, fox, rabbit) and some individuals, however, it has been found to be on the acid side, and in others it is distinctly alkaline.

We shall not discuss in detail the chemical composition of seminal plasma, but we shall call attention to a few peculiarities of various species. Fructose occurs in the semen of virtually all mammals, being especially high in that of bulls and goats and considerably lower in that of stallions and boars (both of which ejaculate large volumes of semen). Cock semen contains no fructose, and rabbit semen contains fructose and glucose, the latter being absent from bull, ram, and human semen. In most mammals seminal fructose comes from the seminal vesicles, but in the rat it comes from the dorsal prostate. Citric acid in the semen of boars and bulls is produced in the seminal vesicles, but in men it is secreted by the prostate. The seminal vesicles of boars and rats secrete very large amounts of inositol (these vesicles, in fact, are the richest known source of inositol), but bull and human semen contain virtually no inositol. Though these differences are perplexing and their significance in the metabolic activity of the sperm of the various species remains unexplained, they point up the conclusion that different species may solve the same fundamental problem in different ways. It appears probable that inositol plays a role in the sperm metabolism of the boar, for it is secreted by that animal in large quantities, and that other mammalian sperm do not need this vitamin, for it is absent from their seminal plasma.

SUMMARY

This chapter lays the groundwork for the understanding of much of what is to follow. It discusses the basic macro- and microanatomy of male and female reproductive systems. It contains enough information to refresh the memories of students who have had courses in histology, embryology, and anatomy. Because the endocrine system controls the development of the end organs discussed here, it is necessary to have a thorough knowledge of the basic structure and the histology of the reproductive systems as well as of their embryonic origins.

REFERENCES

S. A. Asdell. 1946. *Patterns of Mammalian Reproduction.* Comstock (Ithaca, N.Y.).

F. W. R. Brambell. 1956. "Ovarian changes" in Marshall's *Physiology of Reproduction,* Vol. I, Part 1, 3rd ed. Longmans (New York).

P. Eckstein and S. Zuckerman. 1956. "Morphology of reproductive tract" in Marshall's *Physiology of Reproduction,* Vol. I, Part 1, 3rd ed. Longmans (New York).

T. R. Forbes. 1947. "The crowing hen: early observations on spontaneous sex reversal in birds." *Yale J. Biol. Med.,* **19**:955.

R. J. Harrison. 1948. "The changes occurring in the ovary of the goat during the estrous cycle and in early pregnancy." *J. Anat.,* **82**:21.

T. Mann. 1954. *The Biochemistry of Semen.* Wiley (New York).

A. Maximov and W. Bloom. 1957. *Textbook of Histology,* 7th ed. Saunders (Philadelphia).

S. R. M. Reynolds. 1949. *Physiology of the Uterus,* 2nd ed. Hoeber (New York).

V. A. Rice, F. N. Andrews, E. J. Warwick, and J. E. Legates. 1957. *Breeding and Improvement of Farm Animals,* 5th ed. McGraw-Hill (New York).

K. C. Richardson. 1935. "The secretory phenomena in the oviduct of the fowl" *Philos. Trans. Roy. Soc.* London (B), **225**:149.

E. Seiferle. 1933. "Art- und Altersmerkmale der weiblichen Geschlechts-organe unserer Haussäugetiere, Pferd, Rind, Kalb, Schaf, Ziege, Kaninchen, Meerschweinchen, Schwein und Katze." *Z. Anatomie Entwickelungsgeschichte,* **101**:1.

H. Selye. 1943. "Factors influencing development of scrotum." *Anat. Rec.,* **85**:377.

S. Sisson and J. D. Grossman. 1940. *The Anatomy of the Domestic Animals.* Saunders (Philadelphia).

L. M. Winters, W. W. Green, and R. E. Comstock. 1942. *Prenatal Development of the Bovine.* University of Minnesota Technical Bulletin, 151.

E. Witschi. 1951. "Embryogenesis of the adrenal and the reproductive glands" in *Recent Progress in Hormone Research,* Vol. VI. Academic Press (New York).

chapter 3

The Endocrinology
of Reproduction

Introduction and Definitions

Sexual reproduction, even in the lower vertebrates, depends on synchronizing systems. The shedding of eggs by the female frog, for example, must be closely followed by the shedding of sperm by the male. Here the problem is rather simple; all that is needed is a system that will assure the simultaneous shedding of gametes by two individuals of opposite sex in the same vicinity of the pond at the most propitious season. In more complex animals a whole series of interlocking and synchronized events must follow one another if reproductive efficiency is to be attained. The shedding of gametes, fertilization, gestation, parturition, and lactation are all events that require accurate timing, and all of them must occur in such a way that the young life depending on them has a good chance of surviving. Without synchronization and cyclic repeatability, reproduction would become a chaotic and completely inefficient game of chance. The problem was solved in several ways in the different species; but, regardless of the details of the solution, all animals evolved an intricate and interrelated system of checks and balances, a time clock which actually consists of two interlocking systems—the endocrine system and the nervous system. These two systems usually function as a unit, although, as we shall see, one system may on occasion override the other, depending on the task to be performed. For ease of discussion we shall consider each system separately before we ask the question of why *two* interlocking systems have evolved to control reproductive events, to determine the end of one episode and the beginning of the next one.

Most of these reproductive events are chains of interdependent, mutually controlling, and cyclic reactions. The final result is frequently the product of a whole series of phenomena, all of which must occur in a properly timed sequence if they are to culminate in a normal and predictable effect on the end organ they affect. In order to understand the intricacies of the hormonal interplays that produce the final results, one must think of the whole chain of events rather than of the single events that make up the chain. One of the basic patterns of the type of interaction involved is shown here. Some of the interrelations are simpler, and most are more complex, but basically they all follow the same scheme.

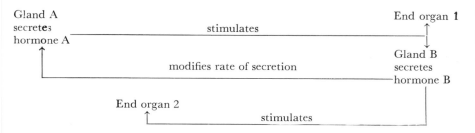

The governing parts of the reproductive system are the glands, the hormones secreted by them, the end organs (such as the ovaries and the uterus) that are acted on by the hormones, and, under certain circumstances, the nervous system.

The endocrine (or ductless) glands can be defined as specialized groups of cells that have the primary function of forming and elaborating chemical substances called hormones, which they secrete directly into the blood stream or the lymph. Hormones, which have also been called distance activators, can be defined as substances made by endocrine glands in one part of the body and carried by the blood or the lymph to other parts of the body, where they modify the activity of certain genetically conditioned end organs. The specifications "genetically conditioned" and "end organ" are important because, as a rule, all hormones are highly specific and selective in their action. Many hormones cause growth; but estrogen causes growth of the uterus and not of the comb, androgen causes growth of the comb and not of the ovaries, and growth hormone causes general body growth, not growth of the uterus, comb, or ovaries. Just what gives an end organ its inherent ability to respond to one hormone but not to another (while all the hormones are reaching the end organ via the blood stream) remains unknown in detail. In Chapter 6 we shall present some ideas on the possible mechanism of hormone action and on the probable reasons why hormones show tissue specificity and how tissues recognize their own trophic hormones and ignore others. Note especially that hormones *modify* the activity of genetically conditioned end organs. They do not initiate reactions that are not normally performed by the cells of those organs. Such cells are endowed with the ability to perform certain highly specialized chemical tasks, which, in the absence of hormones, may be accomplished only slowly and inadequately, but, in the presence of hormones, are speeded up or performed more efficiently.

It is becoming apparent that optimal reproductive performance is possible only in euhormonal organisms, and that the entire endocrine system participates, to a greater or lesser extent, in bringing about this state of well-being. Some of the glands are directly concerned with reproduction proper, and it is of them that we shall speak in greater detail. (The role of the adrenal glands in reproduction will be ignored almost completely, not because it is insignificant, but because it is less precisely defined than the role of glands that are directly involved in this process. Nevertheless, readers are urged to consult textbooks of endocrinology to acquaint themselves with the important roles assumed by all the endocrine glands in the reproductive processes.)

The Pituitary Gland

The pituitary gland, or hypophysis, is located in a bony depression called the sella turcica at the base of the brain and it consists of the adenohypophysis and the neurohypophysis. Each of these can be subdivided into anatomically distinct parts. Thus the adenohypophysis (also called the anterior lobe of the pituitary gland), consists of the pars tuberalis, the pars intermedia and the pars distalis, the latter forming the major part of the anterior lobe. A part of Rathke's pouch, which is an entodermal outpocketing of the stomadeum, forms the pars intermedia, while the floor of this pouch gives rise to the pars distalis of the adenohypophysis. In contrast to the entodermal origin of the adenohypophysis, the neurohypophysis (which is also known as the posterior lobe of the pituitary gland or the pars nervosa), is derived from the diencephalon and is thus ectodermal in origin. The neural lobe consists of the pars nervosa and the median eminence and it is through the latter that both the anterior and posterior lobe of the hypophysis derive their blood supply. According to the best available evidence, only the pars nervosa is innervated, the nerves coming to it via the pituitary (hypophyseal) stalk from the hypothalamic region. Recent evidence makes it seem probable that the hormones usually associated with the posterior lobe are produced in the hypothalamus and find their way to the posterior lobe through nerve tracts connecting that lobe and the hypothalamus. If these tracts are blocked, secretory granules, presumed to be hormone precursors or even the hormones themselves, accumulate on the hypothalamic side of the block and gradually disappear on the pituitary side. This type of evidence makes it seem likely that the posterior lobe itself does not secrete the hormones found in it, but only stores and releases them.

The pars tuberalis is the most vascular portion of the pituitary gland. It is found in all vertebrates, but its endocrine function is not known.

The pars anterior, or anterior lobe, is also called the adenohypophysis. Most recent studies show that the anterior lobe is not innervated, but there is no complete agreement on this question. Evidence to be presented later shows that many reproductive phenomena are controlled by nerve impulses which may signal the adenohypophysis that this or that hormone should be released. If the adenohypophysis were innervated such messages could reach the anterior lobe directly and speedily. However, recent work has shown that the nerve impulses terminate in the hypothalamic region where the command for the release of hypophyseal hormones is translated into humoral agents (of which more will be said later), which in turn reach the adenohypophysis via the hypothalamo-pituitary portal system. It would seem that this system of relaying commands should be inefficient because of its relative slowness as compared to the direct and instant relay possible via the nervous system alone. Of course, this concern may be simply a reflection of our present ignorance of the rapidity with which hypothalamic humoral agents may be released into the portal system and the rapidity with which they may cause release of hypophyseal hormones.

Histology of the Anterior Lobe

Pituitary cytology is too involved and unsettled at the present time to warrant a detailed discussion. There are at least three distinct and important types of cells in the anterior lobe of the pituitary gland. The chromophobes, the largest of the three, are so named because they do not stain as readily as the other two types, of which they are generally assumed to be the progenitors. They are not, at present, associated with the secretion of any hormone. The acidophilic chromophiles are smaller than the basophilic chromophiles. Both stain readily with the appropriate biological stains, and both are secretory.

The proportions of the three types differ with species, age, sex, and reproductive stage. Castration, pregnancy, various thyroid states, and other endocrine states have a profound effect on the appearance and number of the acidophiles and basophiles. These observations provide a basis for associating the secretion of certain hormones with one or the other of the two secretory cell types, as will be shown later in this chapter.

Hormones from the Anterior Lobe

Before discussing the different hormones that are known to be produced by the anterior lobe of the pituitary gland, let us see how the information about the identity of the hormones secreted by that gland has been obtained. Endocrine experimentation usually involves the removal of the gland, followed by replacement therapy. If, for instance, we want to find the endocrine function of testes in the cock, we first remove them surgically. We find that the comb shrinks and eventually becomes very small and dry. We conclude that the growth of the comb in some way depends on the testes. But we do not know (1) whether there is a neural connection between the testes and the comb, (2) whether the action of the testes on the comb is direct, or (3) whether it is indirect, via some other gland, which secretes the hormone responsible for growth and maintenance of the comb.

To resolve these uncertainties, we use replacement therapy. We can either inject an extract of testes into a castrated cock, or we can implant the testes into such an animal. In either case growth of the comb is resumed. We have thus confirmed the initial observation of a relation between testes and comb, and, because testicular extract was effective, we have eliminated the possibility that a neural connection is essential to growth of the comb. We still do not know whether the action of the testes is direct or indirect—via some intermediate gland and hormone. At this point it becomes necessary to use the technique of hypophysectomy, or the surgical removal of the pituitary gland. P. E. Smith perfected the parapharyngeal approach to that gland in the rat and made this technique a laboratory routine. By means of this technique endocrinology became a much more exact branch of physiology and made impressive advances between 1927 and the present. The operation, since the original one on rats, has been used on all laboratory animals—cats, dogs, chickens, pigeons, frogs, pigs, and goats. It had been used therapeutically even earlier in human beings.

Hypophysectomy, by removing the gland that is now known to control the function of every other endocrine gland in the body, creates an endocrine vacuum, for all the other glands depend on pituitary gland secretions for normal functioning. It is probable, to be sure, that even in hypophysectomized animals other endocrine glands continue to function, but at such a low level that their secretions can usually be ignored.

We now return to the relation between the testes and the comb of the cock. If a cock is hypophysectomized, both testes and comb shrink. We shall temporarily ignore the information that the testes seem to depend on pituitary gland secretions not only for size but also for functioning (the comb decreased in size!) and concentrate on the original problem of the testes-comb relation. If we inject a testicular extract into a hypophysectomized cock, growth of the comb is resumed. Since the pituitary gland has been removed, we know that it cannot be intermediary between the testes and the comb. It is conceivable that the extract may have produced growth of the comb by acting on one of the remaining glands and causing it to secrete the hormone that is responsible for such growth. To test this possibility, we can remove, in turn, the thyroids, the adrenals, etc., from hypophysectomized cocks and inject testicular extract. Or we can inject hormones from these other glands, but not testicular extract, into hypophysectomized cocks. In this way we can eliminate the contributions of all other glands and conclude that a hormone produced by the testes is directly responsible for growth of the comb (Fig. 3-1).

This example also illustrates two types of endocrine events: (1) the simple one-step reaction from the testes to their end organ, the comb; (2) the more complex two-step reaction from the pituitary gland to one of its end organs, the testes, and from the testes to their end organ, the comb.

If we have removed the whole pituitary gland from the cock, we have no way of knowing whether the hormone acting on the testes was secreted by the anterior or the posterior lobe. In some laboratory animals and in the chicken it is possible to remove only one lobe and to leave the other in place to continue secretion of its peculiar hormones. It is also quite easy to separate the two lobes in glands obtained from slaughtered animals and to assay each of the lobes separately for the hormones it contains. If we were to do this, or if we were to remove only one of the lobes, leaving the other one in place in the cock, we should find that only hormones from the anterior lobe are capable of

B

D

Figure 3-1. *Effect of hypophysectomy and replacement therapy on male chickens. Compare the size of combs and wattles and the size and color of earlobes in the four pictures, and note that in* **D** *the feathers are long and narrow (thyroid deficiency) and the legs short, and that the bird appears juvenile. The fact that chickens have externally visible and measurable secondary sex characters (comb, wattles), and the fact that even traces of pituitary tissue will cause partial or normal testicular or ovarian function, make chickens good experimental subjects for endocrine research.*

A. Normal control.

B. His hypophysectomized brother, 30 days after the operation.

C. Another hypophysectomized brother, injected with LH for 8 days.

D. Hypophysectomized male that remained untreated for 14 months after the operation.

stimulating the testes to secrete the hormone that causes growth of the comb.

It is also possible to subject the two lobes of the pituitary gland to chemical fractionation and to extract from them several distinct hormones, which have different physiological effects.

It is now known that all pituitary hormones are either polypeptides or proteins (see Chapter 6). The chemistry of the others is inadequately known, but experiments of the type discussed and chemical fractionation have provided evidence of the secretion of at least six distinct and physiologically different hormones by the anterior lobe. Since there are only three types of cells in that lobe, and only two of them are considered to be secretory, one is forced to conclude that the acidophiles and basophiles each secrete several of the pituitary hormones. Investigators have obtained evidence on this point by correlating pituitary cytology with certain physiological states of animals: in dwarf mice, for example, no acidophiles are found in the anterior lobe; and in certain types of gigantism and acromegaly, acidophiles frequently form tumors and become very numerous. These observations lead to the assumption that the acidophiles secrete the growth (somatotrophic) hormone.

Castration causes vacuolation of basophiles, which are then called signet-ring cells because of the acentric nucleus and the large vacuole in the cytoplasm. In some cases of precocious sexual maturity, basophilic tumors occur in the anterior lobe. These findings suggest that the gonadotrophic complex (there are two different hormones) is produced by basophiles. Thyroidectomy also modifies the basophiles, suggesting that the thyrotrophic hormone also is secreted by them (then called the "thyrotrophs"). Similar evidence implicates the basophiles as the probable source of the adrenocorticotrophic hormone. Prolactin is assumed to come from the acidophiles. Much of the evidence presented here has been contradicted or corroborated by various staining techniques that are too complex to be discussed in detail. (See Cowie and Folley, *The Hormones,* Vol. III, pp. 310–316.)

The Pituitary-ovary Relation

One of the most important observations resulting from the early experiments with hypophysectomy was that, when this operation was performed on immature rats, the gonads failed to become functional; when the operation was performed on adult rats, the gonads shrank and eventually atrophied. These observations, together with the fact that the gonads of hypophysectomized animals could be restored or maintained by the injection or implantation of pituitary tissue, conclusively established the dependence of the gonads on pituitary hormones. There remained the intricate job of finding out how the pituitary gland causes the cyclic behavior of the ovary. This was accomplished in a series of beautiful experiments by early endocrinologists, who laid the foundation for the currently accepted interpretation.

According to this interpretation, the pituitary gland secretes the gonadotrophic complex, which consists of two distinct substances. The identity of these two gonadotrophic hormones was first established by the use of female rats as test animals. The two hormones were therefore named, with reference to their effects on the ovary, the follicle-stimulating hormone (abbreviated as FSH) and the luteinizing hormone (or LH). Later it was shown that both hormones are also secreted by the pituitary glands of males. Occasionally the term "interstitial-cell–stimulating hormone," or ICSH, is used instead of LH when the discussion is restricted to the effects of LH in males. There seems little justification for the term ICSH, for it is identical with LH, and no effort has been made to rename FSH when its effects in males are discussed. We shall use the terms FSH and LH whether the discussion pertains to males or to females.

Some endocrinologists also consider prolactin a gonadotrophic hormone, largely because of the luteotrophic effect of this hormone on the corpora lutea of rats and mice. But as is pointed out elsewhere, prolactin is not the LTH of other mammals and for this reason should not be classified as a gonadotrophin. In fact, in many mammals and birds it has an antigonadotrophic action since, if it is injected into mature males or females with functional gonads, the latter can be made to regress completely if the dose of prolactin is sufficiently high and if the injections are continued for several days. These antigonadotrophic effects of prolactin can be counteracted by the simultaneous injection with prolactin and FSH and/or LH, suggesting that exogenous prolactin inhibits the synthesis or the release of FSH and of LH.

Stage 1: Follicular Phase.   It is probable that both FSH and LH are secreted by the pituitary gland throughout the cycle, but the proportion in which they are secreted varies during the cycle. When FSH predominates, it causes the growth and maturation of ovarian follicles. As the follicles grow, they secrete increasing amounts of the female sex hormone estrogen. The increasing concentration of estrogen in the blood stream gradually suppresses the secretion of FSH by the pituitary and brings about the release of LH, which, when it reaches a sufficiently high concentration in the blood, causes the rupture of the ovarian follicle. This is the traditional interpretation of the relations between the pituitary gland and the ovary; it will be modified later in this discussion.

Because, at this stage of the cycle, the follicle is the dominant component of the ovary (both physiologically and morphologically), this stage is called the follicular phase of the estrous cycle.

It is now time to support some of the statements made concerning the endocrine relations between the pituitary gland and the ovarian follicle. Even some of the earliest attempts to fractionate the gonadotrophic complex and to purify its components showed that nearly pure FSH causes follicular growth without luteinization. Such FSH, when injected into immature hypophysectomized rats, should, even in large doses, produce only follicular growth. The data shown in Table 3-1 illustrate the effects produced on the ovary by FSH and LH. In the experiment cited none of the ovaries acted upon by FSH alone showed formation of corpora lutea or any signs of luteinization.

Table 3-1. Effect of FSH and LH on ovarian and uterine weights of immature hypophysectomized rats

FSH (days)	LH (days)		OVARIAN WEIGHT (milligrams)	UTERINE WEIGHT (milligrams)
4			16.3	15.7
7			17.9	14.1
8			18.2	16.7
9			14.0	12.5
10			15.1	12.9
7	plus	2	23.4	49.5
8	plus	3	29.4	61.1
9	plus	4	26.2	78.2
10	plus	5	22.8	101.4
Hypophysectomized controls			6.7	12.4

SOURCE: Data adapted from Greep, Van Dyke, and Chow. 1942. *Endocrinology*, 30:635.

In this experiment, and in others like it, FSH alone, while causing an increase in ovarian weight, did not cause an increase in uterine weight. Since the uterus is a sensitive end organ for estrogen, this fact suggests that follicles grown with FSH alone (without LH) are not capable of secreting estrogen. Evidence from intact females, however, indicates that estrogen is secreted by follicles during the follicular phase of the cycle, which suggests that not only FSH but also LH is secreted by the pituitary gland during that phase. This and similar evidence lead to the assumption that the gland never secretes either gonadotrophic hormone alone and that only the proportion between FSH and LH varies during the cycle. Additional evidence on this point will be presented when the endocrine control of ovulation in chickens is discussed.

That estrogen is able to inhibit the gonadotrophic hormone produced by the pituitary gland has been shown so often that there can no longer be any doubt about this effect. The degree of inhibition is proportional to the amount of estrogen. The important question is whether estrogen, in the minute amounts that are most likely to be present under the physiological conditions of reproductive cycles, is capable of governing the hormone output of the pituitary gland. In adult rats, quantities of estrogen too small to cause weighable uterine growth do cause a decrease in ovarian weight, which is attributed to a decrease in the amount of FSH produced by the gland. This conclusion is strengthened by the finding that the gonadotrophic hormone content of the pituitaries of rats treated with small quantities of estrogen (0.015–0.175 microgram of estradiol daily) is lower than that of untreated rats. This shows that the gonadotrophic hormone content of pituitary glands can be modified significantly even by slight changes in the amount of injected estrogen.

Larger quantities of estrogen inhibit the secretion of the gonadotrophic hormone completely. If enough estrogen is given, effects very similar to those caused by castration or hypophysectomy are produced, for the suppression of secretion of the gonadotrophic hormone and eventually of some of the other pituitary hormones is probably complete. This effect of estrogen has been found of value in producing in animals a condition of "physiological hypophysectomy," which makes them especially useful for certain types of hormone assays. Large doses of estrogen (implants are used for the sake of simplicity) completely inhibit the animals' own pituitary glands, and such animals can then be used in the assay of gonadotrophic hormones (and probably of other pituitary hormones), for the high estrogen titer does not seem to interfere with the assay to any appreciable extent. This method is particularly applicable in males, in which there are no important target tissues for estrogen.

In females, large amounts of estrogen lead to a complete arrest of the physiological and morphological development of the ovary, similar to the arrest produced by hypophysectomy, but here the Müllerian duct system responds to estrogenic stimulation by enlarging greatly. This complicates the situation enough to make estrogenized females unsuitable as assay animals for the gonadotrophic hormone.

With sufficiently high doses of estrogen not only the secretion of the gonadotrophic complex but the entire endocrine activity of the pituitary gland may be inhibited. The gonadotrophic hormone is inhibited first and with the smallest amounts of estrogen; inhibition of the thyrotrophic hormone requires greater amounts, and that of somatotrophin still greater amounts. Even after very large doses of estrogen, apparently some growth hormone continues to be secreted, for neither chickens nor rats can be stunted with estrogen to the same extent as by hypophysectomy. The possibility remains that the failure to arrest growth is not due to incomplete inhibition of growth hormone secretion, but is due to general metabolic upsets, such as an abnormal degree of fat deposition, caused by estrogen. This effect is especially noticed in chickens.

Finally, let us consider the evidence of the part played by ovarian hormones in the release of LH. Experimentally, the ability of estrogen to cause ovulation has been shown in a variety of animals, including cows, rabbits, rats, and sheep. It seems possible that this is one of the roles played by estrogen in the normal cycle. However, progesterone also is capable of causing release of LH, and hence ovulation, in the animals listed above and in chickens. At first it is difficult to see how this particular hormone can have anything to do with ovulation, for it is usually associated with the formed and functional corpus luteum, which is not formed until after ovulation. Recent work has shown that in at least some animals progesterone is secreted by preovulatory follicles; this may or may not be evidence that luteinization begins before ovulation has taken place. This statement will be discussed further in another connection; for the time being let us keep in mind that progesterone can release LH in experimental animals and that it may be the hormone that causes release of LH during the ovulatory cycle of mammalian females.

There remain two other mechanisms by which estrogen and progesterone may produce their effects. It is possible that neither hormone "releases" LH. Instead, they may sensitize the follicle to the action of LH and thus make ovulation possible, or they may incite the hypothalamus to give the anterior lobe of the pituitary the necessary (humoral?) stimulus for the release of LH. Further data on this point will be presented later.

The three models in Figure 3-2 show graphically the ways in which

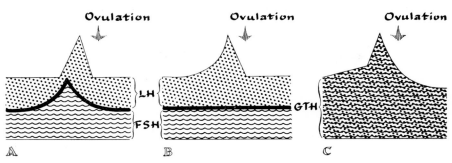

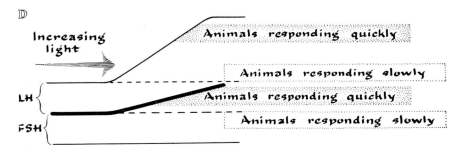

Figure 3-2. *Three of the possible ways in which the pituitary gland may control the cyclic ovarian function. In A the classical assumption is made that both FSH and LH fluctuate and control the rate of follicular growth and later ovulation. It is equally plausible to assume (B) that the rate of FSH release remains constant and that only LH fluctuates. Both follicular maturation and ovulation can also be explained on the assumption (C) that the pituitary gland releases a gonadotrophic complex, not FSH and LH as separate entities. D is a model of the relationship of the onset of anestrous season in sheep. Decreasing light would cause the onset of the breeding season by reversing the hormone levels (see text).*

the ebb and flow of pituitary gonadotrophins may account for the events of the reproductive cycles of females. In models A, B, and C, ovulation (indicated by an arrow) takes place after the greatest out-pouring of the "ovulating hormone" has occurred. In all three models cognizance is taken of the observation that the total gonadotrophic potency of the pituitary glands of animals in heat is low. In A and B the "ovulating hormone" is assumed to be LH. In A it is assumed that both FSH and LH fluctuate during the cycle but that, contrary to traditional theory, the secretion of neither even approaches zero. In B it is postulated that FSH secretion remains constant throughout the cycle and that follicular maturation and the "ovulatory spurt" are due to slowly increasing rates of LH secretion, ovulation following the greatest out-pouring of LH. In C the assumption is made that FSH and LH are artifacts of chemical fractionation and that the pituitary gland secretes a mixture of these two hormones—a true gonadotrophic complex. In this case follicular maturation is accomplished by fluctuations in the rate of secretion of the complex as a whole. Here the "ovulating hormone" is the gonadotrophic complex and not LH alone.

Good experimental evidence is available for each of these models, but none of them can be supported completely. There is considerable evidence in favor of B, which has the advantage over A that it does not call for the simultaneous control of both FSH and LH and is thus much simpler than A. All three models are in accord with the theory that the release of gonadotrophic hormones from the pituitary gland is controlled neurohumorally—by one or both of the ovarian hormones and a neurally released (chemically unidentified) humoral substance of hypothalamic origin.

In all three models it is suggested that the rates of secretion of FSH and LH by individual females fall within the areas delimited by the lines. So long as the rates of secretion are within these limits, reproductive performance is normal; when the rate of secretion of one or of both of the hormones is outside these limits, reproductive performance becomes erratic or even completely abnormal. The ovulation rate would be higher in females secreting larger quantities of hormone than in those secreting smaller quantities.

Model D gives one possible explanation of the onset of the anestrous season in sheep. It is known that increasing light causes sheep to cease breeding in the spring. It is also known that the pituitary glands of sheep contain more gonadotrophic hormone during the nonbreeding season than during the breeding season. It is assumed that, if increasing light increases the rate of secretion of gonadotrophins by the pituitary, the concentrations of these hormones will rise beyond the limits (broken lines) within which normal reproductive performance is possible. Animals that respond to light slowly may continue to reproduce normally long after animals that respond to light more quickly have entered the nonbreeding season.

Stage 2: Luteal Phase.   One can no longer believe that the information which has been obtained on the endocrinology of the luteal phase on the laboratory rat or mouse holds for other mammals. In fact, the rat must now be considered as an exception to the rule; work done on other mammals suggests a different endocrine mechanism operating in the formation and the maintenance of corpora lutea. This is so because prolactin, which is generally assumed to be responsible for the maintenance of the formed corpus luteum, is luteotrophic only in the rat and in no other mammal in which it has been tried. Even though it can be argued that in other mammals the role of prolactin may be assumed by another as yet unidentified luteotrophic hormone (LTH), there are other problems (to be mentioned later) which make it advisable to discuss the luteal phase in rats separately.

LUTEAL PHASE IN RATS.   As already noted, LH induces ovulation. It is also responsible for the mobilization and deposition of cholesterol in forming the corpora lutea of rats. If there is no mating, no LTH (prolactin) is released and, according to the best available evidence, the corpora lutea of the normal estrous cycle of the rat do not produce progesterone. Supporting this statement is the evidence that there are no changes in the uterine endometrium which are usually attributed to progesterone action (see Chapter 4). If the rat mates, LTH is released and the corpus luteum becomes activated to secrete progesterone by synthesis from the stored cholesterol, and progestational changes occur in the endometrium.

LUTEAL PHASE IN OTHER MAMMALS.   In contrast to the rat and mouse, prolactin has no effect on the life span of corpora lutea of guinea pigs, rabbits, women, cattle, or swine, with, perhaps, a very temporary effect in sheep. Thus it appears that prolactin is not the LTH of these species. It seems possible that no trophic agent other than LH is required for the formation of corpora lutea and for their ability to synthesize progesterone.

The experimental evidence underlying these considerations is as follows. We already know that estrogen and other steroid hormones, if given in large enough doses, inhibit the release of hypophyseal hormones. If one administers (by feeding or injection) large doses of progesterone to such animals as pigs, sheep, or guinea pigs during pregnancy, their corpora lutea either completely disappear or are reduced very greatly in size. The conclusion seems justified that the administered progesterone prevents the release of a luteotrophic agent from the hypophysis, resulting in partial or complete luteolysis. If the progesterone is administered to nonpregnant animals (pigs) with normal cycles and if the treatment is started as close as possible to the expected time of ovulation, it develops that in spite of the continuous administration of high doses of progesterone (which in pregnant pigs resulted in luteolysis), the formation of normal corpora lutea of the cycle is not prevented. They remain functional for the same length of time during the cycle as do corpora lutea of normal untreated pigs. In fact, the only way it was found possible to prevent the formation of corpora lutea was to initiate progesterone treatment early enough in the cycle to block LH release and thus prevent ovulation. These experiments led to two conclusions: (a) the luteotrophic agent could be released together with, or very close to, the time of release of LH; and (b) for complete formation of corpora lutea no sustained presence of a luteotrophic agent is necessary. If formation of corpora lutea were to depend on sustained support of a hypophyseal hormone, then the progesterone treatment begun at the time of ovulation would have blocked the release of the luteotrophic agent and formation would have been only partial or the resulting luteal structures would have been defective.

The obvious technical defect of this experiment was the presence of the intact, albeit blocked, pituitary gland, and one further experiment was performed to shed light on the mechanism of corpus luteum formation and maintenance. Again, advantage was taken of the ability of progesterone to block the hormonal output by the pituitary gland. This time the animals (pigs) were continuously treated with progesterone until all components of the ovary had degenerated and only very small follicles (1–2 millimeters) were present. Continuing the progesterone blockade, the pigs were now injected with a gonadotrophic hormone (Pregnant Mare Serum, PMS), which resulted in the formation of follicles of ovulable size. These follicles were ovulated with a *single* injection of an LH-containing hormone (Human Chorionic Hormone, HCG) and resulted in the development of corpora lutea, even though the pituitary gland continued to be blocked by progesterone for the 8 to 10 day period during which their evolution was completed. This time of 8–10 days is the period of the normal estrous cycle during which corpora lutea usually retain morphological and physiological integrity. At autopsy these artificially induced corpora lutea were found to be of normal weight and morphology, and they contained as much progesterone as did corpora of the same age taken from control pigs. It should be remembered that the former were formed following a *single* injection of a luteinizing hormone and during a period during which the animal's own pituitary gland was blocked by the progesterone treatment. Thus, no luteotrophic substance is presumed to have acted on these induced corpora lutea during the period (8–10 days) during which they developed and formed histologically normal corpora lutea capable of secreting progesterone.

Recently, Denamur and Mauleon and their coworkers have succeeded in perfecting a method of surgical hypophysectomy in adult sheep and pigs. Although the work on pigs is still in its beginning, hypophysectomy of adult ewes has confirmed the results obtained by the indirect method (physiological hypophysectomy) outlined above. Ewes hypophysectomized either shortly before or immediately after ovulation can and do form histologically and morphologically normal corpora lutea which persist for the same length of time as they do in intact nonpregnant sheep. Furthermore, it appears on the basis of preliminary results that corpora lutea formed in the absene of hypophyseal support are just as efficient in synthesizing progesterone as are corpora lutea of comparable age of intact animals. These experiments show that, in sheep and probably in pigs, once ovulation has occurred the corpora need no further support from the hypophysis.

The evidence, derived both from pituitary blockade and from hypophysectomy, permits one to propose the following probable mechanisms of corpus luteum formation in mammals other than rats and mice (for reference and further details see Nalbandov, 1961, and Short, 1963).

1. It appears possible that the mere act of ovulation (e.g., the rupture of the follicle) may be enough of an impetus for the luteinization of the follicle cells and for the eventual formation of corpora lutea.

2. Equally plausible is the premise that LH has the double action of being an ovulating hormone and a luteotrophic agent.

3. A luteotrophic substance other than LH may be released by the pituitary. On the basis of available evidence it is impossible to say whether this substance is released together with LH. Neither is it possible to speculate on how long this release lasts, other than to say that it exerts its action on corpus luteum formation in less than 1 or at most 2 days (in guinea pigs possibly 3 days) after ovulation. After that time the corpus luteum of the *cycle* needs no further hypophyseal support to complete its development and to remain functional until about the midpoint of the cycle, when it begins to degenerate morphologically as well as to lose its ability to synthesize progestrone. The same argument would hold regardless of whether the luteotrophic agent is an as yet unknown hormone or whether it is LH. Further support for the hypothesis of a single and temporally limited release of a luteotrophic agent (vs. continuous support during the luteal phase) comes from recent experiments with guinea pigs; in these experiments it was also found that corpora lutea of the cycle continue to develop and to

synthesize progesterone even after hypophysectomy, which was performed shortly after ovulation.

We have stated that progesterone is unable to prevent formation of corpora lutea of the cycle but that it can readily cause luteolysis of corpora lutea of pregnancy. This suggests that, while the corpus of the cycle needs only a single impetus of relatively short duration, the corpus of pregnancy needs sustained and continuous support from a hypophyseal luteotrophic agent. As will be pointed out in another context, uterine contents seem to play a role in being able to signal to the hypophysis (via the hypothalamus) that the uterus is pregnant and that the corpus luteum should not be allowed to degenerate—for example, that additional luteotrophin should be released (see Chapter 3, Implantation).

If one grants the assumption that in the rat and in the other mammals corpora lutea of the cycle are formed solely as the result of ovulation, then there is no need for a trophic hormone which "directs" the mechanism of follicular luteinization beyond the initial stages immediately following ovulation. This assumption is supported, to some ex-

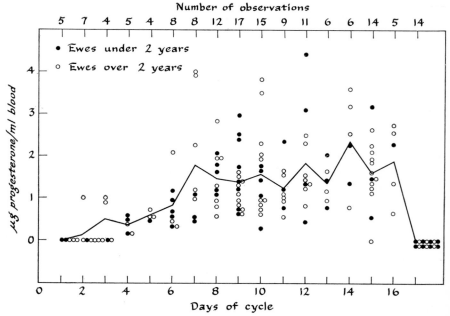

Figure 3-3. *Concentration of progesterone (determined chemically) in the ovarian venous blood of ewes during the estrous cycles (Adapted from Short and Moore, 1959, J. Endocrinol. 19:288).*

tent at least, by experimental evidence. The difference between rats and "non-rats" lies in the fact that in rats and mice corpora lutea of the cycle do not become "functional" (they do not secrete progesterone), while in animals with long cycles corpora lutea do secrete progesterone. To make corpora lutea of the cycle functional and to cause them to persist in mice and rats, the trophic stimulus of prolactin is needed, which, in these species, is released in response to mating. In other species the prolongation of the life span of corpora lutea depends on successful implantation of a conceptus, which results in a signal for the release of an as yet unidentified luteotrophic hypophyseal substance. In support of this contention are data obtained on sheep hypophysectomized after day 30 or 40 of pregnancy in which pregnancy continues while the corpus luteum degenerates completely.

According to the most recent evidence obtained from animals with long cycles (sheep), the corpus luteum synthesizes and releases progesterone into the ovarian vein almost for the entire duration of the cycle (Fig. 3-3). This finding is difficult to reconcile with the fact that histologically the corpus luteum of sheep begins to show degenerative changes as early as day 10 of the cycle and that luteal cells have become very atrophic by day 14. In contrast, in the guinea pig, which also has a 16-day cycle, progesterone concentration in corpora lutea begins to decline on day 6 of the cycle (Fig. 3-4). This decline coincides nicely

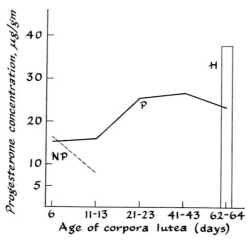

Figure 3-4. *Progesterone concentration in corpora lutea of guinea pigs during the estrus cycle, pregnancy and after hysterectomy (NP, not pregnant; P, pregnant; H, hysterectomized). (Data from: Rowland and Short, 1959, J. Endocrinol. 19:81.)*

with the degeneration of the luteal cells. To reconcile the discrepancies noted requires additional work.

As a general rule, which holds for all animals except for primates, removal of the uterus causes maintenance of corpora lutea, just as would pregnancy or pseudopregnancy. In rats, for instance, hysterectomy performed shortly after ovulation causes functional corpora lutea to be maintained for a period longer than they would have been in pseudopregnancy, but shorter than in pregnancy. In hysterectomized guinea pigs, corpora lutea are maintained for the same length of time as they are in pregnant females, and they contain the same amount of progesterone as do those of pregnant females (Fig. 3-4). Corpora lutea of hysterectomized pigs, sheep, and cattle remain functional at least for the duration of pregnancy typical of the species, and perhaps longer.

In hysterectomized pigs, cattle, and guinea pigs an involution of corpora lutea can be caused by the administration of either estrogen or progesterone, just as it can in pregnant females of these species. This suggests that a hypophyseal factor is involved in the maintenance of corpora lutea after hysterectomy, which can be blocked by the injection of steroids. It also hints at the possibility that normally the uterus either neurally or humorally prevents this luteotrophic substance from being secreted. Furthermore, it is in apparent contradiction to the hypothesis to be invoked elsewhere that uterine contents (inert beads or implanted living blastocysts) signal the pituitary gland via the nervous system that pregnancy has been initiated and that the corpora should be maintained. In the absence of more data it is impossible to resolve this dilemma other than to suggest that the uterus may constantly maintain a positive signal *not* to secrete the luteotrophic substance—that is, an inhibiting signal rather than a releasing one. In the presence of a conceptus or in the absence of the uterus the inhibition is removed and luteotrophin is now secreted freely. We shall encounter another instance of a signal *not* to release a hormone, when we discuss the mechanism of ovulation in birds. We should also recall the evidence presented elsewhere that when the hypophysis is under hypothalamic control, the latter normally *inhibits* release of prolactin (the LTH of rats), a principle which may or may not have general validity for other animals.

It also appears that the uterus may have a direct effect on ovarian structures in addition to a possible pituitary mediated one. Du Mesnil du Buisson (see Anderson et al. in Nalbandov, 1963) has performed partial uterine ablations in pigs in which he removed a part of the uterine horn at the tubal end on one side, but left the opposite side undisturbed. He killed 54 animals, 33 to 115 days after the operation, and found apparently functional corpora lutea on the side on which the piece of uterine horn was removed, while in the ovary on the undisturbed side they had regressed, so that the ovary contained only small follicles. If the ovary on the "hysterectomized" side in which the corpora lutea persisted was removed, the remaining ovary underwent normal cycles, including ovulation and corpus luteum formation. No explanation is available for this asynchronous function of the two ovaries, although it is obvious that both "local" and systemic neural and hormonal effects are operating in this paradoxical situation.

Bioassay of Pituitary Glands

Since the initial demonstration of the relation between the pituitary gland and the ovaries, much work has been done on the characterization of the gonadotrophic hormones. All bioassays used for this characterization are built on the fact that the ovaries of immature females can be stimulated to greater growth by the injection of exogenous gonadotrophins, and that (within limits) the response of the ovaries is proportional to the amount of hormone injected. Although intact, immature females can be used for this assay under certain conditions, hypophysectomized females, for reasons discussed earlier, are preferred.

In a typical assay, the increase in ovarian weight produced in hypophysectomized female rats or mice receiving two injections daily for 4 or 5 days is used as an index of the amount of gonadotrophic hormone present in the substance injected. The degree of luteinization or follicular development gives a rough clue to the proportions of FSH and LH in the substance. An ovary that is much heavier than the ovary of control animals, and that contains only "clear" follicles, can be assumed to have been stimulated by "pure" FSH. Cloudiness of the follicles and some uterine growth indicate contamination by LH; the formation of corpora lutea points to the presence of much LH without giving a clue to the exact proportion in which FSH and LH are present. LH alone has no effect on the ovaries of hypophysectomized females and must be assayed by other methods. If crude pituitary gland tissue is being assayed, low ovarian weight may indicate low concentration of both FSH and LH. For this reason, this type of test is not very satisfactory, and the results must be interpreted with caution. The situation is improved somewhat if comparison is made between the potencies of glands belonging to some logical sequence, such as the days of a cycle, the different stages of pregnancy, or males vs. females.

Before discussing the results obtained from bioassays of pituitary glands, we shall consider the kind of information obtained from such assays. Does an assay reflect the amount of hormone that happened to be stored in the gland at the time when it was collected? Or does it represent the residual amount of hormone that remained in the gland after some of it had been released? The pituitary gland may produce and store gonadotrophic hormones regardless of the needs of the target tissues. To permit cyclic functioning, as in the ovary, gonadotrophic hormones may be released in response to a humoral or neural stimulus emanating from the reproductive end organs. It will be shown later that this is the way one of the gonadotrophic hormones, LH, is released. It is also possible that the production of gonadotrophins is regulated by the needs of the target tissues. If this were so, the hormone content of the pituitary gland would be related to the needs of the ovaries and would vary with the cyclic variation of the ovarian function. If this assumption were correct, the assay of a pituitary gland would reflect the physiological needs of the end organ at the time when the gland was collected, and the end organ would reflect the rate at which the gland was producing the hormone. To obtain information on this point, investigators compared the gonadotrophic potencies of individual pituitary glands of pigs with the morphological appearance of the ovaries of the same pigs during the estrous cycle. The results obtained (Table 3-2) bring out a number of points and raise several interesting questions. A highly significant and close correlation ($r = +0.69$) between gonadotrophic potency and ovarian activity suggests that the bioassay of glands of mammals does indeed measure the rate at which hormones are being produced and secreted into the blood stream. Similar conclusions have been reached by Byrnes and Meyer for the rat. The pituitary glands of pigs in heat show a very low hormone potency because they contain primarily LH. This confirms the findings of most other investigators and is compatible with the theory that FSH secretion has been inhibited by increasing amounts of follicular estrogen.

Further support for the idea that there is a good correlation between the amount of hormone found in the hypophysis and the amount of physiological effect produced on the end organ, comes from studies which show that the amount of hypophyseal growth hormone is proportional to the growth rate of pigs, rats, mice, and humans. In pigs it was also shown that the genetic selection for rapid or slow rate of

Table 3-2.   Changes in ovarian morphology and gonadotrophic potency
of pituitaries of pigs

DAY OF CYCLE	PERCENT FOLLICLES IN CLASS					AVERAGE NUMBER FOLLICLES IN BOTH OVARIES	GTH IN AP*	STAGE OF CYCLE
	FOLLICLE SIZE (mm)							
	5	5–7	8–10	10	CYSTS			
4	100	...	...	...	...	13	14.7	
5	...	100	...	...	...	19	13.5	
6	56	40	...	...	4	24	17.2	
7	47	53	...	...	...	19	14.1	
8	75	25	...	...	...	49	23.5	Luteal phase
9	...	89	...	...	11	49	29.6	
10	62	38	...	...	...	42	26.1	
13	68	30	...	...	2	51	28.1	
14	51	46	3	...	...	37	22.5	
16	40	59	1	...	...	40	23.1	
17	47	52	1	...	...	45	26.4	
18	56	33	10	...	...	39	33.5	Follicular phase
19	44	9	47	...	...	57	20.5	
20	84	16	...	...	...	62	22.5	
1	5	9	76	9	1	16	13.7	Heat
1	...	...	69	31	...	13	17.1	

Source: From Robinson and Nalbandov. 1951. *J. Animal Science*, 10:469.
* Total gonadotrophic hormone in the anterior lobe of the pituitary gland measured by weight of testes (mg) of day-old chicks.

growth in reality is a selection for the ability of the hypophysis to synthesize more or less somatotrophic hormone.

During the early luteal phase in pigs (days 3–7 of the cycle), the gonadotrophic hormone potency of the pituitary gland remains low. The reason for this may be that the gland has not yet recovered from estrogen inhibition, although after experimental inhibition the gland rebounds in a much shorter time. It seems significant that on day 8 of the cycle both the gonadotrophic activity and the number of ovarian follicles rise suddenly, and that gonadotrophic potency remains high until day 20. At that time it drops just as suddenly as it had risen earlier. Because of the abruptness of the changes in pituitary activity and ovarian morphology, and because of the close correlation between these changes, the question arises whether a control mechanism other than estrogen may not be involved in the regulation of pituitary activity.

Although the number of follicles is very closely correlated with pituitary potency, the size is not. As late as 3 or 4 days before the expected ovulation, 90 percent of the follicles are much smaller than the ovulatory size. The follicles of most mammals grow very little during the luteal phase and most of the follicular phase, but undergo the "ovulatory spurt" very shortly before the expected ovulation. In the pig the ovulatory spurt may occur as late as the first day of heat, but as a rule it occurs from 1 to 3 days before ovulation. Along with the great increase in follicular size there is a drastic decrease in the number of follicles to the number that is destined to ovulate.

The reason for the ovulatory spurt is not clear. It may be due to a gradually increasing LH secretion, which, acting synergically with the available FSH, could account for the more rapid follicular growth just before ovulation, which is then precipitated by a sudden and heavy outpouring of LH. If the role of estrogen as a hormone controlling the rate of FSH secretion is accepted, the ovulatory spurt cannot be ascribed to increased FSH secretion, for this would have to coincide with the highest rate of estrogen production by the follicles. The decrease in number of follicles may be due to the shutting off of FSH; or, if one is looking for a control mechanism not involving estrogen, one can assume that FSH production remains unchanged, but that follicular atresia occurs at this time because, with rapidly increasing follicular size, there is no longer enough FSH to maintain all the follicles that started to develop earlier in the cycle. This interpretation is supported by the finding that a much larger number of follicles than is normal for the species will reach ovulatory size and ovulate if exogenous FSH and LH are injected to augment the endogenous gonadotrophin. Similarly, if a polytocous female is unilaterally castrated, the remaining ovary ovulates about as many eggs as were previously ovulated by both ovaries. This again indicates that the factor determining the number of follicles to be matured and ovulated is not of ovarian origin. When as much hormone is available for one ovary as was formerly available for two, the number of follicles is increased in response to the greater hormone stimulation.

Breeding Seasons

Since evolutionary advantage has been on the side of animals that reproduced at times when environmental conditions were most favorable for the pregnant or incubating mother and for the newborn, most of our domesticated animals, before their domestication, had distinct

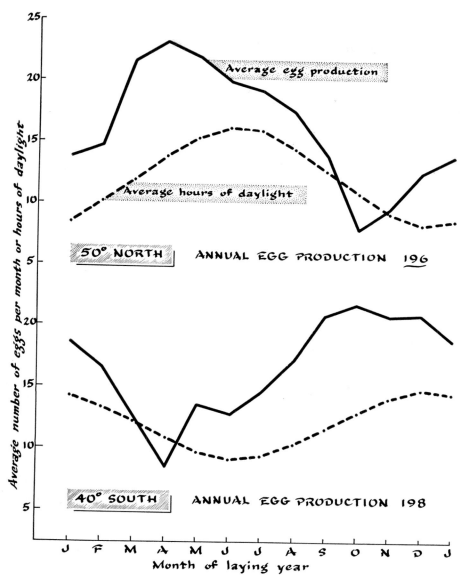

Figure 3-5. *Comparison of rates of egg production by chickens in the northern and southern hemispheres. Note that the production and light curves for 50° N (border of Canada and U.S.A.) and 40° S (southern third of Argentina) are nearly mirror images of each other. Note also that for both latitudes the rate of egg production begins to decrease or to increase somewhat before the corresponding change in the light curve. (Data from Wetham, 1933, J. Agric. Sci., 23: 383.)*

breeding seasons, just as their wild prototypes and relatives have such seasons today.

Continuous Breeders

With domestication, environmental exigencies became tempered to the point where reproductive efficiency was less dependent on adequate food supplies and on proper temperatures than it had been in the wild. As food and shelter were provided for domesticated species, their latent genetic potential for prolonged breeding seasons asserted itself, even making it possible for some species to become continuous breeders. The world "continuous" should not be understood, however, to mean unvarying; in most of these species, peaks of reproductive activity are noted. Man has distinct annual peaks of prolificacy, which vary with the latitude. In the northern hemisphere conceptions occur significantly more often in May and June, the resulting births taking place in February and March. In the southern hemisphere these peaks of conception and parturition are reversed. Similar peaks and valleys of fecundity have been noted in other continuously breeding species, such as chickens (Fig. 3-5). In chickens there also appears to be a definite correlation between the rate of reproduction and the amount of light. This correlation was noted by naturalists a long time ago, and light is still considered a prime factor in the reproductive activity of birds and mammals. (As we shall see shortly, however, the situation is not simple enough to be explained by changes in any single climatic factor such as light, temperature, or precipitation.)

Before we consider the mechanisms that may control reproductive periodicity, a few general statements concerning breeding cycles are in order. We have already noted that all species of animals can be divided into two categories: the seasonally breeding and the continuously breeding. The former include species in which the gonads of both sexes regress completely and become inactive; in other species, however, only the females become periodically sexually inactive, the males showing continuous spermato- and spermiogenesis, which appear to be independent of season. In the species that have become continuous breeders, more or less distinct peaks of prolificacy are discernible. In addition to the peaks already noted for man and chickens, similar peaks are known to exist in other species that are usually classed as continuous breeders.

On the North American continent horses breed during the spring and early summer; during the remainder of the year heats are sporadic and of unpredictable length. Conceptions, however, may occur throughout the year. Cows conceive at any time of the year, and their tendency to show seasonal peaks is disguised by the intervention of man, who, guided by such considerations as milk prices and the availability of pastures for calves, controls conceptions and creates somewhat artificial peaks of conception. If such restraints are not exercised, however, cattle show a decided peak of prolificacy in the fall, spring, and early summer, the chances of conception being distinctly less in the winter. Whereas wild rabbits show a distinct breeding season from December through July, domestic rabbits have become continuously breeding animals; they may conceive at any time of the year, but under North American climatic conditions they show a definite low point in reproductive ability during July, August, and September. There is no complete agreement whether reproductive efficiency varies seasonally in laboratory rats and mice, which are also continuously breeding species. (The sex ratios of laboratory rats and of all human populations studied are significantly higher during spring and summer.) There is, however, no doubt that the wild rat shows seasonal periodicity; its peak of prolificacy occurs from December through June. During the remainder of the year both the number of pregnant females and the litter size of those females are significantly smaller; in this species, therefore, both the efficiency of conception and the rates of ovulation and fertilization may be affected.

The examples cited leave no doubt that in most if not all continuous breeders there are peaks and troughs of prolificacy, the peaks roughly coinciding with the periods of maximum length of daylight.

Seasonal Breeders

Animals belonging to this classification may show one or two annual breeding seasons, which are separated by periods of complete sexual inactivity. During this anestrous period the gonads of females—and in some species those of males—involute completely. The testes of males are retracted from the scrotum into the body cavity; gametogenesis stops in both sexes, and the gonads resemble the gonads of sexually immature juvenile members of the species. All structures dependent on sex hormones also involute during the anestrous period.

Migratory birds are the best-known example of seasonally breeding animals, and their urge to migrate seems to be intimately connected with the functional state of the gonads. The whole problem of bird migration and its causes is too little understood and too complex to warrant discussion here. Migration is certainly not caused by one factor alone (such as gonadal recrudescence), but is probably due to an interplay of a whole series of factors, which are probably endocrine but certainly not simple.

The complexity of the problem of seasonal breeding in mammals can be illustrated by domestic sheep. A hundred sheep were checked for heat daily without being allowed to conceive over a period of three years. The average date of onset of the breeding season in each of the three years, together with the standard deviation, was found to be:

> 1951: July 8, ±40 days
> 1952: August 27, ±26 days
> 1953: September 1, ±9 days

The average dates of onset in 1952 and 1953 do not differ significantly from each other or from the average dates for other groups of sheep observed since that time at the University of Illinois. But the year 1951 was outstanding with regard to earliness of onset of the breeding season—not only for this experimental flock but for other flocks in this and neighboring states. Climatological data were obtained for these three years, but no correlation was found between the onset of the breeding season and the temperature, the average daily cloud cover, or the precipitation. The failure to find significant correlations in these data, and in similar but more extensive data covering twenty-four years and four different breeds, was disappointing because of the following experimental data: (1) It has been shown that one can control (prevent or hasten) the onset and the termination of the breeding season in sheep by manipulating the duration of the light to which they are exposed. (2) Exposure of sheep to an environmental temperature of about 45°F and to normal daylight caused them to come into heat and to conceive 30–40 days earlier than the controls, which were kept at a normal environmental temperature (Dutt and Busch, 1955). The failure to find similar cause-and-effect relations under normal conditions is puzzling and further emphasizes the difficulty of the problem involved.

Sheep also furnish an outstanding example of the fact that the breeding season is a very labile characteristic and can be modified by genetic selection. At least one Asiatic and one South American breed of sheep are known to be continuous breeders, and the Merinos and the Dorset

Horn have more prolonged breeding seasons than other common breeds.

The lability of the breeding season is further illustrated by birds. Mallards in capitivity will easily lay 60–120 eggs yearly (if they are not given a chance to incubate them), and sparrows and flickers may lay 50–80 eggs consecutively if the eggs are removed from the nests daily and the females are not allowed to brood. Similarly, the wild ancestors of domestic chickens normally lay 12–20 eggs and then incubate them, but they can be induced to lay many more eggs if they are deprived of the chance of incubating those they have laid. Because of the lability of the genetic mechanism controlling reproductive cycles in birds and mammals, it has been possible to convert seasonally breeding animals into continuously breeding ones; but it has not been possible to eliminate all the manifestations of the initial pattern of seasonal breeding, which continues to assert itself in the greater prolificacy at certain times of the reproductive year.

Effects of Light on Reproduction

There can be no doubt that light plays an important role in determining the reproductive periodicity of animals. In some animals, light governs only macroperiodicity, as it does experimentally in sheep, by determining the onset of the breeding season, but apparently does not play a major role in governing estrous cycles within the breeding season. In chickens and presumably in other birds, light governs microperiodicity as well, for not only the breeding season itself but also the laying of eggs within clutches is controlled by light. Just as there are "long-day" and "short-day" plants, so there are "long-day" and "short-day" animals, breeding activity in the former being initiated by increasing, in the latter by decreasing, length of day.

Long-day Breeders. Before we consider the role of light in reproductive events in detail, a few general comments are in order. One can easily demonstrate the effect of light by exposing seasonally breeding animals—such as sparrows, ferrets, or goats—to additional light during their nonbreeding seasons: their gonads enlarge to the size usually seen only during the breeding season, and complete gametogenesis occurs. In a series of experiments begun by Bisonette and continued by Benoît and others, it has been established that light usually acts on the retinas of the eyes and that its effect is relayed from them via the optic nerves to the hypothalamus, which responds by releasing a substance that stimulates the pituitary gland. This chain is neurohumoral. In ducks it has also been shown that neither eyeballs nor intact optic nerves are necessary for the transmission of the light stimulus to the hypothalamic region, and that the transmission to photoreceptors in the hypothalamus occurs directly through the tissue of the orbit; but if the pituitary stalk—connecting the hypothalamus and the pituitary gland—is cut, the ducks can no longer respond to light. This leads to the postulate that in normal animals light acting on the hypothalamus causes it to secrete a substance that reaches the pituitary gland via the portal system and stimulates that gland to produce or to release the gonadotrophic complex.

It does not follow, however, that the reproductive behavior of all seasonally breeding animals is totally dependent on stimulation by light. Ferrets kept in complete darkness and blinded ferrets show estrus at the same season as control animals kept under normal light conditions. Cows that are blind because their optic nerves are completely atrophied, as a result of vitamin A deficiency, show perfectly normal reproductive cycles, with normal rates of ovulation and fertilization. The reproductive activity of Eskimos is not reduced during the long winter night. Male chickens raised in total darkness show a growth of testes and combs that is, on the average, significantly below that of control birds kept under normal daylight conditions; but they do, though significantly later in life than the controls, achieve spermatogenesis. When 99 percent of the control males have testes with active spermatogenesis, only 25 percent of the males kept in the dark may have reached that stage. From these observations it appears that light is not essential for the complete development of reproductive organs but has the ability to hasten development. The most important role of light in governing reproductive functions may lie in its ability to synchronize reproductive events in all the members of a local population, causing them to be in similar reproductive states at any time of the year. Light is one environmental factor that can be expected to affect both sexes of a species in a uniform manner. Without the synchronizing effect of light, reproductive rhythms would still be possible, but reproductive efficiency would probably be greatly impaired, for the periods of reproductive readiness in different individuals would be out of phase, and their coincidence would be purely a result of chance.

Short-day Breeders. The cases briefly discussed above, including most birds and the smaller seasonally breeding mammals, all seem to have one factor in common: they respond to increasing light by increased reproductive activity. They can be properly called the "long-day" species. In contrast, the "short-day" species respond to increasing light by decreased reproductive activity (anestrus); their breeding season, in fact, is brought on by decreasing light. A prime example of such animals is the domestic sheep. We have already commented on the fact that in sheep the control of seasonal breeding seems to be very labile; we find a complete gradation from continuous breeding in some breeds, through prolonged seasonal breeding in other breeds, to very restricted breeding seasons, which, in at least one South American breed, is said to consist of 3–5 estrous cycles each year.

A series of experiments initiated by J. F. Sykes and extended by N. T. M. Yeates showed that one can hasten the beginning of the breeding season by reducing the amount of light normally available in the spring, and that one can end the breeding season before its normal end by increasing the amount of light. It was found that the breeding season starts 13–16 weeks after the change to decreasing length of day is made, and that the season ends 14–19 weeks after the length of day begins to increase. These findings may seem hard to reconcile with the idea that light "stimulates" pituitary gland activity (as it does in chickens), for the reproductive activity of sheep follows decreasing amounts of light and hence decreasing stimulation of the pituitary gland. In Figure 3-2D an attempt is made to reconcile these seemingly contradictory ideas. On the basis of the finding that the total gonadotrophic potency of a sheep's pituitary gland is significantly higher during the nonbreeding season than during the breeding season, it is postulated that the pituitary glands of all birds and mammals respond to light by greater activity. In sheep the rate of secretion of the gonadotrophic complex that is compatible with reproductive functioning is below the maximum capacity of the gland for such secretion. With increasing light the pituitary gland of sheep therefore secretes more than the compatible amount of gonadotrophic hormones, possibly leading to an imbalance between the FSH and the LH and making normal reproductive performance impossible. The endocrine limits within which the different species can function normally are apparently quite flexible and subject to modification by genetic selection. This may account for the fact that within ovines we encounter the whole gamut of continuous breeding, prolonged breeding seasons, and very short breeding seasons.

To explain why sheep begin to show cyclic activity of ovarian function with the onset of the breeding season, we should recall that with decreasing length of daylight the amount of gonadotrophic hormone synthesized by the hypophysis drops to a point compatible with follicular growth and estrogen production. Here we must invoke the ovary-pituitary feedback mechanism, which is responsible for cyclic behavior of all ovarian function. That the feedback mechanism does not function perfectly at the beginning of the breeding season (or at its end) is shown in Table 4-1. The reason why the oscillations are not normal at these periods—deviating significantly from 16 days—may be because both at the beginning and at the end of the season not enough follicular estrogen is produced to cause a more precise feedback relationship between the ovaries and the hypophysis.

One further example should be cited to point out that there is significant variation between species with regard to the response elicited by various light regimes. Some birds reproduce essentially normally under a great variety of light regimes, from almost total darkness to continuous light. There is a high positive correlation between the amount of light received and the egg-laying activity of the females. In sheep increasing amounts of light seem to cause an imbalance in the gonadotrophic hormones, resulting in a sexually quiescent period (the nonbreeding season). If rats are exposed to continuous lighting, normal cycles disappear within a very short time after exposure and rats show what is called "continuous estrus." Their ovaries contain no corpora lutea but only large follicles which do not ovulate, the uteri are enlarged, and the vaginas show constant cornification—all testifying to continuous secretion of estrogen. In birds the margin of tolerance is such that the light-induced increase in gonadotrophin results in increased egg layings; in sheep it leads to an imbalance of hormones to which the ovary is incapable of responding; and in rats it leads to an overstimulation of the ovaries and apparently a deficiency in LH, since these follicles are incapable of ovulating.

We may note here that the identical condition of constant estrus can be produced in at least two other ways. One is to place electrolytic lesions in the anterior region of the hypothalamus; the other is to administer to prepubertal female rats (about 5 days old) a single dose of a steroid hormone (for instance, 1.0 milligrams of testosterone). When these animals reach an age at which their controls have begun to show normal ovarian and vaginal cyclic activity, the steroid-treated females show constant estrus, with large ovaries containing many large vesicular follicles; these follicles secrete estrogen, evidenced by continuous vaginal cornification and the absence of corpora lutea. In rats with electrolytic lesions—as well as those in which constant estrus was induced by prepubertal treatment with a steroid—cyclic activity can be induced by injecting them with progesterone, which presumably inhibits LH release and allows it to accumulate to the level where it can cause ovulation. In both types of treated rats ovulation can also be induced quite easily by the injection of exogenous LH. It thus appears that in rats in constant estrus, regardless of how this condition was induced, the breakdown of cyclic reproductive activity occurs because insufficient ovulation-inducing hormone is stored in the pituitary gland.

Finally, it seems important to point out again that no single factor can explain the phenomenon of seasonal breeding or of reproductive rhythm. Light, temperature, adequacy of the food supply, neural stimuli (such as the presence of males or of other animals), time of feeding, and probably a host of other factors—singly or, more probably, in combination—are responsible for the reproductive rhythm of birds and mammals.

The Gonadotrophic Complex in Reproductive States Other Than the Cycle

Pregnancy

Our interest in the gonadotrophic potency of the pituitary gland of pregnant females was originally due to an attempt to explain their suspension of the estrous or menstrual cycle. It was also important to see if there was any correlation between the gonadotrophic potency of pituitary glands and the reproductive efficiency of polytocous animals. In neither cycling nor pregnant pigs is there any correlation between the gonadotrophic potency of the pituitary and the number of eggs ovulated or of corpora lutea formed. This is in sharp contrast to the high correlation between hormone content and the number of ripening follicles and the number of follicles destined to ovulate (Table 3-2). This dissociation between gonadotrophic potency and efficiency of ovulation may have several explanations. The amounts of LH released may be the same, regardless of the number of follicles to be ovulated; or small amounts of LH may be as effective as large amounts in inducing ovulation. If release of LH is a neurohumoral phenomenon even in spontaneously ovulating mammals, as it is known to be in some of them, one would not expect to find a correlation between efficiency of ovulation and the quantity of LH released. However, there always remains the possibility that the assay methods employed are too crude to detect minor changes in LH potency, changes that may nevertheless be of profound physiological significance to the animal.

The gonadotrophic potency of the pituitary glands of both swine and cows is high at the time of conception, but it diminishes gradually during the course of pregnancy and is lowest just before parturition. This seems to be the general rule for all species investigated with the exception of the rat, in which the potency increases. In the cow and the sow, the steady decrease in gonadotrophic potency is coupled with a progressive decline in follicular development in the ovaries. In both species the decrease in pituitary potency is inversely related to the increasing production of estrogen by the placenta during pregnancy. Placental estrogen may be responsible for the inhibition of the pituitary gland during pregnancy. It also suggests that the effect of estrogen is to prevent the formation of gonadotrophic hormone rather than to prevent its release from the gland.

Since, during the first trimester of pregnancy, the total gonadotrophic potency of pituitary glands does not sink below that found in cycling animals, an explanation for the absence of cycles during pregnancy must be looked for elsewhere, possibly in an imbalance of the two members of the complex, an imbalance that may be brought about by the rising tide of progesterone or estrogen or of both.

Castration

The gonadotrophic potency of the pituitary glands of both sexes is always higher in castrates than in intact animals. Here again the power of estrogen (and, to a lesser extent, of androgen) to inhibit the pituitary function is invoked to explain the increase in potency. After the inhibiting influence of the gonadal hormones is removed by castration, the pituitary gland is no longer restrained in its formation of gonadotrophins. This interpretation is supported by experimental evidence; the rise in the gonadotrophic potency of castrates of both sexes can be prevented or returned to normal by the injection of either estrogen or androgen. In such experiments it is found that estrogen is much more efficient than androgen in inhibition of the pituitary, and that androgen is more effective than the other hormones classified as steroids (see Chapter 6).

Breeding Seasons

The problem of breeding seasons will be taken up in detail elsewhere. It is appropriate to point out here, however, that the failure of sheep to show estrus during part of the year is not due to a reduction in pituitary function, as has been commonly assumed. On the contrary, their pituitary glands contain significantly more total gonadotrophic hormone during the nonbreeding season than during the estrous cycle. This is reflected in ovarian activity during the nonbreeding period; the average diameter of all follicles and the diameters of the largest follicles are the same then as during the estrous cycle. There are, however, significantly fewer follicles during the nonbreeding season. Nothing is known about the proportion of FSH and LH in the pituitaries during the two reproductive stages, but it is tempting to assume that the anestrous period is caused by an imbalance of the two hormones. This could be brought about by a disproportionate increase in FSH and a decreased or unaltered rate of LH secretion. This contention is supported by the finding that ovulation can be caused in some anestrous sheep by the injection of LH alone.

Prepubertal vs. Sexually Mature Animals

Because the gonads of most immature mammals will respond to exogenous gonadotrophins, even producing fertilizable and viable eggs, and because spontaneous precocious sexual maturity sometimes occurs, it seems that the onset of sexual maturity is primarily determined by the pituitary function and does not depend on the ability of the gonads to respond to hormonal stimulation. In a recent study, in which the pituitary glands of pigs ranging in age from one to three hundred days were assayed for gonadotrophic potency, it was found that the glands were significantly more potent before puberty than after it. There is a steady decrease in potency from the age of one day to sexual maturity. After the onset of sexual maturity the gonadotrophic potency remains almost unchanged throughout the reproductive life of the animal. Nothing is known about changes in the FSH-LH ratio during this period, but it appears that the prepubertal period (the nonbreeding season of the young!) may be due to an imbalance between the two components of the gonadotrophic complex. The assumption that the pituitary glands of the young secrete primarily FSH is supported by the fact that the ovaries of immature females show considerable follicular development, while the estrogen-dependent duct system shows quite insignificant growth. The prepubertal period may thus be compared to the anestrous period of seasonally breeding mammals such as sheep. In both instances the high gonadotrophic potency of the pituitary glands is correlated with a nonbreeding period and must be lowered (increase in LH secretion?) before normal reproductive cycles can begin.

Fractionation of the Gonadotrophic Complex

Since the demonstration that the two hormones of the gonadotrophic complex cause the cyclic ovarian function, attempts have been made to separate this complex into its components, FSH and LH. This has been accomplished by a variety of chemical and enzymatic means, and recently both FSH and LH of great purity have been obtained. Although the purely physiological evidence leaves little doubt that the pituitary gland produces two hormones that have different effects, there is increasing certainty that neither of the two is ever secreted without the other. There is much evidence (some of it intuitive) that FSH is produced continuously at a steady rate and that the factor responsible for the cyclic behavior of the ovarian function is LH, the production of which fluctuates. The question therefore arises whether chemical fractionation of the complex, which forcibly splits FSH from LH, may not be producing artifacts that have no counterpart in the physiological economy of the normally functioning pituitary gland. Much has been learned about the function of FSH and LH from the fractionation of the complex obtained from crude pituitary gland tissue, but much remains to be learned about the physiological activity of the two hormones when they are still parts of a unit secreted by the anterior lobe and not fragments obtained by chemical fractionation.

Classification of Gonadotrophins

Chorionic Gonadotrophins

In 1927, when P. E. Smith opened the field of endocrinology by his initial experiments with hypophysectomy and replacement therapy,

Ascheim and Zondek discovered a gonadotrophic hormone in the urine and the blood of pregnant women. They assumed that this hormone was of pituitary origin and called it prolan (later subdivided into pro-lan A and B). Subsequent work has shown that this hormone does not come from the pituitary gland but is made by cells covering the chorionic villi (the cytotrophoblasts). It was then called "anterior pituitary like" hormone (APL). Still later this too was found to be a misnomer, and both terms were discarded in favor of "chorionic gonadotrophin" or "hormone of human pregnancy." Chorionic gonadotrophin (HCG) shows largely LH-like effects. Older studies had shown that it appears only during the early stages of pregnancy in women, and that it had no demonstrable effects in hypophysectomized rats and mice. This lead to the supposition that it showed gonadotrophic activity by its effect on the pituitary gland of assay animals, causing that gland to release its own gonadotrophic complex. The most recent work (Lyon and others), however, has shown (1) that chorionic gonadotrophin is present in appreciable amounts throughout pregnancy, the peak of its production occurring during the early weeks; (2) that it does have gonadotrophic action in hypophysectomized females if it is given in sufficiently high doses; (3) that it changes qualitatively from early to late pregnancy (Table 3-3). The fact that this hormone is found in

Table 3-3. **Qualitative changes in urinary gonadotrophins in human pregnancy during period of rapid increase in hormone titer**

DAYS AFTER OVULATION	M.U.U. 24 HOURS	EFFECT ON OVARIES OF RATS			UTERINE WEIGHT (mg)
		FOLLICLES*	CORPORA LUTEA†	WEIGHT (mg)	
5–16	35–100	None	None	8–24	27–43
19–23	150–200	S, M, L	lut F	18–29	38–53
26–33	5,000–15,000	L, cysts	CL	44–88	81–164
35–50	75,000	L, cysts	CL	58–129	117–154
121–238	20,000–40,000	S, M, L	None or lut F	22–60	50–109
Control	. . .	S, few	None	10	22

SOURCE: After Lyon and others. 1955. *Endocrinology*, 53:674.
* S, M. L = small, medium, large.
† lut F = luteinized follicles.

the urine of pregnant women is the basis of most pregnancy tests. In pregnant women, it first appears in the urine at about 30 days, reaches a peak at about 60 days, and decreases in amount at about 80 days. This hormone has been found in the urine of other primates (rhesus monkeys and chimpanzees), but it has not been found in the urine of other mammals.

In women, high urinary gonadotrophic titers are also characteristic of certain malignancies, such as chorioepithelioma and hydatiform moles. It is also noteworthy that substantial amounts of gonadotrophic hormone (largely FSH), which can be detected by the standard pregnancy tests, appear in the urine of men with testicular neoplasms.

Urinary Gonadotrophins

Gonadotrophic hormones are found in the urine of normal non-pregnant women, but at a much lower concentration than in that of pregnant women. A rise in the concentration of gonadotrophic hormone occurs midway between two menstrual periods. This "ovulatory peak" is thought to coincide with or to precede ovulation. The hormone is probably of pituitary origin and shows predominantly FSH effects when given to test animals.

Surgical or physiological castration (menopause) causes an increase in urinary gonadotrophins. This hormone, too, shows mostly FSH activity and is of pituitary origin.

Normal men have in the urine small quantities of an FSH-like hormone, which greatly increases in amount after castration.

Pregnant Mare's Serum (PMS)

In 1930, Cole and Hart made the important discovery that the blood of mares between the 40th and 140th days of pregnancy contains large quantities of a gonadotrophic hormone (called by them equine gonadotrophin). Unlike the hormone of human pregnancy, which is formed by placental tissue, the equine gonadotrophin of pregnancy is probably formed in the endometrial cups of the pregnant uterus; and, whereas human chorionic gonadotrophin is found in high concentrations in the urine, PMS occurs almost exclusively in the blood. PMS remains in the blood stream not only in mares but also in animals into which it is injected. For this reason a single injection is as effective as the same dose divided into a larger number of injections—in distinct contrast to other gonadotrophins, which are metabolized rapidly and are more effective in multiple divided doses.

Whereas human chorionic gonadotrophin shows predominantly LH effects, PMS shows both FSH and LH effects. When PMS is given to hypophysectomized female rats in small doses, it has predominantly an FSH effect; when the doses are increased, the LH effect asserts itself and produces ovulation or luteinization, depending on the conditions under which the PMS is injected. However, the PMS complex is not comparable to the pituitary gonadotrophic complex. All attempts to fractionate PMS chemically, and to divide the complex into FSH and LH, have thus far failed.

PMS is a useful tool in endocrine research. It is easily available commercially, and one can prepare it under ordinary laboratory conditions by bleeding mares at the right stage of gestation. It can be easily standardized, a quality that makes it especially valuable for certain therapeutic or experimental purposes. It produces primarily follicular growth when given subcutaneously, ovulation when subcutaneous injection is followed by intravenous injection. Because it has high FSH activity, it frequently produces cysts instead of follicles, especially when the doses are large and the period of injection is prolonged. By use of the minimum effective doses over the shortest possible time, this difficulty can frequently be overcome.

Pituitary Gonadotrophins

The pituitaries of all vertebrates studied are known to secrete a hormone complex consisting of FSH and LH. There are significant differences among the species, however, in the ratio at which the two components of the complex are produced. We have already pointed out how this ratio differs within the estrous cycle of one species. When the FSH and LH potencies of the pituitary glands of different species are compared during the same stage of the cycle, considerable differences are found. The pituitary glands of cattle are very rich in LH and low in FSH; the reverse is true of human pituitary glands and those of horses. The significance of these differences is not known, for cattle, sheep, and pigs manage to reproduce quite well though they have a high LH content, and rabbits, rats, and horses though they have a high FSH content. The duration of heat, or sexual receptivity, is generally longer in animals in which the FSH-LH ratio is high. The ratio increases successively in the species cattle, sheep, pigs, horses, and women, and the duration of sexual receptivity is 18 hours for cattle, 1 day for sheep, 2–3 days for pigs, 5–10 days for horses, and the whole 28 days of the menstrual cycle for women. There seems to be an inverse relationship between the amount of LH found in (and secreted by?) the pituitary gland and the duration of sexual receptivity.

Interrelation Between the Hypothalamus and the Hypophysis

During the infancy of endocrinology, scientists were quite content to think simply in terms of hormonal feedback mechanisms and ascribed to them the major role in controlling the rate of flow of this or that hormone, which in turn governed the rate of function of the glands controlled by these hormones. A classical example of such a hormonal feedback mechanism is the interrelationship between hypophyseal FSH and follicular estrogen. Increasing amount of FSH cause growth of follicles, which secrete estrogen; as the blood level of the latter rises, due to follicular enlargement, estrogen inhibits FSH production and release and follicular growth slows down. When follicles reach ovulatory size, the same hormonal feedback mechanism (of which we shall speak in another connection), releases hypophyseal LH, resulting in ovulation. Similar feedback mechanisms were postulated and successfully demonstrated for the rate of thyroid function—in which the blood level of thyroxine governs the rate of release of TSH—and for the rate of adrenal function—in which the blood level of adrenal steroids signals for increased or decreased ACTH release. For many years these mechanisms of maintaining hormonal homeostasis were thought to be perfectly adequate to explain the phenomena of the cyclic behavior of the ovaries and the normally steady state of the thyroids and the adrenals. However, within recent years it has developed that the hormonal feedback system represents only half of the whole control system that regulates the endocrine events of the body. The other half of it is the nervous system, both the nervous and endocrine system being closely interlocked.

General Considerations

For the time being (qualifying statements will be made later), let us say that no hypophyseal hormone is released without a direct or indirect signal for such a release from the internal peripheral environment. Such signals may be intended either for the adenohypophysis or for the neural lobe.

If they are intended for the neural lobe the problem is relatively easily solved because the latter is innervated so that the demand for the release of either oxytocine or vasopressin can be and is obeyed instantly. It is now established beyond reasonable doubt that the neural lobe of the pituitary serves only as a reservoir for the hormones that are actually synthesized in the paraventricular and supraoptic nuclei of the hypothalamic region (see Fig. 3-6), from where they migrate along the supra-optic pituitary tract that connects the hypothalamus and the neural lobe. If this tract is cut and blocked, an accumulation of neurosecretory granules occurs on the hypothalamic side of the block, and depletion occurs on the neurohypophyseal side as the neural lobe is being emptied of its hormone stores. This arrangement probably explains why, as we shall see later, the removal of the neural lobe does not always lead to symptoms of deficiency of oxytocin or vasopressin.

If the signals from the periphery are intended for the anterior lobe of the hypophysis, the problem of relaying the signal becomes much more complicated because that gland is not innervated. Instead it is connected to the median eminence and the hypothalamic nuclei by a very elaborate blood system—called the portal system of the hypothalamo-hypophyseal unit. In general it is correct to say that blood flows mainly in one direction, from the hypothalamus down to the adenohypophysis. The afferent nerve endings from the periphery are known to terminate at the neurosecretory cells of the hypothalamus. (At this point Fig. 3-7 should be studied carefully and fully understood.) The demand for the release of a hormone of adenohypophyseal origin is in most cases transmitted via the afferent nerve endings, and the hypothalamic neurosecretory cells respond by elaborating *releasing factors;* these factors are transported through the portal system directly to the anterior lobe, which responds by the release of the appropriate, previously synthesized hormone.

Several releasing factors have been identified and separated out by function and they are known to be polypeptides. The ones that are best known are the corticotrophin-releasing factor (CRF), the thyrotrophin-releasing factor (TRF), and the luteinizing hormone-releasing factor (LRF). Whether some of these releasing factors (especially CRF) are oxytocin or vasopressin is at present not quite clear. It is true that in the intact rat or chicken these hormones cause ACTH release; but researchers favoring the hypothesis that CRF is chemically distinct from the neurohypophyseal hormones point out that they can act by releasing CRF, which in turn releases ACTH.

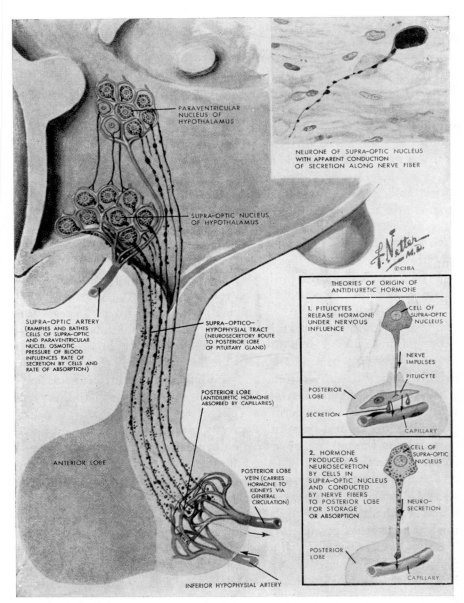

Figure 3-6. *Relation of the hypothalamus to the posterior lobe of the pituitary gland. In contrast to the anterior lobe, the posterior lobe is innervated by the supra-optico-hypophyseal tract. The secretion products are conducted along the nerve fibers from the hypothalamus to the capillaries. (Copyright 1956 by Clinical Symposia, 8:4, published by CIBA Pharmaceutical Products Inc.)*

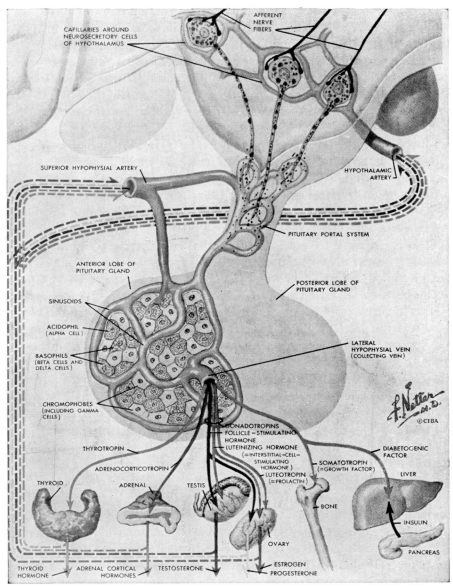

CAPILLARIES AROUND
NEUROSECRETORY CELLS
OF HYPOTHALAMUS

AFFERENT
NERVE
FIBERS

SUPERIOR HYPOPHYSIAL ARTERY

HYPOTHALAMIC
ARTERY

PITUITARY PORTAL SYSTEM

ANTERIOR LOBE OF
PITUITARY GLAND

POSTERIOR LOBE OF
PITUITARY GLAND

SINUSOIDS

ACIDOPHIL
(ALPHA CELL)

BASOPHILS
(BETA CELLS AND
DELTA CELLS)

LATERAL
HYPOPHYSIAL VEIN
(COLLECTING VEIN)

CHROMOPHOBES
(INCLUDING GAMMA
CELLS)

GONADOTROPINS
FOLLICLE–STIMULATING
HORMONE
LUTEINIZING HORMONE
(=INTERSTITIAL–CELL–
STIMULATING
HORMONE)
LUTEOTROPIN
(=PROLACTIN)

DIABETOGENIC
FACTOR

THYROTROPIN

SOMATOTROPIN
(=GROWTH FACTOR)

LIVER

ADRENOCORTICOTROPIN

THYROID

ADRENAL

TESTIS

BONE

INSULIN

OVARY

PANCREAS

THYROID
HORMONE

ADRENAL CORTICAL
HORMONES

TESTOSTERONE

ESTROGEN
PROGESTERONE

Figure 3-7. *Relation of the hypothalamus to the anterior lobe of the pituitary gland. Note that the humoral substance from neurosecretory cells in the hypothalamus passes to the anterior lobe of the pituitary gland through the portal system. Compare with Figure 3-6. (Copyright 1956 by Clinical Symposia, 8:4, published by CIBA Pharmaceutical Products Inc.)*

The existence of these releasing factors has been demonstrated both *in vivo* and *in vitro,* the necessary criteria being that the adenohypophysis, either *in situ* or in tissue culture, must "release" a hormone corresponding to the releasing factor injected. Thus, if CRF is injected into an appropriately prepared animal, the adrenal must respond by an increased synthesis of adrenocortical hormones because the CRF caused release of hypophyseal ACTH. If TRF is added to a pituitary gland *in vitro,* it must release TSH into the culture medium. Recently, evidence has been presented for the existence of the newest and least-known releasing factor—that for growth hormone. If the existence of such a releasing factor is substantiated, it would appear unlikely that it too is under neural control as are the other releasing factors; it would seem more logical if that factor were controlled by a humoral feedback mechanism.

It is interesting to note that hypothalamic extracts yielding these releasing factors also contain measurable quantities of hormones which are physiologically similar or perhaps identical with the hypophyseal hormone themselves. LH, FSH, TSH, and ACTH all have been demonstrated in extracts which themselves show potent "releasing" ability. The physiological meaning and significance of this coexistence of releasing factors and hormones in hypothalami and the median eminence, remain unknown. Pertinent here are recent experiments at the Department of Animal Science, University of Illinois. The ability of adrenals to produce corticosterone in normal and hypophysectomized cocks was compared. It was found that after hypophysectomy the rate of corticosterone synthesis was drastically reduced in some animals and only slightly reduced in others. The explanation for the dichotomy of steroid production lay not in incomplete hypophysectomy (as confirmed by serial sections of the area), but in the degree of damage to the stalk and to the median eminence. In those birds in which neither the stalk nor the median eminence were damaged, the levels of steroid production were significantly higher (although not reaching the rate of production of the controls), than they were in birds in which these structures were severely damaged or destroyed. This shows that an ACTH-like substance is being produced by the stalk and the median eminence for as long as 40–50 days *after* hypophysectomy in sufficient quantities to cause synthesis of corticosterone in significant amounts. This finding also raises the question whether ACTH itself, or a precursor of it, is being made somewhere in the hypothalamus and is stored in the median eminence and the stalk. Since these regions contain other hypophyseal hormones as well, one wonders whether they themselves or their precursors are being made in the hypothalamic region as well as in the hypophysis.

At least one of the peptides of hypothalamic origin is not a "releasing" but an inhibiting factor. In rats, it has been established that this factor inhibits the production of prolactin (or LTH).

Evidence for the existence of releasing factors has been obtained in many ways, including chemical extraction of hypothalami and by the separation and purification of these factors, at least one of which (CRF) is close to being completely characterized chemically (see Guillemin, in Nalbandov, 1963). Other approaches to this problem involve the electrical stimulation of specific areas of the hypothalamus that leads to release (or inhibition of release) of specific hormonotrophic factors such as CRF, TRF, or LRF. A map of the hypothalamo-hypophyseal region in which the various "releasing" and "inhibiting" areas are postulated is presented in Fig. 3-8. Of interest to us is the rather wide separation of the postulated LH and FSH "areas" on the map. An FSH-releasing factor may or may not exist. FSH release may be an all-or-none phenomenon, an assumption supported by results with hypothalamic lesions. Lesions placed in the basal part of the hypothalamus of sheep (corresponding to the area of the arcuate nucleus in Fig. 3-8) caused continued normal cyclic ovarian behavior but with an absence of behavioral heat. This shows that neither FSH nor LH release were hindered; however, this area is presumably the target area for estrogen and acts as a control center in determining whether the ewes will go through the necessary changes for the manifestations of psychological heat. That this area may be a "sex center" is further suggested by the observation that lesions for this general area in rats cause precocious sexual maturity significantly advancing the day of vaginal opening as well as the age at first estrus (see Ganong, in Villee, 1961).

We started this discussion by noting the curious fact that in the thirties and early forties endocrinologists were perfectly contented to get along with the endocrine system as the sole member of the mechanism maintaining homeostasis; they felt no urgent need to search for additional controls to complete the picture or fill a gap in our knowledge. Several examples of participation of the nervous system in reproductive events were then known but were considered as curious exceptions, evolutionary adaptations of this or that species, without significance for endocrine events in general. Now we find ourselves with two closely interlocked systems, the endocrine system having been demoted to coequal partner to the nervous system in the control of hormonal events. The question now seems appropriate of how these

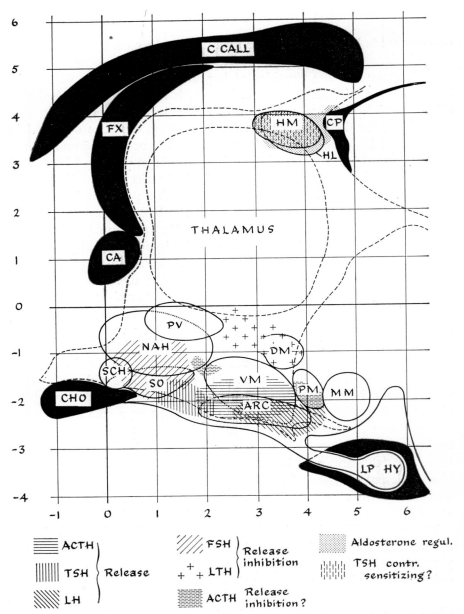

Figure 3-8. *Stimulation or electrolytic lesions of the areas shown led to the release or the inhibition of release of the hormones shown. (Redrawn from: Szentagothai, Flerko, Mess and Halasz. 1962. Hypothalamic Control of the Anterior Pituitary. Adademiai Kiado. Budapest.)*

ARC—arcuate nucleus
PM—premammilary nucleus
DM—dorso-medial nucleus
VM—ventro-medial nucleus
SO—supra-optic nucleus

SCH—supra-chiasmatic nucleus
NAH—tantero-hypothalamic nucleus
HM—habenular nucleus
CHO—optic chiasma

two systems have evolved. After all, the more complex a control system, the greater the chances for a breakdown.

Events controlled by hormones fall roughly into two categories: those requiring a status quo and those in which a sudden and rapid release of hormones is needed to cope with an emergency or to cope with a situation in which a temporary sudden copious release of a hormone is needed. In the first category would fall hormonal needs for follicular growth—a steady progressive process. The rate of FSH release can, therefore, be controlled by the slow and relatively sluggish hormonal feedback system; this, as we know, involves a gradual rise in the level of estrogen, which would eventually reduce the rate of release of FSH. In the same way we can visualize that the daily normal needs for such hormones as mineral- or glucocorticoids can be adequately provided for by the interplay between the output of these steroids by the adrenals and their feedback effect on the rate of release of hypophyseal ACTH. On the other hand, there are stress situations which call for a sudden increase in the output of these steroids, and the usual hormonal feedback system would be probably too slow to provide such a sudden rise. We can then visualize the nervous system entering into the picture, signaling for CRF to cause a rapid and immediate release of ACTH, which results in an immediate increase in mineral- and glucocorticoids.

The increased LH blood levels needed for ovulation can also be regarded as a "stress" situation (in a broad sense of that word), in that follicular rupture is thought to occur not as the result of a slowly rising blood LH level but as a sudden and short-lived increase of this hormone. In the same manner one can regard the release of milk in response to suckling as a stress situation in that the young expects to obtain milk immediately when hungry. A much longer time would be required to translate his needs into results if the slower hormonal feedback system rather than the nervous system were involved in the signal.

At the present time it is not clear whether all signals, be they neural or humoral, pass through the hypothalamus and are there translated into releasing factors or whether some signals (for instance, the depression of FSH secretion by estrogen) act directly on the pituitary gland. Certain results suggest, but do not prove, that some effects may be directly elicited from the pituitary gland. Thus, for instance, a pituitary *in vitro* will respond to added estrogen by increased prolactin synthesis and release into the medium. Since estrogen is known to have the same effect on prolactin production *in vivo,* it could be argued that in this case the hypothalamus is bypassed and the signal acts directly on the adenohypophysis.

Effects of Interrupting Connections Between Hypothalamus and Pituitary Gland

Stalk Sections. Because both the neural and the vascular connections between the hypothalamus and the pituitary gland run through the pituitary stalk, it is fairly easy to study the interrelation by cutting the stalk and thus interrupting humoral and neural intercommunication. It was learned early in such studies, however, that mere cutting of the stalk is not enough to break all connection, for the stalk regenerates, and both the neural and the vascular connection may be reestablished. One can prevent this by inserting a disk of metal, paper, or plastic between the cut ends of the stalk. When this precaution is taken, the pituitary function becomes abnormal or even stops completely with regard to the gonadotrophic hormone. Rats and rabbits thus treated fail to have estrous cycles, the testes and accessory glands shrink in both mammals and birds, and the ovaries and combs become completely atrophic in chickens. There is good evidence that section of the stalk in mammals impairs the pituitary function with regard to all pituitary hormones, but the gonadal function is affected most spectacularly. In the chicken only the gonadotrophic function of the pituitary gland appears to be affected. This fact suggests that in this species pituitary malfunction is not due to an ischemia of the gland caused by the interruption of the portal system, for it does not seem probable that ischemia would affect the formation and release of the gonadotrophic hormone without interfering with the secretion of the other pituitary hormones. In mammals as well as in birds the portal system is not the only blood supply to the pituitary, and stalk section does not reduce the systemic circulation to the gland (Fig. 3-5). It is nevertheless true that profound histological degenerative changes occur in the gland after stalk section. In mammals, the secretion of TSH, of ACTH, and possibly of the lactogenic and growth hormones is reduced, but the effect on these secretions is not nearly as drastic as that on the gonadotrophic complex.

Confirmation of the conclusions drawn from the results of stalk section has been obtained by other techniques, such as electrostimulation of the hypothalamic region, which causes ovulation in rats and rabbits, milk ejection in lactating sheep, goats, and rabbits. Direct stimulation of the pituitary gland itself is either ineffective or effective only in a minority of the animals stimulated. The use of drugs that block nervous impulses and prevent stimuli from reaching the hypothalamus furnishes additional evidence of neurohumoral control of the pituitary. The adrenergic blocking drug Dibenamine prevents ovulation in rats, rabbits, and hens by blocking the neurohumoral LH-releasing mechanism. Atropine blocks or delays ovulation in rats, rabbits, and cows but has only a slight effect in chickens. Similarly, Nembutal anesthesia blocks ovulation in rats; in chickens, however, it is completely without effect and may, in fact, hasten ovulation.

A number of nonspecific substances, such as picrotoxin, copper acetate, cadmium salts, and Metrazol, cause ovulation when injected into rats or rabbits. How these substances work (while some closely related ones do not) is not quite clear, but it is possible that some of them work directly on the anterior lobe of the pituitary, causing it to release LH, and that others work on the nervous system, which, in turn, acts via the hypothalamus, the portal system, and the anterior pituitary.

Pituitary Autografts.   The interdependence of the anterior pituitary gland and the hypothalamus has been further emphasized by experiments in which the pituitary gland is taken out of its natural location and away from its normal humoral and neural connections with the hypothalamus and is transplanted to the subcapsular pocket of the kidney or to the eye chamber, where it usually becomes well established.

However, the results obtained in these experiments are not nearly as clear-cut as one would want them, especially when comparisons of effects of such autotransplants are made between species. If, in female rats, the pituitary gland is removed from the sella turcica and placed in a blood-rich organ such as the kidney capsule, it becomes vascularized and, after a time, regains some semblance of normal histological organization, although it is not typical of the pituitary gland in its normal location. Such translocated pituitary glands no longer synthesize and release the normal amounts of hormones typical of the adenohypophysis; they shift to the synthesis of predominantly one hormone, prolactin. In female rats with new corpora lutea the copious release of LTH leads to pseudopregnancy (with placentoma formation if challenged) or to pregnancy if the autotransplant was performed at the proper time. The usual feedback mechanisms do not operate because pseudopregnancy is found to continue almost indefinitely and pregnancy will last beyond the normal 21-day period and until the young die *in utero* and are resorbed. No detailed studies of the rates of synthesis have been made, but the consensus is that synthesis of both TSH and ACTH is markedly decreased, although growth hormone production seems to continue.

One can retransplant such deranged hypophyses into the sella turcica and they will resume production of all the expected hormones, the gonadotrophic complex being released again in the typical cyclic manner. It is also possible to transplant the hypophysis into the third ventricle of the brain in such a way that the gland either does or does not touch the median eminence of the hypothalamus, the hypophyseotrophic area. If the gland does touch, that part of it immediately abutting the median eminence regains normal histological appearance and produces the expected hormones, some of them cyclically. Glands not touching the hypothalamus behave like those transplanted to the kidney capsule; they remain histologically abnormal and do not synthesize and release the hormones normally expected from them. Finally, it has been shown that the adenohypophysis of male rats—which normally does not function in the distinctly cyclic manner of hypophyses of females, with regard to the release of FSH and LH—when transplanted to the sella turcica or to the third ventricle of females, is able to change pace and to release the gonadotrophic complex in such a manner as to support perfectly normal ovulatory cycles of the female host.

These facts seem to boil down to this. So far as the hypophysis is concerned, there is some virtue in being in the proximity of the hypothalamus from which the former derives signals (releasing factors? other factors?) that tell it whether it is supposed to be a "male" or a "female" pituitary, what hormones it is supposed to synthesize, in what quantities, and when. The hypothesis also tells us that hypothalamus normally produces a substance which inhibits the synthesis or the release of LTH (see also "General Considerations" and "*In vitro* culture of pituitary glands").

Unfortunately, this clean picture became muddied when R. Courrier made transplants of the hypophysis to the kidney in males instead of female rats. Quite unexpectedly he found that the transplanted pituitaries frequently continue to secrete enough gonadotrophic hormone to maintain testes weights, completely normal spermatogenesis, and normal weights and function of all the male accessory glands. Whether thyroid function is depressed is not clear, but it is known that the adrenals become atrophic or function below the level of those of normal intact males. There is no evidence as to whether these transplanted glands in males secrete abnormal quantities of prolactin. The growth rates of intact males and of those with hypophyseal grafts are identical.

At present there is no rational basis on which we can decide why, in one sex, the pituitary is utterly dependent upon the hypothalamus for directions as to what hormones to secrete, while in the other sex it depends for such guidance on the hypothalamus for only one or perhaps two hormones. Is this difference in the "sex" of the hypothalamic centers?

If we now consider the situation in another species, birds, we realize that we are far from being able to generalize on the problem of the interrelation between the hypothalamus and the hypophysis. In chickens, separation of the pituitary gland from the influence of the hypothalamus, by such means as the cutting of the stalk to the anterior lobe, causes rapid and complete involution of the gonads, but this operation has no apparent effect on the secretion rate of either TSH or ACTH. If the adenohypophysis is autotransplanted to the kidney of growing male chickens, the testes and the comb regress to the size typical of hypophysectomized birds. But in such birds neither the thyroids nor the adrenals nor the growth rates are affected. After hypophysectomy the iodine uptake by the thyroid becomes minimal, but the adrenal continues to produce corticosterone provided that the stalk and the median eminence have not been damaged during the operation.

From these experiments it appears that in the chicken the hypophysis is completely dependent on hypothalamic proximity only for the release and perhaps the synthesis of FSH and LH. TSH and somatotrophin are apparently secreted at normal or near-normal levels by the transplanted pituitary, which also responds by graded reduction of TSH production if one injects graded doses of thyroxine; this seems to block TSH output, just as it would in a pituitary *in situ*. We already know that there is an extrahypophyseal source of ACTH, but it is not certain whether the transplanted pituitary secretes ACTH. No comparable studies have been made in mammals, and the degree of dependence of the hypophysis on hypothalamic proximity (for the synthesis and release of hormones other than the gonadotrophins) remains unknown.

Induced Ovulation, Pseudopregnancy, and Delayed Ovulation

Two reproductive events that are clear-cut examples of neurohumoral phenomena are induced ovulation and pseudopregnancy, both of which are discussed in some detail elsewhere (pp. 162 and 257). In induced ovulation the nerve impulse resulting from copulation is known to culminate in release of a luteotrophic substance; but the triggering mechanism, especially in rabbits, is extremely sensitive, not being confined to the genitalia, and events leading to release of LH may be initiated by external physical contact of females penned together. Spontaneous pseudopregnancy, on the other hand, does not occur in the absence of genital stimulation. A phenomenon comparable to these is found in the hen and possibly in birds in general: the presence of a foreign body (an ovum) in the oviduct prevents the release of LH and hence ovulation, both of these events occurring in their proper order as soon as the foreign body is removed or the egg is laid (p. 146). Here, to be sure, the nerve impulse appears to inhibit hormone release rather than to stimulate it, as it does in the previous two cases.

Implantation

An age-old and important question (to be further discussed in Chapter 11) is: How do the ovaries "know" that the uterus is pregnant and that the corpora lutea should be maintained for the duration of pregnancy rather than being allowed to degenerate as they normally do when a female does not become pregnant?

One explanation is that the uterine contents may in some way signal the pituitary to secrete a luteotrophic substance that maintains the corpora. This theory is based on the finding that implantation of beads into the uterine lumen of sheep sometimes causes, through nondegeneration of the corpora lutea, a significant prolongation of the estrous cycle. In the presence of beads, the corpora were maintained for an average of 21 days instead of the normal 9–10 days. The brevity of the effect of the beads is not surprising if we remember that beads are inert and of a fixed size, whereas the embryo and its fluid-filled membranes are growing constantly and establishing an intimate union with the maternal uterine tissues. The degree and intensity of neural stimuli originating from a living embryo and its uterine attachments are certainly much greater than those of stimuli coming from beads.

In the guinea pig, uterine contents (beads) also significantly modify the life span of corpora lutea, causing a prolongation of the cycle. A balloon inserted into the uterine lumen of the cow shortly after heat causes a significant shortening of the subsequent cycle; but since this is the only time during the cycle when this experiment was tried, it remains unknown whether this foreign body inserted later would have led to prolonged maintenance of corpora lutea, as it did in sheep. In contrast to sheep, cattle, and guinea pigs, foreign bodies placed into the uterine lumina of pigs at different times of the cycle have no effect whatever on the life span of their corpora lutea. The reasons for these species differences remain unknown (see Anderson et al. in Nalbandov, 1963).

Of greater significance is the recent finding that partial resection of the pituitary stalk or total section of the nerves going to the uterus prevents implantation and pregnancy in sheep (Nalbandov and St. Clair, unpublished). If either of these operations is performed, estrous cycles remain normal in length (about 16 days), and ovulation occurs at normal times. However, if the females subjected to such operations are mated with fertile rams, even as many as five times, most of them do not become pregnant. The eggs ovulated by them are fertilized and cleave normally, but apparently implantation cannot proceed normally. One operation interrupts the neural pathway from uterus to hypothalamus, the other the pathway from hypothalamus to pituitary gland, and either prevents the signal for release of luteotrophic hormone from reaching the pituitary gland. That this explanation is probably correct is suggested by one case in which a degenerating blastocyst 18 days old was recovered from the uterus and a 16-cell egg was flushed from the oviduct of the same ewe.

Milk Ejection

Another complex neurohumoral mechanism is associated with milk ejection and, to some extent, with milk formation. Stimulation of nipple or breast by suckling or milking initiates the release of certainly one and possibly two hormones from the pituitary gland. In lactating females of many species a corpus luteum of lactation is formed, which persists, as a rule, until the young are weaned. It is postulated that the act of suckling causes the release from the anterior lobe of a luteotrophic substance that maintains the corpora lutea of lactation. The suckling reflex may cause the flow of several pituitary hormones (among them luteotrophin), for it is now known that maximal galactopoiesis can be induced experimentally by combinations of growth hormone, thyroid-stimulating hormone (TSH), and lactogenic hormone (see p. 278). That the formation of milk in a breast is not due to the local irritation of suckling or to the emptiness of the breast resulting from removal of milk can be shown, for example, in rats; if one tapes most of the glands and allows the young to suckle at only one or two of them, milk formation in the unused glands appears to be as copious as in the used ones.

Much better understood is the role of the posterior lobe in milk ejection, which is commonly called milk "let-down." Among the earliest hints that a neural pathway is involved in this mechanism were the observations that anesthesia of lactating females reduces the milk yield to a small fraction of the normal amount, and that embarrassment in women and emotional stress in all lactating females prevent the let-down of milk temporarily or even permanently. Recent work has succeeded in explaining the relation between stimulation of the nipple and the let-down of milk. In classical studies, first Gaines and then Ely and Petersen showed that oxytocin is the hormone that is responsible for the ejection of milk. Even more recently it has been found that the nursing stimulus causes the release of oxytocin from the posterior lobe, and that this hormone acts on the myoepithelial "basket cells" around the alveoli, causing them to constrict and to squeeze out the milk contained in them.

If oxytocin is injected into lactating females under deep anesthesia, milk ejection is normal; in the absence of exogenous oxytocin it is not. Similarly, injection of oxytocin into cows with cannulated teats causes unrestrained and immediate gushing of milk. Milk ejection can also be initiated by the electrical stimulation of the paraventricular nucleus of the hypothalamus in lactating sheep and rabbits. All these observations strengthen the theory that oxytocin is the normal milk ejection hormone and that the pathway from nipple through hypothalamus to posterior pituitary gland is neural. The posterior lobe responds by immediate release of oxytocin into the pituitary vein.

Transport of Sperm in the Female

Finally, a few words are in order about the neurohumoral mechanism involved in the transport of sperm in the female reproductive tract. It has been known for a long time that the propulsion of semen from the site of ejaculation to the oviduct (where fertilization takes place) is not due to the automotive ability of sperm cells but is completely accomplished by contractions of the female duct system. Since, in all species in which such propulsion has been timed, it has been found to require not more than a few minutes (less than one minute in the rat and about two and a half minutes in the cow), there is no relation between the rate at which semen is propelled and the distance separating the cervix and the vagina from the oviducts. It is also known that lactating cows and women eject milk from the mammary glands during coitus. In view of the preceding discussion of the mechanism of milk ejection, this fact suggests that the act of mating also causes release of oxytocin. The question whether oxytocin is involved in uterine contractions during mating was answered affirmatively by VanDemark and Hays (1952), who found that mating causes a rise in intramammary pressure in the cow and that strong uterine contractions were induced in cows through stimulation of the genital system by natural mating, by artificial insemination, by manipulation of the vulva, or even merely by the sight of the bull. Furthermore, increased activity was noted in isolated uteri perfused with oxytocin, and even in such preparations semen deposited in the cervix was transported to the oviduct in five minutes.

All these observations taken together are interpreted to mean that coitus induces nervous impulses that reach the posterior lobe of the pituitary via the hypothalamus, activating the release of oxytocin, which then causes the uterine and oviducal contractions that are responsible for the rapid movement of semen from the site of ejaculation to the oviduct.

The Posterior Lobe of the Pituitary Gland

We are accumulating more and more evidence that the posterior pituitary hormones are really formed in the hypothalamus, and that the posterior lobe serves merely as a reservoir. We have seen that the demand for hormones from the posterior lobe may be sudden and may require an immediate response. Birds are especially well suited to the study of the effects of stalk section on the posterior lobe because in them a septum separates the two lobes and it is possible to cut either or both of the two stalks. If the posterior lobe is removed from laying hens, the results are immediate and dramatic. There is no apparent effect on the rate of ovulation or the time of oviposition, but the water intake increases rapidly until birds weighing 1,000–2,000 grams may drink 900–1,000 grams of water daily. Both the polydipsia and the diuresis seem to be permanent, and both can be controlled very effectively by pitressin. Oviposition, which is known to be due to oxytocin-induced contractions of the shell gland and of the vagina, is not affected. It is possible that the amount of hormone required to induce oviposition is small and that the hypothalamus may produce and release enough oxytocin to take care of this need. Neurohypophysectomy in mammals does not usually prevent normal delivery of young, but it makes lactation impossible; young attempting to suckle from mice deprived of their posterior pituitaries starve to death because the mechanism for milk let-down has failed.

The role of oxytocin in its ability to control the output of hypophyseal hormones related to reproduction is not clear. There are several claims in the literature that precocious puberty has been induced in male and female rats and rabbits injected with oxytocin. However, there are also data (and many unpublished experiences) showing that no effect was produced by this treatment. The claims cannot be dismissed without considering the fact that in the early days of study and isolation of the hypothalamic releasing factors, oxytocin and vasopressin were considered as promising candidates for the role of releasing factor. Daily injections of minute quantities of oxytocin into the third ventricle of rats induced a premature opening of the vagina and a very significant increase in the weights of the reproductive organs; uterus and ovaries of treated females weighed 386 and 74.2 micrograms, those of control females 229.8 and 8.9 milligrams. When the same comparison was made in hypophysectomized female rats there was no difference between treated and control females. It was concluded that oxytocin acted on the adenohypophysis, causing it to release gonadotrophic hormones (Corbin and Shottelius, 1960).

In experiments with dairy cattle, Armstrong and Hansel (1959) found that subcutaneous injections of oxytocin immediately after ovulation caused these animals to form small and histologically abnormal corpora and, what is more significant, all oxytocin-treated animals came in heat and ovulated about 7 days after the last heat and ovulation. Experiments on both the rat and the cow can be interpreted to mean that oxytocin stimulates the release of gonadotrophic substances from the pituitary gland. However, the clue to the possible pathway of action of oxytocin lies in the observation that oxytocin lost its ability to shorten the estrous cycle of cattle if it was injected into hysterectomized females; in this case the corpora lutea formed were perfectly normal. Since, in cattle, the uterus appears to be essential for the action of oxytocin, it seems that oxytocin acts on the uterus rather than directly on the adenohypophysis and that signals (neural?) originating in the uterus are responsible for the modification in pituitary function. This is reminiscent of the effect of foreign bodies in the uterus on the length of estrous cycle of sheep, cattle, and guinea pigs, which was discussed before.

The other posterior pituitary hormone, vasopressin, is of less direct importance to reproduction. It too is formed in the hypothalamus and only stored in the posterior pituitary. Its main function is the regulation of water balance in animals; it is called the antidiuretic hormone or ADH. Although both ADH and oxytocin are stored in the neural hypophysis, the mechanisms controlling their release appear to be different. By appropriate experimental manipulation of animals, it is possible to deplete the neural lobe of one of the two hormones without greatly affecting the concentration of the other.

Relation of the Thyroid Gland to Reproduction

General Considerations

It is not within the scope of this book to discuss the endocrine economy of the whole body. The thyroid gland and its hormones, however, play such an important role in reproduction, as well as in regulation of the metabolic rate of the whole body, that they cannot be overlooked. Thyroid hormones probably influence the various reproductive functions at the cellular level. Although there is some evidence that thyroid hormones influence the pituitary-adrenal relation, we shall be mainly concerned with the thyroid-pituitary axis.

In studies of the relation of thyroid hormones to reproduction, the classical procedure of surgical extirpation of the thyroid gland, followed by replacement therapy, has been used. This procedure has the disadvantage that in most mammals and birds extra thyroid tissue— so-called thyroidal rests—is usually present in the thymus gland, making complete thyroidectomy virtually impossible in any animals more than one week old. For this reason it is frequently better and easier to study thyroid physiology by the injection of radioactive iodine (I^{131}), which is selectively picked up by all thyroid tissue (including the rests) and so destroys the tissue by radioactivity. It is sometimes more expedient to use goiterogenic agents (such as thiouracil and thiourea), which prevent the synthesis of thyroid hormones and, if given in sufficiently large doses, can stop all thyroid activity.

That thyroid hormones affect the pituitary-gonad axis can be seen from the facts that administration of them increases the gonadotrophic potency of the pituitary glands of rats and that thyroidectomy decreases the gonadotrophic potency of the pituitary glands of rats, rabbits, and goats. There is considerable evidence that the alteration in gonado-trophic potency in the change from euthyroidism to hypo- or hyper-thyroidism is due to a shift in the FSH-LH ratio and in the rate at which these hormones are secreted.

Of considerable interest are the data obtained by the Michigan group of workers (Table 3-4) who rendered male rats and mice hypo- or

Table 3-4. Effect of thiouracil (T.U.) and thyroprotein (Th.P.) feeding on the response of immature rats and mice to a constant dose of gonadogen

TREATMENT	NO. RATS	TESTES WEIGHT (mg/100 g*)	SEM. VES. WT. (mg/100 g*) (±SE)	NO. MICE	TESTES WEIGHT (mg/100 g*)	SEM. VES. WT. (mg/100 g*) (±SE)
		THIOURACIL FEEDING				
Control	5	549.1	23.6 ± 0.7	8	693.3	58.5 ± 14.7
Gonadogen	5	856.0	49.0 ± 8.2	6	643.3	321.7 ± 4.5
0.1% T.U. for 20 days + gonadogen	5	1,177.2	115.8 ± 24.2	6	139.6	256.5 ± 22.3
		THYROPROTEIN FEEDING				
Control	11	1,003.0	29.2 ± 1.9	9	547.6	142.7 ± 10.6
Gonadogen	10	798.8	80.2	9	572.6	226.9 ± 19.5
0.32% Th.P. + gonadogen	10	871.4	36.0	5	647.7	288.2 ± 24.6
0.64% Th.P.	5	770.8	28.3 ± 2.9	5	630.9	195.9 ± 11.7

SOURCE: Data abridged from Meites and Chandrashaker. 1949. *Endocrinology*, 44:368.
* Per 100 g of final body weight.

hyperthyroid and then treated them with a standard dose of a gonad-otrophic hormone. The two species responded in exactly opposite ways: hypothyroidism increased the ability of rats, and decreased the ability of mice, to respond to gonadotrophin; hyperthyroidism, conversely, de-creased the ability of rats, and increased the ability of mice, to respond to gonadotrophin. This observation shows that the ability of end organs to respond to tropic hormones depends on the thyroid state of the animals; it also shows—what is more important—that the "euthyroid" mouse secretes suboptimal amounts of thyroid hormone (exogenous thyroid hormone increases the responsiveness of its testes and acces-sories to gonadotrophin), and that the "euthyroid" rat is really hyper-

Table 3-5. Effect of thyroidectomy, thiouracil, and thyroid hormone on reproduction of males in different species

SPECIES AND TREATMENT	TESTES WEIGHT*	SPERMATOGENESIS*	ACCESSORY SEX ORGANS, SEC. SEX CHARACTER	LIBIDO	FERTILITY
Chicken					
Thyroidectomy	I	I	Comb, I		
Thiouracil	S, I†	S, I	Comb, I		
Thyroid hormone	S	S	Comb. S		N
Mouse					
Thiouracil	I, N		Sem. ves., I, N	S	
Thyroid hormone	S, N		Sem. ves., S, N	S	N
Rat					
Thyroidectomy	I	I	Sem. ves., N	N	
Thiouracil	N			N	
Thyroid hormone	S, I‡; N**	N, I	Sem. ves., I, N		N
Rabbit					
Thyroidectomy	I	I			
Thiouracil		I		S	
Thyroid hormone		S		S	N
Guinea pig					
Thyroidectomy			Accessory sex organs, S	S	
Thiouracil		N		N	
Thyroid hormone				N	N
Dog					
Thyroidectomy					N
Thyroid hormone		N		N	N
Goat					
Thyroidectomy	I				N
Cattle					
Throidectomy		N			
Thyroid hormone					
Sheep					
Throidectomy		I		I	N
Thiouracil		I			S
Thyroid hormone		S		S	
Man					
Thiouracil				I	
Thyroid hormone				S	S
Clinical hypothyroid	I			I	

SOURCE: Compiled from the literature.
* I = inhibition; S = stimulation; N = no effect.
† Dependent on age and dose.
‡ Thyroid feeding.
** Thyroxine.

Table 3-6. Effect of thyroidectomy, thiouracil, and thyroid hormone on reproduction of females in different species

SPECIES AND TREATMENT	OVARY*	ESTROUS CYCLE	GESTATION
Chicken			
Throidectomy	Decreased	...	No effect on hatchability†
Thiouracil	No effect on egg prod.	...	Lower hatchability†
Thyroid hormone	No effect on egg prod.	...	
Mouse			
Thiouracil	Large follicles, no C.L.	Irregular	No effect
Thyroid hormone	Many C.L.	Progestational uteri	...
Rat			
Throidectomy	Cysts	More variable Lengthened	No effect
Thiouracil	Atrophic ...	More variable Lengthened	Resorptions Abortions
Thyroid hormone	No effect, low dose Degeneration No mature follicles Atresia of follicles Many C.L.	Continuous Leucocytic smears Pseudo-pregnant	...
Rabbit			
Throidectomy	Large follicles No effect	No effect	Still births Resorptions
Thyroid hormone	Few follicles Many follicles	No effect	No effect Resorptions
Guinea pig			
Thyroidectomy	...	Decreased heat	Abortions
Thiouracil	...	No effect	No effect Decreased stillbirths
Thyroid hormone	...	No effect	No effect
Dog			
Thyroidectomy	...	No effect	No effect
Cattle			
Thyroidectomy	Normal	No heat	Normal
Monkey			
Thyroidectomy	...	Amenorrhea	...
Man			
Clinical hypothyroid	...	Amenorrhea	Abortions

SOURCE: Compiled from the literature.   * C.L. = corpora lutea.   † Hatching time lengthened

thyroid, for "hypothyroidism" improves its ability to respond to gonadotrophins. Whether these differences pertain only to gonado-trophic hormones remains unknown, but they should serve as a warning against applying conclusions reached in one species to another species unless experimental proof makes such transfer warranted.

The effects of the various thyroid states on the reproductive performance of males and females of various species are summarized in Tables 3-5 and 3-6.

Effect of Thyroid States on the Reproduction of Females

That female reproductive performance can proceed normally only in euthyroid individuals has been shown in many experiments. In one such experiment it was found that the estrous cycles of rats were lengthened by 1.27 days after thyroid inhibition, and by 2.52 days after thyroidectomy. The deleterious effect of hypothyroidism on embryonal survival and on total litter size are summarized in Table 3-7. Even if

Table 3-7. Effect of hypothyroidism on litter size in female rats

| TREATMENT | NUMBER OF RATS | NUMBER OF YOUNG BORN | | |
		DEAD	ALIVE	TOTAL
Before thiouracil	10	6	83	89
		Av. 8.3		
		No resorptions		
After thiouracil		6	33	39
		Av. 3.3		
		2 females		
		resorbed litters		
Before thyroidectomy	9	1	79	80
		Av. 8.9		
		No resorptions		
After thyroidectomy		10	21	31
		Av. 2.3		
		2 females		
		resorbed litters		

SOURCE: Data from Krohn and White. 1950. *J. Endocrinol.*, 6:375.

the four hypothyroid females that resorbed their whole litter are omitted from the final calculation, it is seen that the hypothyroid females produced only half as many young as the normal controls. The reproductive performance of most guinea pigs, in contrast, remains unaffected over a wide range of hypo- and hyperthyroidism (see Table 3-6); in some strains, however, in which stillbirths and abortions are conspicuously high, administration of thyroid hormone alleviates the condition. These observations further emphasize the fact that it is not possible to generalize from one species to another or even to draw conclusions that will hold true within the same species.

An estimate of the different rates of thyroid activity during the estrous cycles of rats and mice shows that the thyroid of female rats is most active during heat and that that of female mice is most active during proestrus (Table 3-8).

Table 3-8.   Mean I^{131} uptake as percentage of injected dose during estrous cycle of rats and mice

STATE OF CYCLE	RATS $\bar{x} \pm$ SE	MICE $\bar{x} \pm$ SE
Proestrus	9.17 $\pm$ 0.64	13.74* $\pm$ 1.13
Estrus	18.23* $\pm$ 0.65	9.14 $\pm$ 0.81
Metestrus	10.79 $\pm$ 0.67	9.29 $\pm$ 0.56
Diestrus	8.99 $\pm$ 0.78	10.62 $\pm$ 0.66

SOURCE: Data from Soliman and Reineke, 1950. *Am. J. Physiol.*, 178:89. 1954. *J. Endocrinol.*, 10-305.
  * Significantly different at 1% level of probability.

In normal chickens, thyroxine injection can completely inhibit estrogen-induced hyperlipemia, hyperprotenemia, and increase in blood biotin, but it does not interfere with the response of the oviduct to estrogen.

The stimulating effect of thyroid hormone on spermatogenesis and the ovarian function, in such a variety of species as chickens, mice, rabbits, swine, sheep, and cattle, plus the fact that egg production by hens usually declines during the summer, when thyroid secretion is low, instigated work on the effect of feeding thyroid hormone, in the form of thyroprotein, to laying hens. An evaluation of the available data suggests that the treatment does not benefit all birds; for some, however, the summer slump was prevented or alleviated. The feeding of thyroprotein or of thiouracil to laying hens increases the incubation period of eggs laid by them and increases the size of the thyroids of chicks hatched from those eggs.

Effect of Thyroid States on the Reproduction of Males

The response of the secondary sex organs of castrated male mice and of the comb of capons is increased by thyroxine; in the castrated male rat, however, the response of the seminal vesicles to androgen is reduced in the hyperthyroid condition. In the intact mouse thyroid hormone injections do not affect the response of the seminal vesicles to exogenous androgen.

It is well known that the environmental temperature affects the thyroid activity of various species. At high temperature and high humidity the secretion of thyroid hormone is generally reduced; at low temperature it is increased. In several species (mice, rabbits, sheep, and swine) exposure to high temperatures induces degenerative changes in the testes and reduces fertility. The testicular changes in the ram may be, not a direct effect of the high temperature on the testes, as in cryptorchism, but an effect of decreased thyroid secretion. The changes induced by the feeding of thiouracil to rams are similar to those obtained in "summer sterility"; on the other hand, the administration of thyroid hormone sometimes prevents changes in the testes during the summer. Similar testicular changes were found in aged rabbits and in mice and rabbits kept under intermittent high temperatures.

In addition to its direct or indirect action on spermatogenesis, the thyroid has an effect on the mating desire, at least in some species. Guinea pigs and rats are apparently not affected in their sex drive by thyroidectomy. Thyroidectomized bulls lose sexual interest in cows in heat, but their libido returns to normal not only with thyroid hormone therapy but also after treatment with dinitrophenol, which is known to increase the basal metabolic rate.

The beneficial results of thyroid hormone treatment of male swine, sheep, and cattle with poor fertility and libido seem to indicate that there is a definite threshold below which thyroid secretion cannot drop if reproduction is to remain normal.

The effect of thyroidectomy on the reproductive functions varies from a rather mild effect in the guinea pig to severe interference in young rats and chickens, in which, if thyroidectomy is performed during the first two days after birth or hatching, the gonads are severely affected and resemble those of hypophysectomized animals. After spermatogenesis and oogenesis have been completed, the thyroid appears, in most species, to have the function of modulating gonadal performance. Thyroidectomy of female rats causes degenerative changes in the ovary (Table 3-6).

The addition of thyroxine to semen increases the consumption of oxygen if the sperm concentration is above 800,000/cm³. The fertility of the semen of some bulls, as measured by the nonreturn rate of the cows bred with such semen, is also increased by the addition of thyroxine.

SUMMARY

This chapter deals with the fundamentals of reproductive endocrinology. It establishes the fact that both the anterior and the posterior lobe of the pituitary gland are controlled, to a considerable extent, by the hypothalamus. Evidence of this control is given. The relations involved are summarized in the following tabulation. The interested reader should take each of the effects listed and diagram all the events that contribute to it. (For instance, compare induced and spontaneous ovulation: diagram all the events, the end organs they affect, the hormones that participate, and the relations that exist between the duct system, the ovaries, the hypothalamus, and the pituitary gland. Similar diagrams for all the other events listed would clarify the various interrelations and reveal holes in the theories presented in the text.)

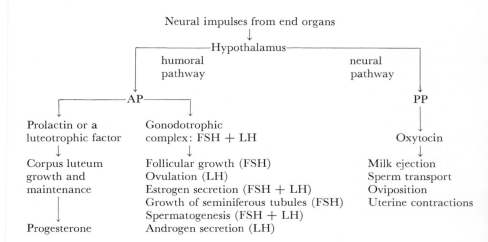

This chapter further deals with the fluctuations of the pituitary gonadotrophic hormones during the estrous cycle, in pregnancy, and after castration (surgical or physiological). The significance of bioassays of pituitary glands is discussed and their pitfalls pointed out. A brief discussion of breeding seasons points out that light is, without doubt, one of the factors, but not the only factor, controlling the onset of the breeding season.

A new and different hypothesis of corpus luteum formation and maintenance is presented and documented. It is pointed out that the mechanisms of corpus luteum formation in animals with short cycles are completely different from the mechanism involved in animals with long cycles (that is, all domestic mammals and man). The role of the uterus in controlling the life span of the corpus luteum and of ovarian function is also considered.

REFERENCES

D. T. Armstrong and W. Hansel. 1959. "Alteration of the bovine estrous cycle with oxytocin." *J. Dairy Sci.*, **42**:533.

S. A. Asdell. 1957. "Reproductive Hormones" in *Progress in the Physiology of Farm Animals*, Vol. III. Butterworth (London).

J. Benoît and I. Assenmacher. 1953. "Rapport entre la stimulation sexuelle préhypophysaire et la neurosécrétion chez l'oiseau." *Arch. Anat. Microscopique Morphol. Exp.*, **42**:334.

H. H. Cole and H. Goss. 1943. "The source of equine gonadotrophin" in *Essays in Biology*. University of California Press (Berkeley).

A. Corbin and B. A. Schottelius. 1960. "Hypothalamic neurohumoral agents and sexual maturation of immature female Rats." *Am. J. Physiol.*, **201**:1176.

A. T. Cowie and S. J. Folley. 1955. "Physiology of gonadotrophins and the lactogenic hormone" in *The Hormones: Physiology, Chemistry and Applications*, Vol. III. Academic Press (New York).

A. T. Cowie and S. J. Folley. 1957. "Neurohypophysial hormones and the mammary gland" in *The Neurohypophysis*. Academic Press (New York).

J. de Groot. 1952. "The significance of the hypophysial-portal system." Van Gorcum's Medische Bibliotheek, Deel 118.

C. W. Emmens, editor. 1950. *Hormone Assay*. Academic Press (New York).

R. J. Fitzpatrick. 1957. "On oxytocin and uterine function" in *The Neurohypophysis*. Academic Press (New York).

J. Hammond, Jr. 1954. "Light regulation of hormone secretion" in *Vitamins and Hormones*, Vol. XII. Academic Press (New York).

G. W. Harris. 1955. *Neural Control of the Pituitary Gland*. Arnold (London).

R. L. Hays and N. L. VanDemark. 1953. "Spontaneous motility of the bovine uterus." *Am. J. Physiol.*, **172**:553.

R. T. Hill. 1937. "Ovaries secrete male hormone." *Endocrinol.*, **21**:495.

M. Maqsood. 1952. "Thyroid functions in relation to reproduction of mammals and birds." *Biol. Rev.*, **27**:281.

A. V. Nalbandov. 1961. "Comparative physiology and endocrinology of domestic animals" in *Recent Progress in Hormone Research*. Academic Press (New York).

A. V. Nalbandov, editor. 1963. *Advances in Neuroendocrinology*. University of Illinois Press, Urbana.

I. W. Rowlands. 1949. "Serum gonadotrophin and ovarian activity in the pregnant mare." *J. Endocrinol.*, **6**:184.

R. V. Short. 1963. "Ovarian steroid synthesis *in vivo*" in *Recent Progress in Hormone Research*. Academic Press (New York).

C. D. Turner. 1960. *General Endocrinology*, 3rd ed. Saunders (Philadelphia).

C. A. Villee, editor. 1961. *Control of Ovulation*. Pergamon Press, New York.

E. Witschi. 1955. "Vertebrate gonadotrophins" in *Comparative Physiology of Reproduction and the Effects of Sex Hormones in Vertebrates*. Cambridge University Press.

N. T. M. Yeates. 1954. "Daylight changes" in *Progress in the Physiology of Farm Animals*, Vol. I. Butterworth (London).

chapter *4*

Reproduction in Female Mammals and Birds

The Estrous Cycle

The patterns of reproduction and breeding behavior of vertebrates, in relation to season, are remarkably varied. In most domestic animals and in man, both sexes breed continuously throughout the year, some of the species showing seasonal peaks of fecundity but none showing breeding seasons in the true sense of the word. In sheep, the males are continuous breeders but the females have a distinct breeding season. In the majority of wild mammals and birds, both sexes have synchronous, alternating breeding and nonbreeding seasons. Most animals can be classified either as seasonal or as continuous breeders, but some, such as the bitch, fit neither category.

Seasonal breeders go through a nonbreeding, or anestrous, period, during which they are sexually less active. In continuous breeders the sexual cycles are repeated more or less continuously throughout the year. All animals except the higher primates permit copulation only during a definite period within each sexual cycle. These periods of proper psychological and physiological state, during which copulation is permitted, are called periods of heat, or estrus. The period from the beginning of one heat to the beginning of the next heat is called an estrous cycle. When in heat, a female is in a psychological state that is distinctly different from her state during the rest of the cycle. Only when in heat does the female permit copulation. And during the remainder of the cycle the male ordinarily shows no interest in her; if he does, his advances are repelled.

The psychological, physiological, and endocrine events are all correlated. In addition to the externally visible manifestation of sexual receptivity, certain changes in the vaginal histology make it possible to follow, without recourse to surgery, the ovarian events that are primarily responsible for the physiological and psychological changes. The uterine endometrium also undergoes cyclic changes. These are, indeed, correlated with ovarian events, but only after surgery can they be used as guides to stages in the estrous cycle.

Heat, or Estrus

Heat, or estrus (from the Latin *oestrus,* possessed by the gadfly, insane, in a frenzy), coincides with the greatest development of ovarian follicles. The psychological manifestations of heat are brought about by a female sex hormone, named estrogen, which is produced by the ovarian follicles. Complete heat can be brought about by estrogen even in ovariectomized females. It is important to keep this fact in mind, for, even though heat is caused by an ovarian hormone, in a sense it is independent of ovarian activity. In intact females, exogenous estrogen causes heat at almost any time during the estrous cycle, and thus heat can be completely divorced from the most important ovarian event, ovulation. This factor in the therapeutic use of estrogen is frequently overlooked in veterinary practice.

In the female guinea pig, a trace of progesterone is necessary before estrogen can cause the female to show full mating response. In the rat, estrogen alone can bring about heat, but less estrogen is required for the full response if the female is pretreated with progesterone. The same situation seems to hold in sheep and possibly in females of other species. One is tempted to assume that priming with progesterone is essential for the full copulatory response in all females, especially in view of the fact that the follicles secrete progesterone before ovulation and before becoming luteinized.

In some domestic animals, especially cows and mares, physiological, or quiet, heat occasionally occurs: all the histological and physiological phenomena, including ovulation, are observed, but the mating response (psychological heat) is lacking. The need of estrogen may be greater in some individuals than in others, and quiet heats may be caused by the failure to secrete estrogen in large enough quantities to bring about the mating response. About 10 percent of mares show quiet heat, especially during March and April. Quiet heat also occurs in dairy cows, and it becomes of great importance when it occurs in an unduly large proportion of the population. The prevalence of quiet heat has brought a Swedish breed of dairy cattle close to extinction, the bulls being unable to tell when the cows are in heat.

Frequently in mares, and occasionally in cows, split heat is observed:

the initial period of sexual receptivity is interrupted by a period of nonreceptivity (one or two days in the mare, a few hours in the cow), which is then followed by another period of heat.

The duration and intensity of heat are variable (Table 4-3). Parous cows have more intense heat and a slightly longer cycle than virginal cows. There is no difference in length of cycle or duration of heat between beef and dairy cattle, but the cycle generally lengthens with increasing age. In sheep, in the middle of the breeding season, both the length of the cycle and the duration of heat are remarkably uniform, but early and late in the season the length of the cycle is extremely variable (Table 4-1). In mares, the cycles and the heat are

Table 4-1. **Changes in length of intervals between heats in mature sheep during breeding season**

MONTH	NUMBER OF CYCLES	PERCENTAGE OF CYCLES			AVERAGE CYCLE LENGTH	
		NORMAL	LONG	SHORT	DAY	SD*
May	12	33	67	0	33.5	8.43
June	61	16	75	8	58.5	8.75
July	49	14	76	10	32.5	4.17
August	99	55	26	19	19.0	1.12
September	330	72	11	17	16.5	0.43
October	375	78	9	13	16.8	0.29
November	365	84	6	10	16.8	0.29
December	394	82	6	11	16.8	0.27
January	373	54	15	31	16.5	0.50
February	156	38	35	27	18.3	0.79
March	21	10	43	48	22.3	2.30

SOURCE: From Williams and others. 1956. *J. Animal Science*, 15:984.
* SD = standard deviation.

variable in length, the cycles being somewhat shorter late in the season (August and September) than in the spring, and they seem to be governed largely by the characteristics of the breed. In swine, heat usually lasts two days in gilts and three days in parous females, but deviations from these norms are common, and increasing age generally lengthens the cycle.

One aberration of heat—common in cattle, less so in mares—is nymphomania. The causes of this condition, which is characterized by sterility and a more or less continuous manifestation of the psychological desire to mate, will be discussed later. It does not occur in sheep, goats, or swine but is said to be known in bitches.

Phenomena Related to Heat.   When in heat, many animals show a greatly increased activity. In walking, sows and cows in heat take four or five times as many steps as during the rest of the cycle. This increased activity is caused by estrogen. Rats in activity cages run spontaneously much more at the height of heat than during diestrus or after castration. Spontaneous activity in rats can be increased during the inactive phase by the injection of estrogen. During the menstrual cycle women show two peaks of spontaneous walking, one (for unknown reasons) during the menses and the other at the time of ovulation.

The sow also shows very significant changes in bioelectric potentials measured externally over the ovarian region of the body at the time of heat. Sows in heat registered 23.2, nonestrous females only 6.6, millivolts. Similar changes in electric potential have been recorded at the time of ovulation in women. In most women ovulation is preceded by a slight dip in basal body temperature; this is followed, either at the time of or shortly after ovulation, by a significant rise in temperature. The fact that such a rise in temperature can be produced by the injection of progesterone may imply that the rise observed in women is caused by increasing preovulatory secretion of progesterone. Similar changes in temperature have been looked for in cows, sheep, pigs, and rhesus monkeys, but the results have been inconclusive, possibly because of the difficulty of obtaining basal body temperatures in animals other than the human female.

During heat (or the greatest follicular development) the cervix secretes the greatest amount of mucus, which is least viscous during heat or, in women, at the time of ovulation. Cervical mucus has a pH of 6.6–7.5 (the average for cows is about 6.9), and this remains fairly stable throughout the cycle. Sperm survive in the cervix much better (up to seventy-two hours in women) than they do in the vagina, where they become nonmotile within a few hours. The vaginal pH is generally alkaline, but it varies greatly among individuals and also within the cycle. In cows, the vaginal pH varies from 7.5 to 8.5. In all animals investigated (cows, mares, women, rats), the vagina is more alkaline in diestrus and becomes more acid during heat (or during the greatest follicular development). That the change in pH is due to estrogen has been shown by the injection of this hormone into ovariectomized women and cows. The vaginal pH of rats is acid but changes during the cycle and under different experimental conditions, as shown on the following page.

These figures are from Asdell (1946).

In diestrus	6.1
At beginning of proestrus	5.4
During heat	6.1
In ovariectomized female	7.0
In ovariectomized female injected with 8 I.U. of estrogen	4.1

Postpartum Heat.   Females of several species come into heat shortly after parturition. Rats have a postpartum heat accompanied by ovulation within forty-eight hours after parturition. As soon as the young begin to suckle, no further heats occur until the young are weaned. Mating at the postpartum heat results in pregnancy, but the interval between mating and parturition is usually significantly longer than normal, for reasons that will be discussed in another connection. An anovulatory condition is said to exist in women as long as they breastfeed their babies, but there appears to be much individual variation in this respect. Sows come into heat within a few days (usually from three to seven) after parturition, but the endocrinology of this event is not clearly understood. The ovaries of the sow show practically no follicular development at this time, no ovulations occur, and mating during the postpartum heat therefore does not result in pregnancy. Sows, however, do come into heat and ovulate if the litter dies or is removed at parturition or a few days later. This fact may be responsible for the general but erroneous belief of farmers that mating during postpartum heat results in pregnancy. Mares show a "foal heat," which begins from five to ten days after parturition and lasts from one to ten days. Ovulation may or may not occur at that time; more frequently than not, mating during foal heat does result in pregnancy.

No postpartum heat is observed in cows, the first heat occurring between thirty and sixty days after parturition. Subsequent heats in cows are not inhibited by lactation, as they are in most other animals. In most domestic sheep, parturition occurs at a time when sheep do not normally show estrous cycles. For this reason few observations on the occurrence of postpartum heat in sheep are available. When ewes were caused to lamb early in the fall, however, most of them showed postpartum heat from one to ten days after parturition if the lambs were not allowed to suckle. No postpartum heat is noted in suckled ewes. The relation of postpartum heat to uterine morphology and to lactation and its endocrinology will be discussed in Chapter 10.

Vaginal Changes During the Estrous Cycle

While the main physiological events of the estrous cycle are occurring in the ovaries, these events are reflected in the changes that take place in the vagina under the influence of the ovarian hormones, estrogen and progesterone. This finding was a significant contribution to the development of the physiology of reproduction, for it made it possible to diagnose ovarian events by simple techniques not involving repeated surgery. Stockard and Papanicolau, and also Long and Evans, observed that the histology of the vaginal epithelium does not remain constant during the estrous cycle. The vaginal epithelium is cyclically torn down and rebuilt, fluctuating between the stratified-squamous and low-cuboidal types. These cyclic changes can be followed by means of the vaginal-smear technique, in which the debris accumulated in the vaginal lumen is swabbed out and the cells obtained are examined under the microscope. The types of cells predominating in the smear give a clue to whether the vaginal epithelium is or is not being stimulated by estrogen.

Changes in vaginal histology during the estrous cycle are found in all mammalian females. The vaginal-smear technique is most useful, however, with animals having short estrous cycles (mice and rats), for in them vaginal histology reflects ovarian events most accurately; in animals with longer cycles, such as all domestic animals and woman, vaginal changes lag from one to several days behind ovarian changes, and vaginal smears are therefore less reliable indicators of ovarian events. Females with long cycles also show considerable individual vari-

Table 4-2.   Events in ovaries and vaginal histology of rats during estrous cycle

NAME OF STAGE	DURATION OF STAGE	OVARIAN EVENTS	TYPES OF CELLS IN VAGINAL SMEAR
Diestrus	½ of whole cycle	Corpora lutea	Nucleated epithelial and leucocytes
Proestrus	12 hours	Follicles growing fast	Nucleated epithelial
Early estrus	12 hours	(mating)	Cornified
Late estrus	18 hours	Ovulation	Cornified
Metestrus	6 hours	Corpora lutea formed	Leucocytes among cornified
Beginning of diestrus or anestrus		Functional corpora during early part	Cornified disappearing

ation, and this also makes the application of the technique less precise and less useful. For rats, in which the cycle lasts about four days, very careful comparisons have been made between ovarian morphology and vaginal histology, and the cycle has been broken down into its component parts (Table 4-2).

The rapid growth and cornification of the vaginal epithelium during early and late estrus have been found to be caused by estrogen. When the level of estrogen drops in the normal cycle after ovulation, or when in castrate females injection of exogenous estrogen is stopped, the cornified vaginal epithelium begins to break down, the scales disappear, and leucocytes become predominant. Histologically, the vaginal epithelium changes from the thick stratified-squamous type produced by estrogen to a thin low-cuboidal epithelium typical of the anestrous phase of the cycle (Fig. 4-1).

A   B

Figure 4-1. *Histology of vaginal epithelia of a ewe in heat.*

A. The epithelium is thick and stratified-squamous, the ewe being on day one of the cycle.

B. The epithelium is low-cuboidal on day 10.

Uterine Changes During the Estrous Cycle

If one follows the histological and morphological changes of the uterus throughout the cycle, one finds that neither the size nor the histology of that viscus is ever static. The most striking changes occur in its endometrium and in its glands. During the follicular phase of the cycle the uterine glands are rather simple and straight, with few branchings (Fig. 4-2A). This appearance of the glands is typical of estrogen stimulation and, in fact, can be duplicated by the injection of estrogen into castrated females, in which the epithelium is much lower, the endometrium thinner, and the glands fewer than they are when estrogen

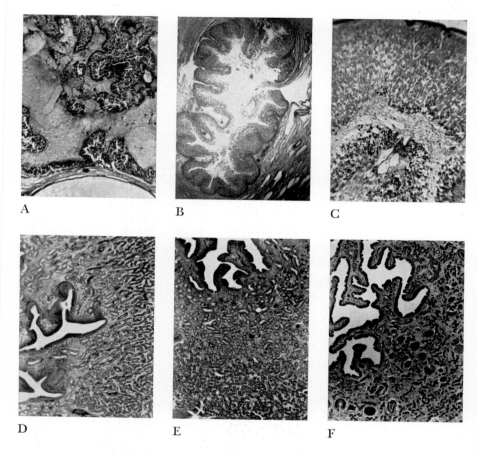

Figure 4-2. *Comparison of uterine endometria and of corpora lutea of swine during the follicular phase and during the luteal phase of the cycle.*

A. A follicle 1 or 2 days after ovulation. Note the folded granulosa layer and the lumen filled with lymph and blood.

B. An ovulated follicle on the way to becoming a corpus luteum. The granulosa layer has proliferated but is still folded. Day 5 of cycle.

C. Almost mature corpus luteum on day 9. Granulosa layer much thicker, almost filling former follicular cavity.

D, E, F. Uterine endometria corresponding to the ages of corpora shown above. Note that the glands in D are still straight but that the glands in E are more convoluted. Compare the epithelial linings of the uterine lumina of D and F, and note that in F (height of luteal function) the epithelium has become crinkled. Note also that in F there are many more blood vessels than in E, and in E more than in D.

is acting on the uterus. Histological sections through estrogen-stimulated uterine endometrium show a multitude of holes, which are the lumina of the simple, nearly unbranched glands. Such endometrial cross sections resemble a cut through a piece of Swiss cheese, and the estrogen-stimulated endometrium is frequently called a Swiss-cheese endometrium.

During the luteal phase, when progesterone is acting on the uterus, the endometrium increases in thickness conspicuously. The glands grow rapidly in diameter and in length, becoming extremely branched and convoluted (Fig. 4-2B). In bitches, rabbits, women, and some other species, the endometrium appears to be perforated by irregularly shaped, fringed openings, which connect with openings from other glands. In histological sections progesterone-stimulated endometria resemble a lace curtain, giving rise to the descriptive term "lace-curtain effect."

During the discussion of the menstrual cycle of primates, one of the main phenomena of menstruation—the sloughing off of the uterine endometrium and its complete replacement by a new endometrial lining—will be described. It is not generally known that in nonprimates, too, there is a cyclic sloughing off and regeneration of the uterine endometrium, a process that seems to be hormone-controlled, just as it is in primates, although the details of it are not yet clear. Endometrial destruction and regeneration in nonprimates involve no bleeding, possibly because only the epithelial layer of the endometrium is involved. In sheep, this occurs during the early follicular phase and is completed in about three or four days (Fig. 4-3). In cows and pigs, a similar process takes place late in the luteal phase and is completed

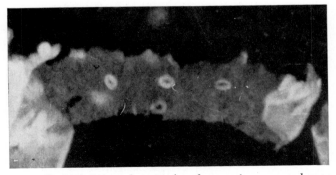

Figure 4-3. *Uterine cast flushed from the uterine horn of a normal ewe shortly after mid-cycle. The holes and projections in the cast (top layer of uterine epithelium) are openings to the uterine glands.*

by the onset of the follicular phase. Rats show an almost continuous sloughing off of the endometrium, and the presence of uterine debris does not seem to be correlated with any hormonal state.

Effects of Estrogen and Progesterone on the Castrate Uterus

The changes occurring in uterine endometria during the normal cycle can be duplicated in castrated or infantile females, both of which have similarly unstimulated uteri. Estrogen causes increased vascularization and greater mitotic activity of the uterus, which result in a great increase in the weight of that organ. In rats and mice, estrogen therapy leads to an accumulation of water in the uterine lumen; in other mammals, there is no significant accumulation of water in the lumen, but the uterine interstitium becomes very edematous. Myometrial smooth muscles undergo hyperplasia and hypertrophy. The increase in the weight of the uterus is proportional to the amount of estrogen injected and is due to the sum total of the effects mentioned.

Small physiological amounts of progesterone have very little if any effect on the uteri of castrate or infantile females. Very large amounts can produce the effects typical of that hormone, but progesterone alone, without estrogen, is not very effective. For this reason the effects of progesterone are best studied after "estrogen priming." The priming is accomplished by pretreatment of the female with a dose of estrogen that is too small by itself to cause any morphological or histological changes ascribable to estrogen. After estrogen priming, much smaller doses of progesterone are required to produce typical progestational effects, including an increase in the thickness of the endometrium, which is primarily caused by coiling and convolution of the endometrial glands. Other typical effects of progesterone on the uterus will be discussed later.

The estrogen and progesterone effects discussed here can be produced in castrated females of all species. The same uterine changes are produced by these hormones when they are secreted by the ovaries during the estrous cycle. But the uterine changes occurring during the cycle are not always as clear-cut as they are in castrates treated with estrogen alone or with progesterone after estrogen priming, probably because during the normal cycle there is considerable overlapping in the secretion and action of these two hormones, so that the uterus is never acted upon by either alone. Since the uterine endometrium of rats and mice does not undergo the changes that are typical of females with long cycles, it is thought that the corpora lutea of rats and mice do not become functional during the short cycles and do not secrete progesterone. Exogenous estrogen and progesterone, injected into castrated rats and mice, cause the typical changes in the uterine endometria, just as they do in other mammals.

In species with longer cycles, the change from the follicular to the luteal phase is distinct and typical. There is great variation within a species, however, in the time, during cycles of similar length, when the change occurs. In a homogeneous group of sheep (in which there is very little variation in length of cycle after the breeding season becomes established), it is possible to separate the ewes in luteal phase from those in follicular phase by the histology of their endometria. But there is great variation in the onset of the luteal phase. The endometria of some ewes still show the full progestational effect on day 10 of the cycle, but others, at the same time and with the same length of cycle, show the full estrogenic effect. Some ewes may have progesterone-stimulated uteri for the whole sixteen days of the cycle even though the corpus has regressed morphologically and histologically. After considerable experience it is possible to evaluate the reproductive state of women, ewes, and pigs from the histology of the corpora lutea and the uterine endometrium, and this method is very useful in the analysis of the reproductive physiology of domestic animals. In cows, the evaluation of uterine histology is even more difficult than it is in sheep and pigs because the differences between the luteal and follicular phases in cows are not as clear-cut as they are in the other two species. Even with the limitations cited, however, uterine histology provides a good guide to ovarian activity, especially in cases of abnormality, such as cystic ovaries or nonfunctional corpora lutea.

Ovulation

The culminating event of the estrous cycle is the rupture of the follicle and the shedding of the ovum. Because the endocrine control of ovulation and the physiology of the phenomenon are discussed elsewhere, we shall confine ourselves here to the relation of ovulation to the rest of the estrous cycle.

All the events of the cycle are related to ovulation in anticipation of the possibility that the egg will be fertilized and that pregnancy will ensue. It is in preparation for this latter possibility that the uterine changes described in the preceding portions take place. During heat, the female permits or encourages frequent matings and thus increases the chance that viable sperm will be present in the reproductive tract for fertilization when the eggs arrive. In the great majority of spontaneously ovulating females, ovulation occurs shortly before or shortly after the end of heat. In induced ovulators, the egg is shed within a few hours after copulation. Table 4-3 summarizes the length of cycle, the

Table 4-3. Cycle length, duration of heat, and time of ovulation in some animals

SPECIES	LENGTH OF CYCLE (days)	DURATION OF HEAT OR SEXUAL RECEPTIVITY	TIME OF OVULATION
Mare	19–23	4–7 days	From 1 day before to 1 day after end of heat
Cow	21	13–17 hours	12–15 hours after end of heat
Sow	21	2–3 days	30–40 hours after start of heat*
Ewe	16	30–36 hours	18–26 hours after start of heat
Goat	19	39 hours	9–19 hours after start of heat
Guinea pig	16	6–11 hours	10 hours after start of heat
Hamster	4	20 hours	8–12 hours after start of heat
Mouse	4	10 hours	2–3 hours after start of heat
Rat	4–5	13 or 15 hours	8 or 10 hours after start of heat
Woman	28	Continuous	Days 12–15 of cycle
Dog	†	7–9 days	1–3 days after start of heat
Fox	‡	2–4 days	1–2 days after start of heat
Rabbit	——	——	10½ hours after copulation (induced)
Mink	8–9	2 days	40–50 hours after mating (induced)
Cat	——	4 days	24 hours after mating (induced)
Cat	15–21	9–10 days	If no mating occurs
Ferret	**	——	30 hours after mating (induced)

    * Some breeds may ovulate as early as 18 hours after heat starts.
    † Two heats yearly, fall and spring, no cycles.
    ‡ Season December–March, no cycles.
    ** In absence of male, continuous heat from March to August.

duration of heat, and the time of ovulation in relation to the onset of heat or, in induced ovulators, to the time of copulation. For many species, only ranges are given, generally because in these species the intervals vary with breed, strain, age, and, possibly, other factors such as season. The times of ovulation given for most species apply to the majority of individuals studied. Of the cows studied, for instance, 75 percent ovulated 12–14 hours after the end of heat; the others ovulated as early as 2½ hours before the onset of heat or at late as 22 hours after the end of heat. Similarly, most women ovulate about day 14 of the cycle, but there are cases on record in which ovulation occurred during the menstrual flow or very early or very late during the cycle. For this reason the figures given in the table should be regarded simply as a guide to the reproductive behavior of the majority of the females belonging to the group in question but should not be considered as absolute figures that apply to all females under all conditions.

In a few animals, on the other hand, variability in the time of ovulation is insignificant. The vast majority of all rabbit does, regardless of breed, ovulate 10–11 hours after copulation or after the injection of an ovulation-inducing hormone. In rats and mice, the length of cycle and the time of ovulation are quite constant within each of the various strains, in most of which the cycle lasts four days and in a few of which it lasts five days.

The time required for the completion of the ovulatory process in polytocous animals, after the first follicle has ruptured, is not accurately known. In pigs, ovulation may be completed within six hours; in rats and rabbits it takes much less time. In pigs, the intervals between the ruptures of follicles are very uneven, unovulated follicles being found occasionally as late as four days after the end of heat. It is probable that these lagging follicles are retained and persist as cysts into the next cycle.

The mare has the longest heat of all spontaneously ovulating non-primate females. Among the wild Equidae, repeated matings during the whole heat, lasting from four to seven days, are probable. Under domestication, however, the long heat presents a problem: it is difficult to time the mating in such a way as to have viable sperm present in the oviduct at all the times when ovulation could occur. To increase the chances of fertilization, one can take advantage of the fact that LH-containing hormones (such as chorionic gonadotrophin) cause ovulation of the mature follicle well before the normal time. The time of ovulation can thus be controlled by the breeder, who can avoid repeated breeding of the mare by causing ovulation through hormone injection and by timing the breeding to ensure the presence of viable sperm when the egg arrives in the oviduct. According to some authors, stallion sperm remains motile in the reproductive tract of the mare for as long as five days, but it is not known how long it retains its ability to fertilize the egg.

The dog and the fox (and possibly other Canidae) are unique in that in them the first polar body is not extruded at the time of ovulation (as it is in all other mammals). Fertilization of the egg in these females does not occur for a considerable time after ovulation, but it is not known whether the delay in fertilization is due to the delay in the extrusion of the polar body.

Bizarre Phenomena Related to Estrous Cycle

We have described female reproductive cycles as rather steady phenomena, delimited by such cyclically repeated events as psychological estrus, menstruation, ovulation, corpus luteum formation, etc. As we know, these phenomena are controlled by interrelated neuroendocrine mechanisms, and one might think that once a cycle has begun it must run its course in an orderly fashion before the next cycle can begin. This expectation of neuroendocrine stability, which is held generally responsible for the predictability of the length of the estrous cycle, the time of ovulation, onset of menstruation, duration of heat, etc., has suffered some disconcerting jolts within the last few years, and the derangements of these reproductive phenomena are too drastic and too well documented to be ignored.

We are presently at the very beginning of studies of animal behavior as it affects reproduction, but the fragmentary information available makes it clear that much future effort can be expended profitably to increase our understanding of the mechanisms that permit psychogenic factors to modify the function of the neuroendocrine mechanism. Such studies have much theoretical and practical importance. For these reasons a brief summary of the best-documented phenomena will be made here in the hope that this review will stimulate further study of animal behavior as it relates to reproduction.

In reading this summary it should be remembered that each of the effects discussed is due to a significant modification of one or of several of the basic neuroendocrine control systems discussed earlier. The reader is further urged to think about the drastic endocrine shifts that must have occurred to produce results which deviated so greatly from the expected.

It all began with the finding that such exteroceptive signals as the odor of the male can significantly modify the length of the estrous cycle, hasten or delay ovulation, prevent implantation of fertilized eggs, etc. These phenomena were first studied in detail by Whitten and by Parkes and Bruce (details in Nalbandov, 1963), and the reproductive effects are appropriately called by the names of their discoverers.

To them we shall add a few other effects that seem to fall into the same category.

The Whitten Effect.   Whitten housed 10 to 30 female mice in a single box. Subsequently, each mouse was placed singly in a clean box with one vigorous male. Because in mice the cycle lasts 4 to 5 days, one would expect about $\frac{1}{4}$ or $\frac{1}{5}$ of all the mice to mate on each of the succeeding 4 or 5 nights after pairing. What was actually found was that there was a highly significant shift in the numbers of mice mating on each of the 5 nights. In one typical experiment, involving 317 females, the observed mating frequencies (as judged by the presence of vaginal plugs), were distributed as follows:

> First night: 43 females mated
> Second night: 44 females mated
> Third night: 146 females mated
> Fourth night: 42 females mated
> Fifth night: 14 females mated
> Remainder: 28 did not mate at all

Assuming a 4- to 5-day cycle as typical for this group, on a purely random basis 58 mice should have mated each night (if the 28 mice which did not mate at all during the observation period are subtracted). It is of great interest that in the mice which should have mated on days 1 and 2, heat and ovulation must have been delayed, while in those mice which should have mated on days 4 and 5, these events must have been hastened. Whitten has evidence that the odor of the male (or perhaps ingestion of the male feces by the female) was the immediate cause of this modification of the cycle.

The Bruce Effect.   The experiments involved two strains of mice which, for the sake of simplicity, will be identified as A and B. Miss Bruce allowed females of strain A to mate with males of strain A. Half of the females exposed were then left in peace and most of them, as expected, became pregnant or pseudopregnant. The other half of the females were exposed to males of an alien strain, B, within 24 hours after they had mated with males of their own strain, A. These females *remated* with males of strain B and, what was most amazing, most of them gave birth to young which were gentically identifiable as having been sired by B males. To explain these results it must be postulated that after exposure to B males, corpora lutea formed after the mating with A males degenerated, that a new crop of follicles must have matured and ovulated, the resulting ova now being fertilized by sperm from B males and, finally, that eggs from the previous ovulation which were fertilized by sperm from A males, must have degenerated and yielded their rightful place to the newcomers from the second mating. It is important to pause here and to reflect on all the endocrine upheavals which must have occurred to make the events just described possible.

Some of these events could be initiated by placing A females, following their mating with A males, into boxes which have previously housed B males. This was sufficient to interrupt the original (A × A) pregnancy, and most A females either resumed normal cycles or became pseudopregnant. The contraceptive effect of B males was traced to their odor, which is able to initiate the whole train of events described. Obviously, the action of an "odor" on the central nervous system can profoundly affect the reproductive behavior of other individuals. To contrast these external agents to internal ones (hormones) the term "pheromones" or "carriers of excitation" was introduced. That pheromones play an important role in the sexual integration of invertebrates has been known for some time. For instance, the queen bee secretes a substance which, when ingested by the workers, keeps their sexual apparatus underdeveloped. It appears now that pheromones may play an important role in vertebrates as well.

Signoret and Mouleon removed the olfactory bulbs from sexually mature pigs and found that the subsequent cycles became either very irregular or ceased completely. The ovaries of such females contained no corpora lutea but many vesicular follicles, which were somewhat smaller than the follicles of ovulatory size. In no sense were the ovaries of these females atrophic and they bore a striking morphological resemblance to the ovaries of constant estrus rats. In anosmic pigs the hypophysis is unable to provide sufficient quantities of LH for ovulation.

Much additional work will be needed before we can understand the neuroendocrine pathways involved in this phenomenon. To underscore the importance of olfaction further, mention should be made of a congenital genetic defect in man, which results in either absence or malformation of the olfactory bulbs. In this condition genital agenesis is noted quite frequently.

Part of the explanation of the Bruce effect lies in the nonmaintenance of the corpora lutea formed after the initial mating of A females with A males. The overriding contraceptive effect of B males can be halted if, immediately after mating to A males, the A females are injected with prolactin, the LTH of mice and rats. This prevents the degeneration of the first set of corpora lutea formed and allows the inference that the odor of B males is able to block the continued secretion of the LTH necessary in mice and rats.

Miscellaneous Effects.   Both the Bruce and the Whitten effects could be classified as being triggered by such exteroceptive signals as olfaction. The other effects to be discussed have not been studied in sufficient detail to permit us to classify them in detail with regard to the triggering mechanisms involved, and we shall confine ourselves to their enumeration. The question, to what extent the modification in the reproductive behavior is caused by stress, proximity of males (olfaction, actual physical contact), or by other environmental factors remains unresolved.

Reminiscent of the Whitten and Bruce effects are the observations that in sheep the onset of the breeding season may be advanced by several weeks if the ewes are exposed to rams several months prior to the expected onset of the breeding season, as compared to ewes not exposed to males.

In the discussion on sterility (Chapter 12), evidence is presented that sexually mature pigs which are "sterile" on their home farms, in spite of estrous cycles of normal length and in spite of frequent matings to fertile males, will conceive to the first mating after they have been moved from the home farm to a new location. The move by truck from one location to another is apparently the only change undergone by these animals, since they did not remain in the new location sufficiently long to benefit from any possible amelioration in management or diet. Similarly, normal, sexually mature pigs, when moved from one location to another, show a tendency to synchronize their sexual activity (both heat and ovulation) in relation to the moving day. Thus, a significantly higher proportion of them show heats 5 to 8 days after being moved than would have had they been left in the original habitat.

There also appears an effect of "travel" on the onset of puberty in swine. In a well-documented study, Du Mesnil Du Buisson and Signoret reported what happened to 1043 prepubertal gilts which were shipped to an experiment station and checked for heat twice daily. A group of 858 females of the same breed and age and of similar weights was slaughtered. Seventy percent of them had infantile ovaries and reproductive tracts, while 30 percent had "some follicular development" or had ovulated one or more times. On the basis of this slaughtered sample it is presumed that the 1043 animals which remained alive (and were used in the experiments) were in a similar stage of reproductive development. Of the experimental group, 277 females (26.5 percent) showed heats 4, 5, and 6 days after arrival at the station; an additional 188 females showed heats on days 1, 2, and 3, or on days 7, 8, and 9. Thus, 465 females (45 percent of the total) showed heat 1 to 9 days after arrival at the station. It should be kept in mind that these animals were predominantly prepubertal and that, according to the evidence of the slaughtered group, only about 190 of them should have shown sexual activity had they remained on their native farms.

It appears that both hastening of the onset of puberty and synchronization of cycles as occurred in this sample of pigs. It remains unknown whether the stress of transportation, the new environment, or the daily exposure to males produced this remarkable shift in the reproductive behavior of these females.

In women, failure of menstruation—sometimes lasting for several months because of fear of pregnancy—is a well-known phenomenon, menstruation frequently occurring within a few days after a negative pregnancy test has been communicated to them. Culmination of this psychosomatic modification of the menstrual cycle is the so-called pseudosiasis in which a neurotic desire for pregnancy may lead not only to a complete cessation of menstrual period but also to an enlargement of the breasts, swelling of the abdomen, and, in extreme cases, even labor pains at the expected time, as if a fetus were present.

When in heat, females of several species show a lordosis reflex in which they become rigidly immobile when a hand or finger is placed on the back. When the pudendal region is touched the back is arched in concave fashion, the hind legs are rigidly extended, and the pudendal region is everted and presented in such a manner as to facilitate and to invite copulation. Females not in heat try to escape the touch of the experimenter and do not show the lordosis reflex. This reflex can be used as a reliable means of detecting heat in laboratory mammals such as rats (in which to the above symptoms there is also added a characteristic twitching of the ears), guinea pigs, and cats.

Domestic mammals show a variant of the lordosis reflex, which has been analyzed in some detail in pigs by Signoret. He has confirmed the observations of many practical pig breeders that a sow in heat will become rigidly immobile when, in the absence of a boar, a man sits on her back or even simply exerts manual pressure on the back. The degree to which this response can be obtained is apparently genetically controlled; in cross-bred swine used for experimental work at the University of Illinois, 90 to 100 percent of all females respond to the test by rigid immobility. In the breed (Large White) used by Signoret, only about 50 percent of the females in heat responded to the signal while the other 50 percent of the females in heat—and, of course, all females not in heat—escaped the experimenter's attempts to sit upon them or his attempts to exert manual pressure. Signoret noted that the proportion of females responding could be greatly increased if a male was present, and he proceeded to fractionate the role of the male in eliciting the reflex. He found that 90 percent of the females showed the reflex if they could smell the males, the odor being produced by infiltration of the area with male urine, and if they could listen to a recording of his typical rutting call. If, in addition to the odor and the call, they could also see the male, a further 7 percent showed the reflex; if they could also have physical contact with him, the remaining 3 percent showed the reaction. The recorded call alone raised the response from 46 to 71 percent, but if the rhythm of the call was altered only an additional 9 percent of the females responded. Odor alone raised the percentage of positive responses from 50 to 81 percent.

How the phenomena of sound and odor can intensify psychological heat, which is normally attributed to the action of estrogen on the central nervous system, remains completely unknown and invites further study. Of great interest is the fact that there is a very significant relationship between the readiness with which the rigidity reflex can be induced and the fertility of swine. This will be discussed in greater detail in Chapter 12.

The Menstrual Cycle

The estrous cycle of nonprimates is characterized by short heats, during which the female permits mating; ovulation takes place either shortly before or shortly after the end of heat. Menstruating primates, in contrast, do not have unequivocal peaks of sexual desire and, as a rule, permit copulation throughout the whole cycle. Ovulation in primates occurs midway between two menstrual periods. In both the estrous and the menstrual cycles the endometrial linings of the uterus are sloughed off, but bleeding accompanies this breakdown only in primates and does not occur at that particular time in other mammals.

Before discussing the physiological basis of menstruation, we shall present the results of experiments that formed the basis for the under-

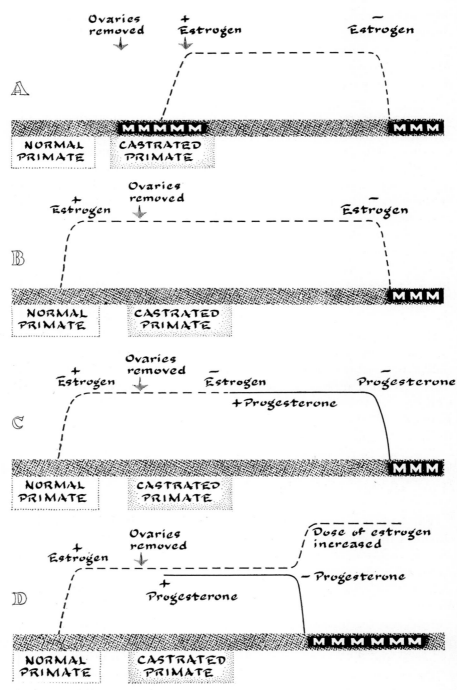

Fig. 4-4. A-D. *For explanation see facing page.*

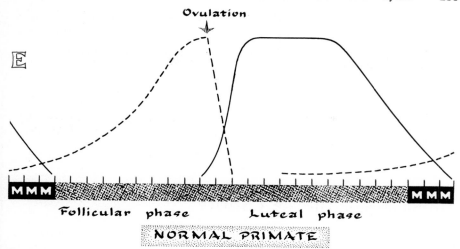

Figure 4-4. *Relation of hormonal states to menstruation in primates. The broken line indicates the estrogen level, the solid line the progesterone level.*

A—D. Effects of castration and hormone administration on menstruation (MM).

E. Postulated hormone levels of a primate female during the normal cycle.

standing of the mechanism of menstruation. One of the earliest observations showed that the removal of ovaries from intact primate females precipitated menstrual flow within a day or two. This observation led to the assumption that menstruation was caused by the absence of ovarian hormones. That this idea was correct was shown when it was found possible to prevent or to stop postcastration menstruation by the administration of estrogen or progesterone. Menstruation can be prevented by these hormones for as long as they are injected, but cessation of injection causes onset of menstrual flow within forty-eight hours after the withdrawal of progesterone and within four days after the withdrawal of estrogen. This flow is known as withdrawal bleeding. A few basic experiments, which illustrate the different conditions under which menstruation occurs, are shown in Figure 4-4. Graphs A and B show that ovariectomy causes menstruation and that this can be stopped and prevented for as long as either estrogen or progesterone is injected. Comparison of C and D shows that, though progesterone, when it is substituted for estrogen, can hold off menstruation (C), the reverse is not true even though the dose of estrogen is increased (D). From these facts it is inferred that normal menstruation is the result of the withdrawal of progesterone and that it occurs from a progestational endometrium. Under experimental conditions, progesterone, estrogen, androgen, and certain adrenal hormones are capable of preventing or of stopping menstruation. It will be noted (E) that in normally cycling primate females menstruation takes place when the corpus luteum is regressing (withdrawal of progesterone) and before rapid follicular growth has begun. It is not quite clear why menses stop during the normal cycle, but we may assume that the slowly rising level of estrogen coming from growing follicles is responsible.

Morphological Uterine Changes

In animals with long estrous cycles (all mammals except rats and mice), profound uterine changes take place under the influence of sex hormones. There is no basic difference between the effects of the ovarian hormones on the uteri of primates and their effects on the uteri of nonprimates. In both, the presence of sex hormones causes a thickening of the various uterine elements. In the absence of these hormones the structures making up the uterus can no longer be maintained in the lushness of peak hormonal action, and a gradual breaking down of the uterine tissue takes place. A thinning of the mucosa, a leucocytic infiltration, and a decrease in the rate of blood flow are phenomena of both primate and nonprimate uteri during the phase of hormonal withdrawal. Primates (except the New World monkeys) differ from other females in that they have spiral arteries in the endometrium. When, in the absence of progesterone, the mucosa becomes thinner, the spiral arteries become exposed, and bleeding from them begins. It is equally plausible, however, to assume that the absence of progesterone causes vasoconstriction, which leads to local ischemia, to the subsequent breakdown of the endometrium, and hence to menstruation. In any event, menstrual flow is preceded by a thinning of the endometrium, vasoconstriction, and an increased coiling of the spiral arteries. These events lead to local necrosis and to desquamation. Starting with a few isolated patches, this process of gradual necrosis and renewal eventually involves the whole uterine surface and continues until it is completed. Hemorrhages in an area in which local necrosis is in progress last from thirty to sixty minutes.

New World monkeys and all nonmenstruating mammals have no spiral arteries. The former do menstruate, however, though only in microscopic quantities. Domestic animals do not menstruate, but the

and to predict from that when the next ovulation is most likely to occur. A hen with a clutch length of four eggs that has laid the first egg of a clutch at 8:00 A.M. is likely to ovulate the next egg about 9:00 A.M. on the same day. Because about twenty-six hours are needed to finish the ovulated egg, she should lay this egg about 11:00 A.M of the next day. Similarly, the time of laying can be used as a clue to the probable time when the laid egg was ovulated the day before. After a hen's clutch length has been determined over a period of two or three weeks and oviposition of the first one or two eggs of a clutch has been accurately timed, both ovulation and oviposition of succeeding eggs of the clutch become highly predictable. For this reason the hen is an unequaled experimental animal for the study of ovulation and related phenomena.

The mechanisms controlling ovulation (LH release), oviposition, and the egg's rate of travel through the oviduct have been worked out in part, but some of the details remain unknown. The productivity of a hen is generally determined by the length of the clutch, and that depends on the interval between oviposition and the following ovulation. The larger that interval, the fewer eggs will be produced in one clutch. Hens laying twenty, thirty, or more eggs in one clutch accomplish this by two means: by shortening the interval between oviposition and ovulation to a few minutes (hens with very long clutches ovulate even before the egg is laid), and by shortening the time the egg spends in the shell gland to as little as eighteen hours.

Pituitary-ovary Relations

The classical concept of the regulation of gonadal function by pituitary hormones has been amply confirmed in chickens by Fraps and others. In general, the mechanism of this control is approximately the same as in mammals, the gonadotrophic complex governing follicular growth and ovulation directly and egg formation indirectly. A few avian deviations will be emphasized here.

The ovaries of immature mammalian females can be stimulated to endocrine and gametogenic activity long before the females would normally reach sexual maturity. The ovary of the immature chicken, in contrast, is amazingly unresponsive to stimulation by any gonadotrophin of mammalian origin until twenty or thirty days before the chicken would normally reach sexual maturity. The injection of crude chicken pituitary is much more effective: it causes the formation of eggs of almost ovulatory size in sexually immature pullets. This indicates that chicken pituitaries contain a hormone that is necessary for follicular maturation and that is not contained in mammalian gonadotrophic preparations. Additional evidence on this point will be given elsewhere.

The injection of chicken pituitaries is also more effective than that of mammalian gonadotrophins in causing secretion of androgen and estrogen by the ovaries of immature chickens, as is shown by the resulting growth of oviducts and combs.

Hypophysectomy of adult laying hens leads to rapid regression of ovary, oviduct, and comb (Fig. 4-5). Normal laying, or at least ovulation, may be maintained in hypophysectomized laying hens for not more than seven days after the operation if mammalian gonadotrophins are injected and not more than fifteen days if chicken pituitaries are injected. If ovarian atresia is permitted to occur after hypophysectomy, the follicles cannot be brought back to normal ovulatory size, regardless of the amount of mammalian gonadotrophic hormone injected, but they do respond by substantial growth. The proportion of FSH and LH in mammalian gonadotrophins may be such that those hormones can bring about only partial follicular growth in chickens.

Of some interest are studies involving the effect of starvation on the egg-laying ability of hens. Withdrawal of feed from laying hens causes an immediate cessation of laying, and the rate of follicular regression of oviducts and comb very much resemble the effects of hypophysectomy (Fig. 4-5). On the day following withdrawal of feed, most hens laid the finished egg, the yolk for which had been ovulated on the day preceding onset of starvation. After this terminal egg no further ovulations occurred unless the hens were injected daily either with PMS or a crude chicken pituitary powder. With such treatment most hens were able to continue egg laying for as long as eleven days in the complete absence of feed. Considering the chemical composition of the components of yolk and white and the total mass of materials produced, this is indeed a remarkable feat, involving the mobilization of 14.5 percent of the hens' total body reserves. Since only a gonadotrophic hormone was injected, and since for the production of a complete egg a functional oviduct is prerequisite, this means that the single daily GTH injections were able to maintain the flow of ovarian steroid hormones, which maintained the oviduct in a functional state. The ovarian steroids were also able to mobilize the necessary precursors for the yolk and the proteins for the albumen from the body reserves (fat stores and muscle tissue), to direct them to the liver, remobilize them

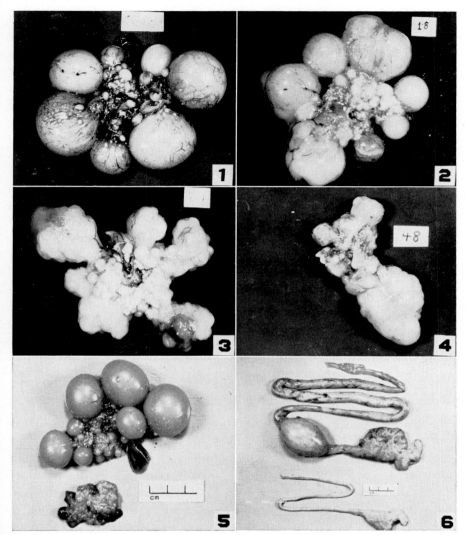

Figure 4-5. *After hypophysectomy follicular atresia is extremely rapid. Compare the normal hen's ovary with those 18 (2), 24 (3), and 48 (4) hours after hypophysectomy. In 5 and 6 the ovaries and oviducts of a normal and a hypophysectomized hen are compared 6 days after operation (Opel and Nalbandov, 1961. Prov. Soc. Exp. Biol. Med. 107:233).*

from there, and finally, under the influence of the GTH, to direct the lipoproteins to the follicles and the albumen protein to the oviduct. The complexity of this whole metabolic performance is impressive.

Hormonal Control of Clutches.   These findings support the contention that the ovary of the hen depends on pituitary gonadotrophins for normal functioning. Clutch length is governed by the amount of gonadotrophin produced by the pituitary gland, as is shown by the fact that exogenous mammalian gonadotrophin injected into hens with short clutches (one or two eggs) increases the clutch length of half of them by one, two, or three eggs.

There remain two questions: how the sequence of follicle maturation and ovulation is governed in hens, and how the flow of FSH is regulated to provide just enough hormone for a graded stimulation of the follicles so that no more than one follicle is ready for ovulation on any one day. Because of the almost continuous and cyclic maturation and ovulation of eggs in chickens with long clutches, it seems reasonable to speculate that in the hen the rate of FSH secretion is not controlled, as it is in mammalian females, by the ebb and flow of follicular estrogen. The pituitary of the hen, furthermore, has been found to be very resistant to estrogenic inhibition (in contrast to mammals of both sexes and to male chickens). For these reasons, and for others that will be given shortly, the assumption seems justified that in the hen there is a continuous flow of FSH from the pituitary. In the hen with the short clutch the valve is set for a low but steady flow of FSH; in the hen with the long clutch the valve is opened wider for a more rapid but still steady outpouring of FSH.

The Endocrine Time Clock.   A clue to the answers to some of the questions raised here was provided by a series of experiments that began as part of a study of the endocrinology of albumen secretion but uncovered, instead, an interesting control mechanism of the pituitary gland. These experiments involved in the introduction of a foreign body (a pellet of paraffin or just a loop of surgical thread attached to the wall of the magnum) into the lumen of the magnum to simulate the presence of a yolk. When this was done in laying hens, ovulation stopped immediately, and no more eggs were laid for three or four weeks after the introduction of the foreign body. The startling thing was that during this anovulatory phase neither the combs nor the ovaries shrank and the ovaries continued to contain follicles of ovulatory size. There was no atresia, and the follicles that were present in the ovary when the foreign body was introduced into the magnum were maintained. Equally important was the fact that the whole oviduct was maintained in its initial size during this anovulatory period. These observations led to the following conclusions concerning the rates of hormone secretion:

1. The rate of androgen secretion remains unaltered. Because androgen secretion in the hen is governed by LH acting on an unknown component of the ovary, the undiminished size of the comb implies that the presence of the foreign body does not completely stop the secretion of LH.
2. The rate of estrogen secretion remains unaltered. Estrogen is known to be secreted in the hen by ovarian follicles, just as it is in mammals, and the rate of its secretion in hens also is controlled by FSH and LH. An undiminished flow of estrogen accounts for the undiminished size of the oviducts.
3. The rate of FSH secretion remains the same. This is indicated by the maintenance of ovarian follicles without atresia.
4. The major change that occurs in the hen after the foreign body is placed in the magnum is cessation of ovulations. Since LH is known to be necessary to ovulation, this observation led to the postulate that there might be a deficiency of LH.

To test this last possibility, the investigators injected LH into hens in which ovulations had been interrupted by the presence of a foreign body in the oviduct: all hens responded by ovulations. In view of the evidence summarized here and the effectiveness of LH in inducing ovulations, the following hormonal relation between the pituitary and the ovary was postulated. It is probable that in the normally laying hen there is a steady and continuous flow of FSH and of *some* LH. At certain intervals a quantity of LH above the steady flow is released. These "ovulatory peaks" of LH are responsible for ovulations.

These results suggest yet another interesting aspect of the reproductive physiology of the hen. The presence of a foreign body in the magnum stops ovulation; removal of the foreign body or injection of LH causes resumption of ovulation. It seems that the contents of the magnum (normally a yolk) control LH release via a neural or neurohumoral mechanism. This theory is supported by the finding that LH release in the hen can be blocked by the drug Dibenamine, which is known to block the nerve system (see the discussion of the mechanism of ovulation in mammals, pp. 162–165). The question now arises whether an egg in the oviduct has the same control over pituitary function as does the foreign body. The evidence on this point is incomplete, but the question is an attractive one, for an affirmative answer would explain how the hen manages to time ovulation in relation to oviposition and, as a rule, to prevent the ovulation of more than one egg and the ovulation of a new ovum as long as the preceding ovum is still in the oviduct. Subsequent experiments attempting to reproduce these phenomena have not always succeeded. Two factors appear to play a role; one is the age of the hen, the other the size of the foreign body or the length of the oviduct exposed to irritation. In young, rapidly laying pullets, in the spring, the introduction of a foreign body either has no effect or only a limited one. It appears probable that in young animals the rate of pituitary function is so great that an artificial foreign body is unable to stem the hormone tide. The thread to be used for the loop must be quite coarse and it must extend through an area of at least 4–5 centimeters of the lumen of the oviduct. Similarly, small foreign bodies are ineffective apparently because the degree of nervous stimulation or the area stimulated is inadequate to produce the signal necessary for the modification of the hypophyseal function.

It was mentioned that in the hen, as well as in mammals, progesterone can induce ovulation. Progesterone in the hypophysectomized hen is ineffective. That the exogenous progesterone does not act on the pituitary gland directly, but rather on a hypothalamic center, has been shown by work of Ralph and Fraps (1960). They found that lesions in the preoptic area of the paraventricular area always blocked ovulation (lesions in other areas of the hypothalamus had occasionally the same effect). Hens with lesions in the anterior ventromedial hypothalamus always failed to respond by ovulation to the injection of as much as 1.0 milligram of progesterone, a dose which does induce ovulation in unlesioned hens. Lesions placed in this area less than six hours before ovulation did not prohibit either normal or progesterone-induced ovulation. Finally, minute amounts of progesterone which, when injected systemically, were ineffective, did induce ovulation in intact hens when the hormone was placed in the anterior ventromedial hypothalamus. These different experimental approaches suggest that the hypothalamus of the hen contains and elaborates an LH-releasing factor.

Adrenal corticosteroids can also induce ovulation in the hen. Both this steroid and progesterone can be assumed to act on hypothalamic areas sensitive to them and cause the release of a factor that then releases hypophyseal LH. The question of whether progesterone (or another steroid) normally participates in the elaboration of LRF, or whether the progesterone effect described is an artifact, remains unknown. The fact that progesterone (or a progesterone-like substance) has been demonstrated in the blood of both laying and nonlaying hens is of considerable interest, but its source remains unknown. Birds do not form a structure that is either histologically or morphologically similar to the corpus luteum of mammals. Reasoning by analogy, some have assumed that the ruptured follicle is the site of progesterone secretion. Thus far, the ruptured follicle in the hen has been associated experimentally only with normal laying: it is found that its surgical removal may cause the egg originating from it to be held in the shell gland from one to seven days beyond the expected time of oviposition. But it is not known whether this effect is in any way associated with progesterone. There also remains the possibility that the progesterone found in chicken serum is a conversion product of another steroid hormone, such as one of the adrenal hormones. That desoxycorticosterone can be converted to progesterone *in vitro* and that progesterone-like substances have been isolated from the adrenal glands of mammals is suggestive. The source of progesterone in the hen and its role in avian reproduction remain to be investigated.

Physiology of the Avian Oviduct

After ovulation, the ovum is picked up by the fimbria of the oviduct and conducted into the magnum. Here it acquires the albumen layers. Albumen secretion in the magnum is controlled by two hormones. One of these is estrogen, which has the primary function of causing the anatomical and glandular development of the whole oviduct. In immature female chicks, estrogen causes a spectacular growth of the magnum and of its glandular elements, but estrogen alone cannot cause formation of albumen antecedents in the glands, nor can it cause the secretion of albumen proper into the lumen of the magnum. A second hormone is required for both the formation and the secretion of albumen. Either androgen or progesterone, acting on an estrogen-developed magnum, can cause the formation of albumen granules and the release of these granules into the lumen. The attempt to decide which of these hormones is actually responsible for these effects in the laying hen presents a dilemma. Because androgen is known to be an indigenous avian hormone, it is more tempting to ascribe the albumen-secreting effect to it rather than to progesterone, whose effectiveness in this reaction and in other physiological phenomena of the hen cannot be doubted, but whose source in the hen remains to be demonstrated.

After the growth of the magnum has been accomplished by estrogen, and the formation of albumen granules has been caused by either androgen or progesterone, there still remains the actual secretion of albumen from the glands into the lumen. This is normally elicited by the presence of any foreign body in the magnum, be it an ovum or a ping-pong ball or even a cockroach, which, on one occasion, had found its way in some unexplained manner into the lumen of the magnum, was later laid, neatly encased in albumen and shell, and almost found itself part of breakfast. The similarity in physiological response between the magnum and the mammalian uterus is striking, even though the result of trauma or the presence of an implanting embryo (the "foreign" body) in one is the secretion of albumen, in the other the secretion of "uterine milk" and the formation of placentomata.

Having acquired albumen during the two and a half or three hours in the magnum, the egg moves on to the isthmus, where the shell membranes are secreted. This part of the oviduct is histologically distinguishable from the magnum, but it too is controlled by the same hormones, which act in the same manner and in the same sequence as they do on the magnum. The egg spends one and a half hours in the isthmus and, having acquired the soft shell membranes and some water, moves on to the shell gland, or the uterus.

It is more appropriate to call this part of the oviduct the shell gland rather than the uterus, for it is not homologous to, and is in no way comparable to, the mammalian uterus. Here the egg spends about twenty-two hours while the calcareous shell is secreted round it. The endocrine control of the shell gland differs from the control of the upper regions of the oviduct in that estrogen alone causes the gland's growth and development as well as the mobilization and secretion of the calcium salts needed for the formation of the shell. Here also lies one of the most interesting aspects of avian endocrinology, one that needs additional work before it is completely understood. It is well known that estrogen causes the mobilization of calcium from bones. This leads to hypercalcemia, which is typical of laying hens and which can be induced by injection of estrogen into nonlaying birds and into males. Equally well established is the fact that estrogen encourages osteoblastic activity in the bone and hence deposition of calcium. It remains unknown how estrogen simultaneously accomplishes these opposite effects—deposition of calcium in bones and withdrawal of calcium from bones—but it is probable that it does so with the cooperation of another hormone (parathyroid?).

It is generally assumed that oviducal motility is caused by posterior pituitary hormones. Additional work on this subject is needed in view of the fact that the egg moves through the various segments of the oviduct at different rates. According to earlier studies, oviposition itself is caused by oxytocin, but more recent attempts to confirm this finding with more purified preparations of this hormone have not been uniformly successful. The effectiveness of oxytocin is inversely related to the length of time the egg has spent in the oviduct and the shell gland. Neurohypophysectomy of laying hens, moreover, does not interfere with normal oviposition, nor does it alter the length of time spent by the egg in the various portions of the oviduct. This, of course, does not prove that the posterior lobe and its hormones play no role in oviducal motility, for it is now known that that lobe may be merely the storage place for oxytocin and pitressin and that both substances are secreted in the hypothalamic region of the brain. It is possible that, once the hen becomes adjusted to the absence of the posterior lobe, the amount of posterior-lobe hormones coming from the hypothalamus is enough to control all functions normally associated with them except polydipsia and polyuria. Neurohypophysectomy probably does not alter the function of the anterior lobe.

SUMMARY

The events of the estrous cycle of nonprimates and those of the menstrual cycle of primates are compared. It is pointed out that all the physiological and morphological changes in the ovaries, the vagina, and the uterus taking place during these cycles are identical except that nonprimates show periodic peaks of sexual receptivity (heat, or estrus) whereas primates do not. In primates, a sloughing off of the uterine endometrium is accompanied by bleeding; in nonprimates, no comparable bleeding is seen. Menstruation in primates is due to an absence of hormones (usually progesterone). Pseudomenstruation in nonprimates (bitches and several laboratory species) is due to diapedesis and is in no way comparable to the menstrual bleeding of primates, for it is usually brought on by the injection of estrogen and occurs normally when the follicle is at the height of its development.

"Uni"-polytocous birds, in which many eggs are matured and ovulated singly but laid in clutches, are contrasted with "multi"-polytocous mammals, such as rats, in which many eggs are ovulated simultaneously. Obviously, the endocrine control mechanisms must be different to permit the maturation and ovulation of but one egg daily throughout a clutch in the one case and the simultaneous maturation and ovulation of many eggs in the other case. How the control mechanisms in these animals differ is not known, but several tentative explanations are offered for consideration. They should challenge the reader to find his own interpretation of the facts and to design experiments that may answer the questions.

Several examples are given in which events associated with the estrous cycle are hastened, delayed, held in abeyance, or otherwise drastically modified by such exteroceptive factors as odor, sound, being moved from one location to another, etc. The mechanism of action of such "carriers of excitation" or pheromones are not understood; but because of the profound shifts they can cause in the neuroendocrine control mechanisms, which are generally considered to be very stable, further study is important.

REFERENCES

M. Altmann. 1941. "Interrelations of the sex cycle and the behavior of the sow." *J. Comp. Psych.*, **31**:481.

S. A. Asdell. 1946. *Patterns of Mammalian Reproduction.* Comstock (Ithaca, N.Y.).

W. R. Breneman. 1955. "Reproduction in birds: the female" in *Comparative Physiology of Reproduction and the Effects of Sex Hormones in Vertebrates.* Cambridge University Press.

J. F. Burger. 1952. "Sex physiology of pigs." *Onderstepoort J.,* Suppl. No. 2, pp. 2–217.

P. Eckstein and S. Zuckerman. 1956. "The oestrous cycle in the mammals" in Marshall's *Physiology of Reproduction,* Vol. I, Part 1, 3rd ed. Longmans (New York).

E. J. Farris. 1954. "Activity of dairy cows during estrus." *J. Am. Vet. Med. Assoc.,* **125**:117.

R. M. Fraps. 1955. "Egg production and fertility in poultry" in *Progress in the Physiology of Farm Animals,* Vol. II. Butterworth (London).

W. Hansel and S. A. Asdell. 1952. "The causes of bovine metestrous bleeding." *J. Animal Sci.,* **11**:346.

C. L. Ralph and R. M. Fraps. 1960. "Induction of ovulation in the hen by injection of progesterone into the brain." *Endocrinology,* **66**:269.

S. R. M. Reynolds. 1949. *Physiology of the Uterus,* 2nd ed. Hoeber (New York).

V. A. Rice, F. N. Andrews, E. J. Warwick, and J. E. Legates. 1957. *Breeding and Improvement of Farm Animals,* 5th ed. McGraw-Hill (New York).

K. C. Richardson. 1935. "The secretory phenomena in the oviduct of the fowl," *Philos. Trans. Roy. Soc. London* (B), **225**:149.

G. W. Trimberger. 1941. "Menstruation frequency and its relation to conception in dairy cattle." *J. Dairy Sci.,* **24**:819.

chapter 5

Follicular Growth, Ovulation, Formation of Corpora Lutea

Normal Follicular Growth

We already know that follicular growth is controlled during the cycle by the hormones FSH and LH, both of which must be present if normal follicular growth and function (estrogen secretion) are expected. During the cycle follicular growth has been found to follow two patterns. In litter-bearing animals (for example, the pig), follicular growth is slow during the luteal phase, and a definite ovulatory spurt is observed during the follicular phase, within the last few days before ovulation (Table 3-2, p. 75). In most monotocous animals (for example, sheep), follicular growth is steady and extends throughout the cycle.

Whether we are dealing with monotocous or with polytocous animals, it is an established fact that more follicles begin and continue to grow until shortly before ovulation than are destined to ovulate. In pigs, from three to four times as many follicles are present in the follicular phase as shortly before ovulation (Table 3-2). Follicles that do not reach ovulatory size degenerate during the follicular phase. It seems that less hormone is required to initiate follicular growth than to maintain larger follicles and bring them to ovulatory size. This is seen from the fact that, when exogenous gonadotrophic hormones are injected at some time during the follicular phase, the number of follicles that reach ovulatory size (and ovulate) is proportional to the amount of hormone injected. Similarly, if one ovary is surgically removed, the remaining ovary produces about as many follicles and eggs as the two ovaries would have produced together. This compensatory effect is probably due to the fact that after unilateral castration twice as much gonadotrophic hormone is available for the remaining ovary as there had been before. These observations further argue for the idea, expressed in another connection, that the rate of FSH secretion is probably quite steady throughout the cycle.

An unconfirmed observation suggests that the large number of follicles started during the follicular phase furnish the estrogen that seems essential for the growth of the follicles chosen to ovulate. This conclusion is drawn from an experiment in which all but one or two of the follicles were destroyed during the follicular phase. It was found that none of the remaining follicles reached ovulatory size and none ovulated. When this experiment was repeated and exogenous estrogen was injected, the remaining follicles were maintained, grew, and ovulated.

Recent work shows that the pituitary glands of prepubertal females contain significantly more gonadotrophic hormone than those of sexually mature females. The ovaries of immature females respond by some follicular growth, but it is apparent from the lagging growth of the duct system that there is little if any estrogen secretion. It is probable that during that period the pituitary secretes mostly FSH, which is able to cause some degree of follicular development. Throughout the prepubertal life of female mammals, waves of follicles grow and become atretic without reaching ovulatory size. Each successive wave of follicular growth reaches a greater degree of development until, at the time of sexual maturity, endocrine conditions reach the most propitious stage for the occurrence of the first ovulation. The first ovulations quite frequently are not accompanied by heat. When the proper balance between pituitary FSH and LH is reached, normal cycles, including heat and ovulation, become established.

Effect of Temperature on Ovarian Function

Normally, the granulosa cells of the ovarian follicle produce estrogen, while the lutein cells of the corpus luteum synthesize progesterone. Only under exceptional circumstances does the mammalian ovary secrete androgen. R. T. Hill discovered that the kind of hormone synthesized by the ovary depends to an important degree on the temperature to which the ovary is exposed. Hill removed the ovaries from rats and transplanted them to the ears of genetically closely related castrated males, where the transplants frequently became established. After a time it was noted that the male accessory glands of the castrated males bearing ovarian grafts did not degenerate but were maintained in full secretory activity and weighed as much as did the prostates and seminal vesicles of intact males. This indicates that androgen is being secreted by the graft but, unfortunately, no data are available on either the chemical nature or the rate of secretion of the male sex hormone. It is also possible to graft the ovary into the tail of a rat belonging to a genetic strain which has a rudimentary prostate but is otherwise a normal female. After the graft has begun to secrete androgen (registered by an increase in prostate size), if the temperature of the tail is raised to body temperature the graft reverts to the secretion of estrogen and causes both uterine growth and vaginal cornification. These experiments show that the kind of hormone produced by the ovary largely depends on the environmental temperature in which the ovary finds itself.

Of interest is the histology of these ovarian grafts. Follicles of ovulatory size are occasionally found in younger grafts but no ovulations occur—perhaps because of the physical confines imposed on the grafts within the ear or the tail. In older grafts, many small follicles may be present but in all of them there is a striking abundance of ovarian interstitial tissue, which in the oldest grafts is the most prominent cell type found. Whether the interstitial tissue is the source of androgen is not known.

Also completely unknown is the role the temperature plays in determining the kind of histological structure the ovary is to assume and the kind of hormone it is to secrete. Women afflicted with multiple ovarian cysts frequently show hirsutism and a coarsening of the skin and facial characteristics. This suggests but does not prove androgen production by ovarian cysts, since such cysts may also secrete progesterone (as they are known to do in swine), which may be metabolized to androgen. This metabolic pathway is a common one in some animals; the pregnant cow is known to convert a good deal of its luteal and placental progesterone into androgen, which shows up in abundance in the feces. Similarly, exogenous progesterone injected into nonpregnant cattle is converted into androgen, which is eliminated in the feces.

Little is known about the extent to which certain histological tissues are restricted in their ability to produce only one type of hormone. Elsewhere in this book we have raised the question of whether follicular granulosa cells are capable of secreting progesterone prior to ovulation or whether this preovulatory synthesis of progesterone occurs only in species whose ovaries have much interstitial tissue. Later in this chapter, we shall present evidence that the corpus luteum of the hypophysectomized rat, when stimulated by LH, produces estrogen, although its normal function is to synthesize progesterone when stimulated by LTH. Avian ovaries are known to secrete androgen normally, but the specific histological structure of the ovary responsible for the synthesis of androgen has never been definitely identified; the interstitial tissue of chicken ovaries contains a cell which may (or may not!) be responsible. It is conceivable that the granulosa cells of the follicles may be able to synthesize estrogen and then progesterone. It should not be inferred, just because there are no obvious changes in the granulosa cells under the microscope, that none has occurred. A change in hormone synthesis may be due to a change of trophic hormones (from FSH to LH) or a change in hormone ratios (FSH:LH) impinging on the receptor system of the granulosa cells.

Effects of Estrogen and Progesterone on Follicular Growth

It has been mentioned that large doses of estrogen can completely inhibit follicular growth in normal animals by suppressing the secretion of pituitary gonadotrophins, whereas small doses of estrogen may enhance follicular development during the normal estrous cycle, perhaps by promoting vascularization of the chosen follicles. Beyond these observations little is known about the role of estrogen in normal follicular growth.

Progesterone has a more clear-cut effect on follicular development. When this hormone is injected into women, sheep (25 milligrams daily), pigs (50 milligrams daily), or cattle (100 milligrams daily), the next expected menstruation and ovulation, or heat and ovulation, do not occur as long as the injections continue. Within two or three days after the injections are stopped, normal cycles, including heat or menstruation and ovulation, return. The ability of progesterone to inhibit heats and ovulations can be used to synchronize the cycles of the individuals of a flock of domestic animals. In this way the heats or ovulations of different individuals can be made to occur at a time desired by the investigator. This new rhythm does not persist, however, and within two or three cycles the females synchronized by the progesterone treatment return to a rhythm in which heats and ovulations occur in the random fashion typical of normal cycles.

Some adverse effects result from this progesterone treatment. Not all females respond by suppression of cycles. In some females (particularly pigs), ovarian cysts are formed in response to progesterone injections, and in them heat and ovulation do not follow discontinuation of the injections. In females in which ovulation takes place, the eggs ovulated show a significantly lower fertilizability and a higher fetal resorption rate than those observed in normal females. For these reasons synchronization of cycles by means of progesterone remains a method that may be used for experimental purposes but cannot be applied in its present form in practice. A good method of synchronizing heats or ovulations would be of great importance to the animal breeder as well as the laboratory worker.

The way in which progesterone acts in producing the effects noted above is not known. It appears probable that in large doses it inhibits LH secretion, thus accounting for the inhibition of ovulation and of estrogen secretion and hence for the occurrence of heat. It also appears that the rate of FSH secretion may not be affected—a fact, if such it is, that may account for the formation of the cysts observed in many of the females treated with large doses of progesterone.

In pregnant females, there is a distinct difference among the species in the ovarian response to large doses of progesterone. If as much as 8 milligrams of progesterone is injected into pregnant rats, there is no noticeable morphological effect on the ovaries. The corpora lutea are indistinguishable from those of untreated rats. In contrast, if pregnant pigs are injected with 300–400 milligrams of progesterone daily between the time of conception and the thirty-fifth day of pregnancy, the corpora lutea degenerate completely, but no ovarian cysts are formed, as they would be in nonpregnant females. In relation to body weight, the 8-milligram dose for rats is about ten times as great as the 400-milligrams dose injected into pigs.

Follicular Cysts

The formation of cysts is one of the most interesting and least understood topics in the physiology of reproduction. Because Selye has provided a good description and classification of the types of cysts found in women, we shall confine ourselves to the types found in domestic animals. Cysts occur in most animals studied, but in some they are more commonly encountered than in others. Only rarely are they observed in sheep and goats. They are common causes of sterility in dairy cattle (but not in beef cattle) and in swine.

Ovarian Cysts in Pigs

About half of the cases of sterility observed in pigs are caused by ovarian cysts. A thorough analysis of this defect has been made in this species and has shown that three types of cysts are commonly found (Table 12-3, p. 291). The "single," or "retention," cysts occur in the normal cycles of swine because one or two normal follicles fail to ovulate at the time the majority of the follicles rupture. These unovulated follicles continue to enlarge during the early luteal phase of the subsequent cycle, until they either become luteinized without rupturing or become atretic. Single cysts do not seem to interfere with normal cyclic behavior and are probably minor accidents that should not be regarded as abnormal.

The other two types of cysts found in swine are definitely associated with sterility. Most common are *multiple large* cysts (Fig. 5-1), which frequently reach the enormous diameter of 10 centimeters. The number of these large cysts is always in the same range as the number of follicles of ovulatory size typical of the individual or the breed. There may be considerable variation in the size of cysts found in the two ovaries.

Figure 5-1. *Multiple large cystic ovaries of a pig with a long history of sterility. The largest cyst measured 5.5 cm in diameter, and the two ovaries together weighed more than 700 g.*

The endocrine causes of these cysts are not known, but it is possible that they are due to failure of LH release. It is significant that these cysts, in spite of their large size, contain less estrogen than normal follicles, either per milliliter of fluid or per total volume of cyst contents (Table 5-1). The large cysts are always heavily luteinized, either

Table 5-1.   Estrogen content of two types of cysts in comparison with normal follicles of swine

MATERIAL ASSAYED	AMOUNT OF ESTROGEN PRESENT (GAMMA)	
	per ml or g	in both ovaries
Large cysts		
Fluid	0.0009–0.0099	0.0228–0.1125
Stroma	0.0014–0.0132	0.0090–0.2323
Small cysts		
Fluid	0.0310–0.0350	1.3950–1.5750
Stroma	0.0361–0.0433	0.6750–1.1570
Normal ovaries		
Fluid	0.1162	0.3490
Stroma	0.0812	. . .
Theca and granulosa	0.1650	0.3257
Corpora lutea from		
Follicular phase	0.0668	0.1024
Luteal phase	0.0164	. . .

SOURCE: From Nalbandov. 1952. *Fertility and Sterility*, 3:100.

along the whole periphery or along part of the cyst wall. In the latter case the cyst wall is said to have lutein patches. The remainder of the wall may be completely naked or may be covered with a very thin granulosa layer, often consisting of only one or two layers of very flattened cells. Because of the heavy luteinization, these cysts are frequently mistaken for corpora lutea, especially before they reach their ultimate large size. Normal-appearing corpora lutea may be present along with the large cysts, but it is not known whether the corpora lutea are retained from previous ovulations, or result from completely luteinized smaller cysts, or are formed after normal ovulations at the time of the infrequent and irregular heats observed in such cystic females. Both the granulosa and the theca folliculi participate in the luteinization of cysts, but usually only the smaller and medium-sized large cysts show complete luteinization or lutein patches on the cyst wall. The largest cysts are usually "naked," showing no signs of luteinization—in fact, showing none of the normal components of follicles, such as the granulosa or the theca folliculi. It is possible that these have degenerated because of the continuous great distention of the cavity with cystic fluid.

Large luteinized cysts secrete progesterone, as can be seen from bioassays of cyst walls and cyst fluids and from the fact that the uterine endometria of sows showing these cysts are of the typical progestational type.

Animals with such cysts have very irregular estrous cycles, with prolonged anestrous periods, the latter sometimes leading to a mistaken diagnosis of pregnancy. There is no nymphomania, but when heats occur their intensity may be greater than normal. Most females with large cysts remain sterile in spite of frequent breedings. Recovery within the reproductive life of such animals rarely if ever occurs spontaneously, and attempts to ovulate these cysts or cause them to regress by the use of hormones have not been uniformly successful. In about 60 percent of the animals that have had large cysts for a long time, the clitoris may reach a length of 3 centimeters (Fig. 12-1C, p. 289). It is possible that the clitoris enlarges as the result of continuous stimulation by progesterone, but it is more probable that the progesterone is converted into androgen and that the androgen is responsible for the enlargement of this female homologue of the penis. Enlargement of the clitoris also occurs in pregnant animals (especially older ones), and for this reason it is not a good diagnostic sign of large ovarian cysts.

Less common than the large cysts are the *multiple small* cysts (Fig. 12-2A), which are distinguished by the fact that they are slightly larger than the normal follicles of ovulatory size. Multiple small cysts are more numerous than the number of follicles of ovulatory size one would normally expect to find in the ovary (Table 12-3, p. 291). Because it is possible to produce such cysts experimentally by overstimulating normal females with a gonadotrophic hormone such as PMS, the guess seems valid that the endocrine cause of multiple small cysts lies in the temporary or continuous overproduction of FSH by the pituitary gland. Both naturally occurring and experimentally induced cysts of this type resemble normal follicles histologically. Small multiple cysts secrete and contain more estrogen than do normal follicles, but even here nymphomania is not observed in afflicted females. Spontaneous recovery from this ovarian defect may occur, but attempts to treat it with hormones have not been uniformly successful. It is impossible to distinguish between small and large cysts by external symptoms, for estrous cycles and intervals between heats are very irregular and unpredictable in both conditions. As a rule, animals with small cysts do not show enlargement of the clitoris. The significance of these types of cysts to the efficiency of reproduction will be discussed in Chapter 12.

 Pregnant swine are frequently found to have ovarian cysts of either the large or the small variety. It is not known whether these cysts arise after conception or whether some animals conceive in spite of them. It is possible that, despite an endocrine imbalance, normal follicles may mature and ovulate in the presence of large cysts and that mating at these times may result in conception. The litter size of most pregnant cystic females is significantly smaller than that of noncystic females.

Ovarian Cysts in Cattle

 A completely different picture is encountered in cattle. Cystic ovaries are much commoner in dairy cattle than in most herds of beef cattle.

 Because nymphomania is frequently associated with cystic ovaries in cattle (as it is not in other species), the assumption has been popular that ovarian cysts in cattle secrete estrogen. Recent work has shown, however, that this is not true; in this respect the cystic ovaries of cattle resemble the large cysts of swine, including the fact that cysts in cattle secrete progesterone. In cattle, furthermore, females with cysts often assume male characteristics, such as general coarsening of the features of the head, deepening of the voice, thickening of the neck, enlargement of the clitoris, and male copulatory behavior. The symptoms of nymphomania may thus be secondary manifestations of an endocrine upset not of ovarian origin, and the cystic condition of the ovaries may be a secondary rather than the primary cause of nymphomania. One of the main reasons for suspecting a cause-and-effect relation between nymphomania and cystic ovaries is the intense sex drive of afflicted females, such a drive being normally associated with estrogen. It is known, however, that the psychological heat can also be induced in females by the injection of large doses of androgen. It is not known whether this hormone itself produces the psychological symptoms of heat or whether it must first be converted to estrogen in the body. These considerations lead to the possibility that nymphomania in cattle may be primarily caused by malfunction of the adrenal glands, which, under these circumstances, may be secreting either androgen itself or an adrenal steroid that is converted into substances having androgenic or estrogenic activity. These guesses are supported by the observed masculinization of the afflicted females. This whole subject has received less study than it deserves because an erroneous assumption, which is completely unsupported by experimental work, that cysts should secrete estrogen and estrogen should cause an intense sex drive, seemed to explain satisfactorily the symptoms associated with nymphomania in cattle.

The issue is further beclouded by the fact that nymphomania may be controlled with some degree of success, at least in its earliest stages, by the administration of gonadotrophic hormones rich in LH (such as human chorionic gonadotrophin), which presumably causes luteinization of the ovarian cysts. This fact seems to focus attention on the ovaries as the primary cause of the disease, which they may be in the earliest stages of the condition, but it does not exclude the possibility that other endocrine glands may be affected as the disease becomes established. Garm (1949) and others have found hypertrophy of the adrenal glands and especially of the zona glomerulosa in cattle with cystic ovaries and nymphomania.

Spontaneous and Induced Ovulations

In most mammalian females, ovulation is a cyclically repeated event, one that occurs at regular intervals except when the female is pregnant. Females belonging to this group are called "spontaneous ovulators." In certain other species, ovulation follows stimulation of the cervix, which, under normal conditions, is provided by the penis during copulation. Females that normally ovulate only after copulation are called "induced ovulators." Among them are the rabbit, the cat, the ferret, the short-tailed shrew, and the mink.

In both spontaneous and induced ovulators, follicles rupture as the result of LH action, but with some differences; LH release in the spontaneous ovulators is cyclic, is independent of copulation, and is provoked by an interplay of the neuroendocrine system; LH release in the induced ovulators occurs only when the proper stimulus, such as copulation or a facsimile of it, is applied to the cervix or to parts of the vagina. The evidence shows that the nervous impulse travels from the cervix to the basal hypothalamic area below and perhaps overlapping with the arcuate nucleus (see Fig. 3-8), where the LRF is presumed to be produced, which then reaches the adenohypophysis via the portal system and causes it to release LH into the peripheral circulation. At present it is not clear what pathway is followed in spontaneous ovulators, since no neural signal is necessary for the release of LH. An LRF has been extracted from the hypothalami of spontaneous ovulators (for instance, cattle and rats), which suggests that an LRF does participate in the release of LH in them, too. Furthermore, ovulations can be caused in rats by injecting them with LRF. It is assumed that the signal for LRF to come into play is neural in that the LRF producing hypothalamic area may be sensitive to one or both of the ovarian steriods. If estrogen or progesterone reach a certain titer in the blood, the hypothalamic area sensitive to that steroid concentration may respond by the release of LRF. From here the pathway is the same as that for induced ovulators. It will be recalled that in the chicken injection of minute quantities of progesterone into approximately the same area of the hypothalamus causes LH release, resulting in ovulation.

Some of the considerations that lead to the interpretation presented above are as follows: In induced ovulators, ovulations rarely occur in the absence of copulation; and, if the pituitary gland is removed within sixty minutes after copulation, or if the pituitary stalk is sectioned within that time, ovulation does not result. If either of these surgical interventions is performed later than the time indicated, ovulation proceeds normally. The length of time required for the copulatory stimulus to elicit the secretion of enough LH for complete ovulatory response argues for the intervention of a humoral agent and against a direct nervous connection from cervix to pituitary gland. That a nervous impulse also is involved, at least in part of this chain, is demonstrated by the finding that ovulation can be prevented, in spite of copulation, if a nerve-blocking agent (such as Dibenamine, or N,N-dibenzyl-chloroethylamine) is injected within one minute after the end of coitus. If the injection is delayed for more than one minute, ovulation is not blocked. Finally, that LH release is the terminal reaction caused by copulation is brought out by the fact that ovulation can be caused in rabbits and other induced ovulators by the injection of LH without copulation. In the rabbit, either copulation or injection of LH leads to ovulation in about ten hours.

In induced ovulators, follicles may occasionally rupture without copulation. In rabbits, 1–5 percent of the females—in some strains as many as 30 percent—may ovulate spontaneously. This usually happens if several females are kept in the same cage, the necessary neural stimulus for the release of LH being obtained from mounting, playing, and other physical contact. For this reason it is important to keep females used for experimental work in solitary cages. Even then as many as 2 percent of them may ovulate spontaneously.

Induced ovulators have no estrous cycle comparable to that of spontaneous ovulators. Theoretically, induced ovulators are sexually recep-

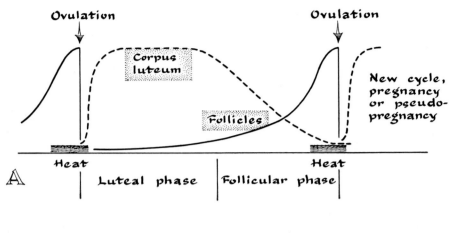

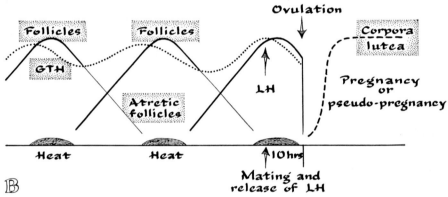

Figure 5-2. *Comparison of ovarian events in females with spontaneous ovulation* (A) *and induced ovulation* (B); *the chains of events are basically similar.*

tive at all times before copulation. In rabbit does, a period of sexual receptivity of two or three days is followed by an anestrous period of approximately equal duration. The endocrinology of these abbreviated cycles has not been worked out in detail, but it seems that the alternation of estrous and anestrous periods corresponds to the growth and atresia of follicles. During follicular growth, estrogen secretion induces sexual receptivity, but rising estrogen levels eventually inhibit the pituitary gonadotrophins. A decrease in gonadotrophic hormones results in follicular atresia and the onset of the anestrous period. Follicular atresia leads to decreased estrogen flow, which is followed by an increased flow of gonadotrophins, the growth of a new crop of follicles, and a new period of sexual receptivity. A graphic comparison of events in induced and spontaneous ovulators is shown in Figure 5-2.

It is interesting to speculate on the advantages of induced ovulation over spontaneous ovulation. The former is found primarily in animals that live singly in field or forest and therefore could not expect to be near a male at the time of the periodic and widely spaced heats. The more or less continuous state of sexual receptivity provides a good chance that at the time of occasional meetings between solitary males and females the latter will be in heat and that mating and reproduction can result. In some species, however, females that lead a solitary life nevertheless ovulate spontaneously. In them the chances of procreation are increased by a gathering of both sexes into droves during the breeding season. Rutting seasons and the endowment of females in heat with an especially pungent odor also attract distant males. It is probably futile to speculate on the advantages of one method of procreation over another or to compare the efficiencies of the different systems. They all serve the purpose for which they have evolved, and they illustrate the enormous potential for variation hidden in the different genetic stocks.

The Mechanism of Ovulation

Though it is established beyond doubt that ovulation is caused by an ovulation-inducing hormone, usually identified as LH, the manner in which this hormone brings about follicular rupture is not known. In rabbits, about 10.5 hours elapse between LH release (or LH injection) and ovulation. In chickens, 8–14 hours must elapse between LH release and ovulation. Comparable intervals have been estimated for other animals. It is reasonably well established, for both chickens and rabbits, that LH release occurs suddenly, over a period of minutes but certainly not of hours. It is not known whether LH, after its secretion into the blood stream, has to act on the follicles over the intervening 10–14 hours before it accomplishes its task of completing follicular rupture. The available evidence speaks against such prolonged action, for it is known that gonadotrophic hormones disappear from the blood stream very rapidly. It is reasonable to assume, therefore, that the LH initiates subtle changes in the follicle wall, which remain microscopically undetected until shortly before ovulation. In the hen, it has been shown that a follicle ovulates normally even if the stalk that connects it to the ovary and hence to the circulatory and nervous systems is severed or clamped off in such a way as to preclude the possibility of either vascular or neural connection. For these reasons it seems most likely that LH only initiates the changes in the follicle wall and that this effect is produced within a short time after LH is released into the blood stream.

Ovulation in several species has been frequently seen and recorded on film, but its mechanism remains unknown. Several of the older theories can be definitely discounted. The follicle does not burst because its "ultimate" size has been reached or because the interior pressure of the liquor folliculi is so great that it bursts the wall. Ovulation is not an explosive process but an oozing one. Under certain experimental conditions (which have been mentioned elsewhere), the follicle can continue to grow long past the time when it should normally have ruptured. Cysts are much larger than follicles of ovulatory size, and the internal pressure of cysts is incomparably greater; yet they do not rupture readily. In some species (especially swine, but also cattle and sheep), follicles become very flabby a few hours before ovulation even though there is no indication of a break in the follicular wall that would permit follicular fluid to escape and thus lower the pressure. The assumption that ovulation is aided by intestinal movements or by the massaging action of the fimbria is equally unfounded, for ovulation in the pig and in the chicken proceeds normally in females in which the fimbriated ends of the oviducts have been amputated. In the chicken, ovulation will even occur *in vitro* if the follicle is maintained at the proper temperature and humidity.

The process of ovulation in the chicken furnishes a clue that may form a basis for an explanation of the mechanism of ovulation. The complex and prominent vascular pattern of the avian follicle is one of the striking features of the maturing and the mature follicle (Fig. 2-5, p. 27). Within a few hours after LH release or administration, the follicle "blanches" because of the drastically decreased blood flow through it. The stigma (which, contrary to general impression, is not avascular) becomes wider, and many of the capillaries that extend across it become constricted and devoid of blood. Finally a small tear appears in one of the corners of the stigma, and the ovum bulges through it. The rip widens, and the whole ovum slips out of the follicle, which collapses. Neither abdominal pressure nor massage by the fimbria contributes to the process of ovulation, for it is possible to prevent these influences from having any effect in properly prepared and anesthetized birds.

Data obtained by Opel strongly support the possibility that IH may cause ovulation by initiating an ischemia in the wall of the follicle destined to ovulate. The evidence for this is briefly the following. In intact laying hens it is possible to hasten the ovulation of the follicle destined to ovulate next by the injection of LH, but under these circumstances it is never possible to ovulate any of the smaller follicles in the hierarchy. If, however, a laying hen is hypophysectomized and injected with LH, it is found that not only the largest but also the second, third, and even smaller follicles can be caused to ovulate. Thus, three or even more ova may be present in the oviduct of hypophysectomized hens (Fig. 5-3), a situation that can never be duplicated in animals with intact adenohypophyses. These findings suggest that normally the hypophysis secretes a factor that inhibits ovulation of any but the largest follicle. The "inhibiting" factor in the intact hen may be FSH, which, by virtue of its folliculotrophic action, may keep follicles from becoming ischemic. This idea found confirmation in experiments with hypophysectomized hens in which FSH was administered immediately after hypophysectomy. It was found that subsequent injection of LH was able to cause the ovulation of only the largest follicle and that in the face of FSH support the follicles of less than maximum size lost their ability to ovulate.

It appears reasonable to view ovulations as a two-stage phenomenon. During the first stage follicles reach their ultimate ovulatory size, which is determined by the total available circulating gonadotrophic hormones distributed via the follicular circulatory system in accord with the vascular capacity of individual follicles. That the amount of "available" hormone limits follicular size is supported by the finding that in both mammals ands birds follicles can be caused to grow beyond their "normal" ovulatory size by the injection of exogenous gonadotrophic hormones. Preliminary observations in chickens support the possibility that, as the largest follicle approaches its ovulatory size, the amount of blood flowing through its vascular system is proportionally less than the amount of blood flowing through the smaller follicles. Hence, the amount of hormone available to each unit of follicular cell is lower in the largest follicle than it is in the smaller ones. Because of this reduction in the concentration of gonadotrophic hormones, the largest follicle can be viewed as having reached a stage of "physiological atresia"—a stage when the hormone concentration is inadequate to maintain active proliferation of the cellular components of follicles. Thus, during the hormone-adequate phase, follicles are capable of rapid growth but are incapable of ovulating, while during the hormone inadequate phase they become physiologically "atretic" and can

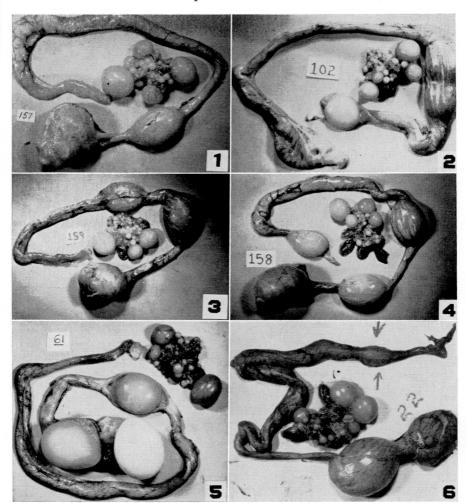

Figure 5-3. *Multiple ovulations are easily induced in hypophysectomized hens injected with a mammalian LH. For explanation see text. Note that in 6 (arrows) a very small ovum was caused to ovulate even though larger ova are present in the ovary. This happens only after hypophysectomy (Opel and Nalbandov, 1961. Endocrinology 69:1029).*

be made to ovulate because they are physiologically essentially inactive.

It is not known, however, what the ovulatory peak of LH does to cause this conversion during the second stage of the ovulatory phenomenon of the follicle that cannot ovulate into one that can. It is also unknown whether LH acts locally on the stigma or on the follicle as a whole.

There is other supporting evidence of this view of the mechanism of ovulation, but the reader should refer to more complete summaries (Nalbandov, 1961 and 1963). The idea that a quasi-necrotic process may be involved in ovulation is supported by the observation made on the ovulatory process in mammals. In cattle, swine, and sheep, the follicle destined to ovulate loses much of its turgidity and becomes soft and pliable as the time of ovulation approaches. The follicle wall is revealed as consisting of several tissue layers. As the outermost layer slowly parts, the two or three inner layers protrude through the breach in the outer layer and form a papilla. Eventually the inner layer too disintegrates, and the follicle collapses. In the species named, there is certainly nothing explosive about the ovulatory event, during which only part of the follicular fluid streams through the newly formed aperture. The ovum, loosened from the cumulus oopherus, now lying unattached in the antrum, is usually washed out with the debris during the initial escape of the follicular fluid. Occasionally it is possible to wash out ova from the cavities of follicles that had already ruptured. Whether such ova eventually leave the follicle or whether they become trapped in the forming corpus luteum is unknown. Because the fimbria closely envelops the ovary at the time of ovulation, and because it shows great motility at that time, it has been asserted that the fimbria plays a role in the evacuation of the collapsed follicle and its contents.

The Formation of Corpora Lutea

One of the most interesting morphological and physiological events during the cycle is the formation of corpora lutea in place of the ruptured follicle. In a short time the cells that secreted estrogen during the follicular phase become transformed into luteal cells that secrete progesterone, the two hormones being chemically related but physiologically completely different. Actually, the change from the secretion of estrogen to the secretion of progesterone may occur even before ovulation has taken place. Circumstantial evidence leading to that conclusion is that the majority of ovariectomized guinea pig females show psychological heat only if they are treated with progesterone before estrogen, neither hormone alone being capable of inducing heat. Since this species ovulates from six to ten hours after the onset of heat, the assumption is made that the progesterone necessary for the interaction with follicular estrogen comes from unovulated follicles. In rabbits, progesterone is normally present in the blood just before ovulation, and mouse ovaries can be caused to secrete progesterone before the follicles ovulate.

In the mole, luteinization of granulosa cells begins before ovulation, and thecal luteinization can be seen at least in some preovulatory follicles in mares. A unique situation exists in the African elephant shrew, *Elephantulus,* in which formation of a corpus luteum is the cause of the rupture of the follicle. The follicular cavity is filled by proliferating, luteinizing granulosa cells, which literally push the ovum out of the antrum.

In most mammalian females, formation of corpora lutea follows about the same pattern, but there is considerable variation among the species. Immediately after ovulation the ruptured and puckered follicular cavity is filled with lymph and blood from broken thecal vessels. In most species postovulatory hemorrhage is minor and does not distend the collapsed follicle to its preovulatory size; in the sow, however, there is a considerable accumulation of blood and lymph, and, by the fourth, fifth, or sixth day after rupture, the blood-filled follicle is much larger than it was before ovulation. In most species the corpus luteum is formed by hypertrophy and hyperplasia of the granulosa cells of the ovulated follicle. The theca interna cells may or may not participate in the formation of this gland; the role of these cells in the formation and maintenance of corpora is not sufficiently well understood to warrant detailed discussion here (see Harrison, 1948).

The easiest way to visualize the growth of the corpus luteum is by imagining a collapsed bag with nonelastic walls. Gradual thickening of the walls, due to hypertrophy and hyperplasia of the granulosa cells, eventually fills out the cavity of the sac, obliterating its central cavity (Fig. 5-2). In some species (rats, pigs, sheep, and others), the central cavity is completely obliterated, leaving only a narrow central scar where the rapidly proliferating granulosa cells from the periphery meet; in other species (women), the process stops short of filling the cavity, the corpus consisting of greatly thickened walls and a substantial central cavity.

The initial increase in the size and weight of corpora lutea is extremely rapid. In some species the corpus reaches 70–90 percent of its ultimate size by the third day after follicular rupture, and it continues to grow until about day 13 of the 21-day cycle. In other species the growth is somewhat slower: in sheep and cattle 50–60 percent of the eventual size of corpora is reached by day 4, the full ultimate size being reached in sheep on days 7–9 and in cows on about day 10. Similar relations exist in other mammalian females. Presumably the rate at which corpora enlarge is roughly correlated with the rate at which they secrete progesterone. In the pig, as early as one day after ovulation, progestational changes can be seen in the uterine epithelium and in the glands; when the corpora are from six to eight days old, they have induced maximal uterine changes, which are then maintained by the progesterone secreted by them until days 12–14 of the cycle.

In the pig, the granulosa luteal cells of the corpus gradually increase in size until about day 13 of the cycle; then an abrupt and rapid decrease in size begins and continues throughout the follicular phase and until the end of the cycle (days 19–21). On about day 14 or 15 the first regressive changes become apparent in the uterus, and these continue until the luteal phase ends and the follicular phase begins. In the cow, the corpus is fully formed by the ninth day after ovulation and begins to regress on day 14 of the 21-day cycle.

It is probably safe to generalize by saying that, in all females with long cycles, the luteal phase lasts a little longer than half of the total cycle. Here again, however, much individual variation is encountered: in some individuals, corpora lutea appear to be histologically in perfectly functional condition well past the time when they begin to regress in the majority. The uteri of such individuals also appear to continue to remain under progesterone stimulation. It should also be kept in mind that in animals with long cycles there is a lag, probably of from one to three days, between the time when the corpus begins to secrete its hormone and the time when the effects of this hormone are visibly registered by the uterine endometrium. Similarly, the corpus begins to wane long before the decrease in hormone secretion caused by this decline is reflected in the end organ. It is not safe to assume that corpora that appear histologically on the decline no longer secrete progesterone, but it is certain that the rate of hormone secretion of waning corpora is greatly reduced.

In the great majority of animals, the spent corpus (now called the corpus albicans) can be recognized as such well into the next cycle, during which new functional corpora lutea and much-regressed corpora albicantia coexist. As a rule, corpora albicantia are no longer macroscopically visible by the third cycle, but they may remain as histologically recognizable scar tissue a little longer. An interesting exception to that rule is the whale, in which degenerated corpora are said to persist for many years, possibly throughout the life of the animal, in macroscopically and microscopically recognizable conditions.

During the histological decline of the corpus, luteal cells shrink, fibroblasts appear in increasing numbers, and large, spindle-shaped cells are seen among the epithelial cells. Shortly before the end of the cycle, rapidly waning corpora lutea are largely composed of connective tissue, which eventually becomes hyalinized. The hyaline tissue becomes greatly reduced and finally disappears.

Corpora lutea are formed in a number of vertebrates below the mammals—for example, in some of the viviparous snakes and lizards. In some reptiles the formation of corpora lutea is not necessarily associated with viviparity, for it occurs also in oviparous forms that retain the eggs in the oviduct.

Contrary to statements in some of the older literature, birds do not form corpora lutea, or, at least, they do not form structures that are morphologically, histologically, or endocrinologically comparable to the lutein tissue of mammals or other vertebrates. It is possibe, however, that the ovulated follicle, at least in chickens, plays a role in determining the time of oviposition.

Hormones Formed by Corpora Lutea

It has been shown repeatedly that corpora lutea contain estrogen of unknown origin. In some species the life span of copora lutea may be prolonged significantly either by the systemic administration of estrogen or by administering it into the corpus luteum directly. The mode of this action of estrogen on the life span of corpora lutea is unknown; it may act either by causing the pituitary gland to secrete prolactin (in rats) or a luteotrophic factor (in other species), or it may act by increasing the vascularity of corpora lutea, thus preventing a more rapid degeneration. In view of what we have said earlier concerning the possibility that LH may be a luteotrophic substance, the following observations are of considerable interest. Parlow (see McArthur, 1961) has found that either HCG or LH (but not FSH), injected into hypophysectomized rats, caused vaginal cornification in the great majority of the treated rats. Even as long as $6\frac{1}{2}$ months after hypophysectomy, 10 out of 13 rats responded to HCG injection with vaginal cornification, which was maintained for 10 days. This suggests that both HCG and LH are luteotrophic, but—surprisingly—in the unusual way of causing corpora lutea to secrete estrogen. Since these rats were hypophysectomized, the action of these hormones must have been directly on the corpora lutea. At the present time it is not possible to speculate intelligently on the mechanism which makes a corpus luteum secrete estrogen in the hypophysectomized rat and progesterone in the intact animal.

In both the cow and the rat, "LH" has been said to be luteolytic; however, in both instances the LH preparations used were far from pure and, at least in the rat, subsequent experiments with more highly purified LH failed to confirm this finding. In the intact rat LH is known to be responsible for the increased movement of cholesterol into the lutein tissue during its formation, the amount of cholesterol stored being directly related to the amount of LH injected. At least in the rat, this stored cholesterol is converted into progesterone under the action of prolactin.

The ability of corpora lutea to synthesize progesterone *in vitro* has been investigated in both pig and cow tissues, and in both instances it was demonstrated that corpora lutea do synthesize progesterone *in vitro* when stimulated by hormones. Significantly, in neither case was progesterone synthesized when prolactin was added to the substrate, but the addition of LH or HCG caused an increased rate of synthesis over that of control corpora lutea. The ability of corpora lutea to produce preogesterone *in vitro* is directly related to their age; that is, corpora lutea which were capable of synthesizing progesterone *in situ* were found to be able to do so *in vitro* under the influence of the hormones mentioned. Those which were taken in late luteal phase, when their ability to produce progesterone *in vivo* is greatly diminished, were also unable to produce progesterone *in vitro*.

Of some interest and possibly of significance is the finding that the uterus may secrete a humoral factor which, at least *in vitro*, has an effect on the ability of corpora lutea to synthesize progesterone. If epithelial scrapings taken from uteri of sows in the early luteal phase are added to corpora lutea cultured *in vitro*, the corpora's ability to produce progesterone is significantly enhanced. In contrast, such scrapings taken from uteri in the late luteal phase have a depressing effect on the rate of progesterone synthesis.

If a rabbit ovary containing no corpora lutea but only preovulatory follicles is perfused *in situ* with LH, HGG, or PMS, progesterone is recovered in significant amounts from the ovarian vein. Just as in the case of the cow and sow corpora cultured *in vitro,* the injection of prolactin did not cause an increase in progesterone synthesis. After the infusion of the hormones is discontinued, the ovary once again resumes the production of estrogen. Even though this observation is obviously of great interest and significance, the rabbit is a somewhat unfortunate experimental animal for this demonstration. The rabbit ovaries contain large masses of interstitial tissue and it remains unknown whether the progesterone recovered is produced by the interstitial tissue or by the follicle cells. Preovulatory progesterone has been demonstrated in the peripheral blood of rabbits, guinea pigs, and women, and in all three species more or less abundant interstitial tissue is present in the ovaries. It was stated earlier that in many species (rat, sow, ewe, cow) behavioral estrus can be induced with significantly smaller doses of estrogen if they are previously primed with progesterone, and that in the guinea pig progesterone is essential for the manifestation of behavioral heat. Thus, intuitively we might guess that preovulatory progesterone would be produced in all species, even in those without ovarian interstitial tissue. But whether this is the case remains to be seen.

In the preceding discussion we have seen evidence to the effect that LH-containing hormones are capable of inducing progesterone synthesis and that prolactin is not. We have also seen earlier that prolactin is luteotrophic only in the rat and we had to use the term luteotrophic *factor* in order to express our ignorance as to what hormone is luteotrophic in species in which prolactin is not. The temptation is strong to suggest that LH may be luteotrophic. However, at present we only know that LH—because of its ability to cause progesterone synthesis —is "progestenotrophic." In other words, this may be its sole role; another, as yet unknown substance may be needed to keep corpora lutea alive. Additional work is needed on the problem of whether LH has both the function of a luteotrophin and of a progestenotrophin. Neither should we ascribe luteotrophic effects to the humoral factor contained in uterine scrapings, because this factor may have only progestenotrophic capabilities.

Though all lutein tissue is basically similar in histology, endocrine control, and function, there are certain special kinds, such as luteinized follicles, accessory corpora lutea, and corpora lutea of pregnancy, pseudopregnancy, and lactation; these will be discussed elsewhere.

The Alternation of Ovarian Function

We have already noted that, though both ovaries may be developed and functional in some of the hawks and owls, in most birds only the left ovary is functional.

In all mammals, both ovaries are developed, but they function to different degrees. In the duck-billed platypus, the right ovary is only about one-tenth as well developed as the left, and only the left ovary is functional, while in Echidna the two ovaries are almost equally well developed. In some of the bats the left ovary is defective but functional. Most other mammals can be divided into right and left ovulators. This means, not that they ovulate unilaterally, but that they habitually ovulate more eggs from one ovary than from the other.

In swine, 55–60 percent of the corpora are found in the left ovary. In the mare, 61 percent of the corpora are found in the left ovary, and the follicles in the left ovary are significantly larger than those in the right.

Sheep and cows are right ovulators, the sheep ovulating from the right ovary 52–59 percent of the time, the cow 60–65 percent. In rhesus monkeys 60 percent of the eggs are shed from the right ovary.

As a rule, the favored ovary is slightly heavier (even in immature females of the species), and the structures in it are somewhat larger. It has been thought that these differences may be due to differences in blood supply, in some species the right ovary being more liberally vascularized, in others the left. Experimental data on this point are not available.

SUMMARY

Some animals (spontaneous ovulators) ovulate at regular intervals in response to an apparently spontaneous release of LH from the pituitary gland. In others (induced ovulators), copulation leads to an outpouring of LH and hence to ovulation. In neither case is it known how LH brings about the rupturing of follicles and the shedding of eggs. After ovulation the empty follicle of mammals is filled with luteal tissue, which is formed by proliferating granulosa cells. Progesterone is secreted by the follicle in small amounts even before ovulation. As the luteal tissue increases in amount, it secretes increasing quantities of progesterone until the corpus luteum begins to wane; then the rate of hormone secretion also declines. Presumably the spent corpus luteum, now called the corpus albicans, secretes no progesterone.

In some species, follicles frequently fail to ovulate at the proper time and continue to grow until they form cystic follicles. In some animals (dairy cattle), cystic follicles cause nymphomania; in pigs, heats become extremely irregular. The usual assumption that cystic follicles secrete more estrogen than normal follicles is not justified.

REFERENCES

N. L. Baker, L. C. Ulberg, R. H. Grummer, and L. E. Casida. 1954. "Inhibition of heat by progesterone and its effects on subsequent fertility in gilts." *J. Animal Sci.,* **13**:648.

F. W. R. Brambell. 1956. "Ovarian changes" in Marshall's *Physiology of Reproduction,* Vol. I, Part 1, 3rd ed. Longmans (New York).

L. E. Casida and A. B. Chapman. 1951. "Factors affecting the incidence of cystic ovaries in a herd of Holstein cows." *J. Dairy Sci.,* **34**:1200.

Otto Garm. 1949. "A study on bovine nymphomania." *Acta Endocrinologica,* Suppl. 3.

H. Hansel and G. W. Trimberger. 1951. "Atropine blockage of ovulation in the cow and its possible significance." *J. Animal Sci.,* **10**:719.

H. Hansel and G. W. Trimberger. 1952. "The effect of progesterone on ovulation time in dairy heifers." *J. Dairy Sci.,* **35**:65.

R. J. Harrison. 1948. "The development and fate of the corpus luteum in the vertebrate series." *Biol. Rev.,* **23**:296.

R. J. Harrison. 1948. "The changes occurring in the ovary of the goat during the estrous cycle and in early pregnancy." *J. Anat.,* **82**:21.

I. W. Rowlands. 1956. "The corpus luteum of the guinea pig." *Ciba Foundation Colloquium on Ageing,* **2**:69.

The following motion pictures are excellent; they show (in color) the processes of ovulation and ova transport. Very highly recommended.

R. J. Blandau. *Physiology of Reproduction in the Rat.* Available from Educational Films, University of Washington, Seattle, Washington.

T. McArthur. 1961. In *Human Pituitary Gonadotropins.* A. Albert, Ed. Charles C. Thomas, Springfield, Ill.

D. C. Warren and H. M. Scott. *The Formation of the Avian Egg.* Available from the Poultry Department, Kansas State College, Manhattan, Kansas.

chapter 6

Some Chemical and Physiological Properties of Hormones

Scattered throughout this book are references to information on the presence and on the concentration of hormones in blood, in urine, or in the glands secreting the hormone. Most of this information is based on bioassay, although recently chemists have provided more sensitive methods, which permit quantitative estimation and identification of some of the hormones by chemical means. The subsequent few paragraphs are intended to provide information on the difficulties involved and to place warning signs for those who are just beginning the task of studying the physiology and biochemistry of hormones. It is not intended to present a complete catalogue of pitfalls and difficulties but to discuss only a few of those which have led investigators astray in the past and which may do so again.

No one has yet succeeded in finding gonadotrophic hormones either in the peripheral blood or in the urine of cattle, sheep, or pigs, but under certain circumstances gonadotrophic hormones are present in these fluids in women and in mares. This is a species difference, and it does not mean that animals do not secrete gonadotrophins merely because they are not demonstrably present. They may be secreted in such small quantities or diluted to such an extent in the blood that no known bioassay method can detect them, or they may be destroyed with such rapidity that they do not reach detectable concentration. In contrast, if one takes blood directly out of the subdural sinus of sheep or cattle, one can easily demonstrate the presence of LH and (with some difficulty) that of FSH. The subdural sinus is located directly under the pituitary gland and it is presumed to drain the two lobes of the hypophysis. The quantities of blood that can be obtained in such large animals as cattle, sheep, or dogs are adequate for most bioassays. At present this is as close as we can get to the source of the hypophyseal hormones; therefore it represents the hormonal output of the gland much more accurately than does hormone concentration in the peripheral blood, but it does *not* tell us anything concerning the amount of hormones that actually *reach* the target gland. We have cited evidence for the fact that the rabbit ovary without corpora lutea can be made to secrete progesterone if LH is injected. This was demonstrated by taking blood directly out of the ovarian vein, where the progesterone concentration is sufficiently large to permit detection and where one is certain that the hormone being measured is actually coming from the ovary and is being produced in response to the treatment.

The measurement of hormone concentrations in the peripheral circulation or in urine has some serious disadvantages. For instance, it is well known that the estrogen concentration in raw urine is only a fraction of the total that can be shown to be there if the urine is first hydrolyzed. The reason for this is that a good part of the estrogen (and of other steroid hormones) is excreted in the form of a glucuronide that cannot be detected by bioassay techniques unless the urine is first hydrolyzed and the linkage thus broken. The question now arises: which estimate is the correct one for the amount of estrogen secreted, the one obtained before hydrolysis or the one after? This dilemma has never been resolved, and it is perhaps fair to say that the main value of studies of the hormone concentration in urine is to detect very sharp rises or falls which may be suggestive of gross endocrine malfunction. Thus, a sharp drop in urinary pregnanediol in pregnant women suggests impending abortion due to inadequate progesterone production; a rise beyond normal in urinary androgen concentration in nonpregnant women is usually associated with cystic ovarian degeneration, etc.

Cattle urines, and probably those of most herbivores, are notoriously difficult to work with because they contain contaminating substances (porphyrines and carotenoids) that are difficult to remove, that interfere with chemical procedures involved in the extraction of hormones, and that behave chromatographically very much like certain steroids, especially estrogen. For these reasons, much of the published work that deals with quantitative and qualitative studies of steroids in bovine urines must be taken with much scepticism and caution.

The cow is able to convert progesterone very rapidly into an androgen, which then appears in great profusion in the feces. This is apparently the normal metabolic pathway of progesterone in pregnant cows since their feces are notoriously rich in androgenic metabolites, which are presumed to come from luteal and placental progesterone. Women convert their progesterone into pregnanediol and excrete it in the urine. In contrast, the urines of cattle, sheep, and swine do not contain significant amounts of pregnanediol.

In spite of such difficulties, the chemical estimation of hormones remains the most desirable method of determining hormone concentration, provided it is made on fluid or tissue samples that can be reasonably assumed to bear a close relationship to the actual hormone output at the source. Thus, if one is interested in the rate of androgen synthesis of a sterile male, the best source of hormone is that contained in the spermatic vein of the testicle; less information will be obtained from sampling the peripheral blood and still less from estimating the hormone level in the urine.

The Gonadotrophic Hormones

All the gonadotrophic hormones have been isolated in reasonably pure form, and all except prolactin have been found to be glycoproteins, the carbohydrate moiety being hexose and hexosamine. In PMS and HCG the hexose is galactose; in FSH and LH it is mannose. In most preparations the hexosamine has not been identified. The gonadotrophins of placental or uterine origin contain a somewhat higher percentage of carbohydrate than the pituitary hormones. Enzymatic destruction of the carbohydrate fraction of the molecule results in inactivation of all four hormones; modification of the protein part leads to lowered activity.

The gonadotrophins are not species-specific in their hormonal capacity; that is, a hormone obtained from one species is, as a rule, capable of stimulating the gonads of another. There is, however, great variability in a gonadotrophin's effectiveness in different species. This lack of species-specificity does not mean, however, that similar hormones from different species are identical in chemical composition. Animals treated continuously with a protein hormone from a different species gradually lose their ability to respond to it. The loss is due to the formation of the so-called antihormones, which may or may not be typical antibodies. Some antihormones are recognized as true antibodies by the fact that they give the typical precipitin test with specific antigen. Examples of these are the antibodies that appear in rabbit serum in response to repeated injections of purified sheep FSH or swine FSH. These are species-specific. But some antihormones, though capable of neutralizing the administered hormone, do not give the classical precipitin test with it and are not species-specific. An example of these is the antihormone found in the serum of human beings receiving purified swine FSH. The rate of formation of antihormones varies with the species; rabbits form them rapidly, but chickens do so slowly or not at all. The degree of purity of the hormone preparation used also influences the formation of antihormones, the rate of formation being inversely related to the degree of purity.

Methods for the isolation and purification of the hormones will not be discussed here; outlines of procedures, as well as analytical data on amino acid composition and the physicochemical constants of various preparations, can be found in the references cited at the end of this chapter.

The Follicle-stimulating Hormone

The follicle-stimulating hormone (FSH) has been obtained in reasonably pure form from the hypophyses of sheep, pigs, and horses. However, even the most highly purified FSH preparations available are contaminated with some LH, and all attempts to eliminate these traces have been unsuccessful. The reason for this ever-present LH contamination may be that the pituitary does not secrete two separate hormones—FSH and LH—but secretes molecules of a gonadotrophic hormone which have FSH and LH properties. It is also possible that FSH and LH share a certain portion of the amino acid sequences that constitute them, a portion of the LH nucleus being essential for the FSH sequence; thus one could not get rid of the LH portion without destroying the biological activity of the FSH sequence. In contrast, it is possible to prepare an LH which is completely free of FSH activity.

By several physical-chemical tests, some FSH preparations appear to have attained a high degree of purity. Thus, a sheep preparation, subjected to biological tests, electrophoresis, and ultracentrifugation, was found to be homogeneous. Its molecular weight was 70,000, and its isoelectric point was at pH 4.5.

Solutions of purified FSH are rapidly inactivated at temperatures higher than 60°C. FSH activity in crude pituitary extracts is not destroyed by trypsin, but extensive digestion with this enzyme, chymotrypsin, or pepsin reduces or abolishes the activity of FSH solutions. Reduction of disulfide linkages in the protein molecule reduces the hormonal activity of FSH.

Precipitating antibodies that are species-specific have been produced in rabbits by administration of purified sheep and swine FSH. Neutralizing antibodies that are not species-specific have been detected in the serum of human patients receiving either the sheep or the swine hormone.

The Luteinizing Hormone

Luteinizing hormone (LH) fractions that have been isolated from both sheep and swine pituitaries are considered to be pure, but the two preparations are different chemically, as their physicochemical characteristics show. The molecular weight of sheep LH is 40,000, and its isoelectric point is at pH 4.6; the corresponding values for swine LH are 100,000 and pH 7.45. The two hormones can also be distinguished immunologically.

The activity of LH solutions is destroyed by digestion with trypsin, chymotrypsin, or pepsin. Disulfide linkages and free amino groups are probably essential for the activity of the hormone.

Prolactin

The lactogenic hormone has been prepared in pure form, as judged by electrophoresis, ultracentrifugation, and solubility behavior, from both sheep and beef pituitary glands. The hormones from the two sources are similar in their electrophoretic behavior, both have their isoelectric point at pH 5.7, and they are antigenically indistinguishable. The last fact is interesting because certain differences in solubility in salt solutions and in amino acid content have been observed. A number of values for the molecular weight of prolactin have been reported, ranging from 22,000 to 35,000. The variability is presumably due to the methods of determination. Prolactin has been crystallized, but it is reported that the procedure for its crystallization is not easily reproducible. Unlike FSH and LH, prolactin does not contain carbohydrate, and there is no evidence of the presence in the molecule of residues other than amino acids.

Prolactin is heat-labile and is rapidly inactivated by pepsin or trypsin. Free amino and disulfide groups and possibly hydroxyl groups are thought to be essential to its activity.

Antibodies to prolactin have been produced in rabbits, mice, and monkeys.

Pregnant Mare's Serum

Because the gonadotrophic hormone present in the serum of pregnant mares (PMS) stimulates both the follicles and the interstitial cells, it was once thought that it was a mixture of two chemical entities. It was shown later, however, that a single substance is responsible for both biological effects. It is not possible to break down PMS by any known procedure into predominantly FSH- or LH-containing fractions. This fact leads to the interpretation that PMS is synthesized by endometrial cups as a single molecule of a gonadotrophic complex possessing both FSH and LH activity. The ratios of FSH to LH in PMS, on the basis of bioassay evidence, differ between mares and less so within mares between pregnancies. In general, the smaller and lighter breeds of horses produce more PMS per liter of serum than do mares of the heavy breeds. One highly purified preparation had its isoelectric point at pH 2.6–2.65. It contained hexose and hexosamine in somewhat larger proportion than the pituitary gonadotrophins. The molecular weight of PMS, which is a glycoprotein, is about 30,000.

PMS loses some of its activity when stored in the dry state. It is more stable in neutral than in acid or alkaline solutions and is more stable to heat in neutral or slightly alkaline solution than in acid. Free amino groups and disulfide linkages are important to its activity, and it is inactivated by pepsin and trypsin.

Human Chorionic Gonadotrophin

Human chorionic gonadotrophin (HCG), which is also a glycoprotein, has been obtained in crystalline form. An amorphous product that behaved as a single protein in electrophoresis and ultracentrifugation had a molecular weight of 100,000 and an isoelectric point at pH 3.2–3.3. The carbohydrate content was somewhat lower than that found in purified PMS, but the hexose-to-hexosamine ratio was the same (2:1).

The purified hormone is stable in the dry state, but in dilute solution it loses activity rapidly on storage at $0°C$. Water solutions of HCG are heat-labile, but glycerol solutions withstand heating at $100°C$ for one hour. Strong acid or alkali destroys the activity of aqueous solutions. Free amino groups are not essential to the activity of HCG. The purified hormone does not contain cystine.

The Gonadal Hormones

The sex hormones are closely related in chemical structure to the hydrocarbon phenanthrene; more precisely, they are cyclopentanoperhydrophenanthrene derivatives. It is hoped that the accompanying formulas and the explanation given below will clarify this formidable nomenclature.

PHENANTHRENE   CYCLOPENTANE   CYCLOPENTANO-
                                            PERHYDROPHENANTHRENE

TYPE FORMULA OF THE STEROIDS

As can be seen from the formulas, the A, B, and C rings of cyclopentanoperhydrophenanthrene are those of phenanthrene, and the D ring is that of cyclopentane. The prefix "perhydro" in the name indicates that hydrogen has been added to the double bonds in the rings. For the sake of simplicity, the term "steroid" has been adopted for substances having this particular fused-ring system. In writing the formulas of steroids, we conventionally omit the symbols of the carbon and hydrogen atoms in the ring system and simply draw a "picture" of the skeleton. We number the carbon atoms as indicated above in order to specify the location of substituents in the various steroid molecules. The ring sytem without substituents is called the steroid nucleus. For compounds in which double bonds occur in the nucleus, these are included in the skeleton formula; if none is indicated, that ring is saturated.

The steroids, which include a large number of other biologically important compounds besides the sex hormones, differ from one another in the nature of the substituents R and R′, in the number and position of hydroxyl groups attached to the nucleus, in the spatial configuration of the nucleus and its substituent groups, and in the number and location of double bonds in the nucleus. The steroid hormones all have a methyl group attached to C_{13}, and the R group, when present, is usually methyl. These are referred to as "angular" methyl groups. R′, at C_{17}, represents a wide variety of substituents in the various steroids; these are relatively simple in the sex hormones.

As mentioned above, one of the characteristics in which steroids differ from one another is the spatial relation within the nucleus itself and between substituent groups. The stereochemistry of these substances will not be discussed in detail here, but the student unfamiliar with the principles of stereochemistry should remember that not all of the carbon atoms of the steroid nucleus lie in one plane. One can imagine the nucleus as a sort of "fluted" structure, the pattern of the fluting varying from one steroid to another. If one imagines this fluted object lying on a flat surface, one can then see that groups attached to it may project upward or downward from the plane on which it is lying. Certain conventions of nomenclature pertain to this property. The Greek letters α and β are used as prefixes to the names of certain steroids to indicate the spatial position of hydroxyl groups substituted on the nucleus. The angular methyl groups project in the same direction from our imagined plane of the molecule. If a hydroxyl group is located on the same side of the plane (that is, is *cis* to the angular methyl groups), it has the β configuration; if it projects in the opposite direction (*trans* to the angular methyl groups), it has the α configuration. In the structural formulas the α configuration is indicated by dotted lines and the β by solid lines. The student should keep in mind that the spatial relations within the molecule of a steroid hormone influence the degree of its biological activity.

The study of the chemistry of any biological compound involves three steps: isolation of the substance from its natural source and purification of it; determination of its chemical structure and configuration by degradation studies; attempted synthesis. Discussion of such studies of the sex hormones is beyond the scope of this book. Here we simply point out that total synthesis of some of the sex hormones has been achieved.

The Estrogens

Estrogenic compounds have been isolated from four endocrine sources: ovaries, placenta, adrenals, and testes. In the nonpregnant female the chief source of the hormone is the ovarian follicle, whereas most of the estrogen present in the pregnant female is produced by the placenta. Estrogen production by the testes is probably under the control of LH. Stallion urine is one of the richest known sources of estrogen. The adrenals of both sexes produce estrogens, but these glands, compared with the gonads and the placenta, are of minor importance in this capacity.

In chemical structure the estrogens are unique among the steroids in that the A ring of the nucleus is aromatic and, since it carries a hydroxyl group, also phenolic. A considerable group of natural estrogens exists; only a few will be discussed here.

The degree of physiological activity of the estrogens is dependent upon such structural properties as the presence of the phenolic hydroxyl group at C_3, the steric configuration of the rings themselves, and the steric position of the hydroxyl group at C_{17}. For example, estradiol, which is probably the compound that is secreted by the

ESTRADIOL-17β   ESTRONE   ESTRIOL

ovary, occurs in two epimeric forms, and of these estradiol—17β is about thirty times as potent as the form with the α configuration at C_{17}.

The following conversion reactions are known to occur in mammals:

$$\text{estradiol—17}\beta \rightleftharpoons \text{estrone} \longrightarrow \text{estriol}$$
$$\updownarrow$$
$$\text{estradiol—17}\alpha$$

The relative activities of these compounds have been considered to be: estradiol—17β > estrone > estradiol—17α > estriol. In the assay of estrogenic compounds, however, several factors influence the results in such a way that the order of potency determined under one set of assay conditions might actually be reversed under another.

A variety of synthetic compounds with estrogenic activity has been prepared. The one that is used most often is diethylstilbestrol.

As to the biosynthesis of estrogens, studies using compounds labeled with C^{14} indicate that the tissues that secrete these hormones build them up from small metabolites such as acetate, and that cholesterol is probably not an intermediate in the process.

The estrogens, like the other steroid hormones, are probably secreted into the blood in the form of the free steroid. They are quickly converted, however, at least in part, to a "bound" form by conjugation with glucuronate or sulfate and by binding with protein. The chief, if not exclusive, site of these processes is the liver. It was once thought that the conjugates were simply excretion forms of the hormones, but some investigators now believe that conjugation of an estrogen, particularly with glucuronic acid, may be a process important to the function of the hormone. In this connection it is interesting that ovariectomy reduces the activity, in uterine and vaginal tissue, of the enzyme β-glucuronidase, which is capable of hydrolyzing steroid glucoronides. Administration of estrogens restores the enzyme to normal or greater than normal activity. Circulating protein-bound estrogen also seems to be conjugated with glucuronic acid. It has been suggested that competition between steroid hormones for specific lipoprotein sites *in vivo* may be a mechanism for steroid hormone antagonisms. Estradiol is more readily bound than most other steroids. This observation has been offered as a possible explanation of the fact that estrogens are physiologically active in much smaller concentrations than the other steroids and that they are capable of antagonizing the biological effects of large amounts of these other hormones.

Information concerning the catabolism of the estrogens is scarce. Both endogenous and exogenous estrogens are excreted, to a great extent, in the bile, and the glucuronides are excreted in the urine. Liver preparations are capable of inactivating estrogens *in vitro* very rapidly, but the quantitative importance of this capacity of the liver in the catabolism of endogenous estrogens *in vivo* has been questioned. There is evidence, from experiments in which isotopically labeled compounds were administered, of complete degradation of the steroid nucleus.

DIETHYLSTILBESTROL

Progesterone

This hormone is known to be produced by the corpus luteum, the placenta, and the adrenal cortex, and it
may be produced by the testes.

Progesterone is a diketone having
strong absorption at 240 millimicrons,
a property typical of α,β-unsaturated
ketones (see ring A in the accompany-
ing formula). The carbon atoms of the angular methyl groups at C_{10}
and C_{13} are numbered 18 and 19, respectively; those of the side chain at
C_{17} are numbered 20 and 21 away from the nucleus. The molecular
structure may be modified in certain ways without complete destruction of progestational activity, but the C_3 carbonyl group in conjugation with the double bond between C_4 and C_5 is necessary for that activity. If the double bond is shifted to other positions in the nucleus, there
is complete loss of activity. Other changes in the molecule, with ring A
in its natural form, result in varying degrees of loss of biological activity.

It has been shown that the human placenta, among the tissues that
produce progesterone, can convert cholesterol-C^{14} to radioactive progesterone. A radioactive intermediate steroid was isolated and identified.

A large proportion of circulating progesterone is probably in the
form of the glucuronide.

There is considerable variation among the species in the catabolism
of progesterone. In most of the species studied (man, chimpanzee, goat,
horse, rabbit) the principal excretion product of progesterone metabolism is pregnanediol, and it appears
in the urine primarily as the glucuronide. Progesterone is probably
metabolized to pregnanediol, by a
series of reductive steps, in the liver.
Fifteen steroids that are considered
to be products of progesterone metabolism have been isolated from
pregnancy urines. These represent
all the theoretical intermediates from
progesterone to pregnanediol. How-

ever, since only two of them have been isolated in increased amounts after injection of progesterone, they may not actually be derived from that hormone. The study of the metabolism of progesterone is complicated by the fact that this steroid and certain of the adrenal cortical steroids have some metabolic pathways in common.

Excretion of pregnanediol has not been demonstrated in the mouse or the rat either during pregnancy or after administration of progesterone. In these species, after administration of progesterone-21-C^{14}, most of the isotope appears in the feces, but a fair amount shows up in the respiratory CO_2. The presence of C^{14} in the expired CO_2 probably represents oxidation of the side chain.

It has been suggested that species variations in the metabolic products of progesterone may be due to differences in the ability to conjugate pregnanediol with glucuronic acid. This explanation assumes that all species reduce progesterone to pregnanediol, part of which is excreted as the glucuronide by species capable of the conjugation. What is not conjugated is presumed to be more readily attacked by oxidative enzymes and therefore to be degraded to still unrecognized fragments, which are excreted; thus the intermediate pregnanediol is never detected in species that do not conjugate it.

The Androgens

There are three known endocrine sources of androgens: the testes, the ovaries, and the adrenals. Only very small amounts of androgens are found in extracts of adrenal tissue, but they are found in adrenal-vein blood in higher concentration than in the general circulation. Certain adrenal tumors greatly stimulate the male secondary sex characters in women and children as well as in men. The ability of the ovary to produce androgen depends, quantitatively, upon the environmental temperature of the ovarian tissue. The normal rat ovary has some androgenic activity; but, if it is transplanted to an exposed area, such as the ear or the tail, where the internal temperature is 2–6°F lower than that of the body cavity, it produces larger amounts of androgens. This production is accompanied by a marked reduction in the synthesis of estrogen. If, however, the transplanted ovary is exposed to an environmental temperature equal to the body temperature of the rat, it continues to secrete estrogen. In chickens, the ovary retains its ability to secrete both estrogen and androgen at the high body temperature of birds. Mammals have lost this ability, but not, it appears, irreversibly, for a change in temperature can cause ovarian cells (not necessarily the same ones that secrete estrogen) to produce androgen.

Many androgens and related substances have been isolated from natural sources or synthesized from other steroids. The formulas of only two of these are included here: testosterone, probably the form secreted by the testes, and androsterone, a biologically active form that is excreted in the urine.

TESTOSTERONE   **ANDROSTERONE**

Testosterone, as can be seen from its formula, bears a close resemblance to progesterone in chemical structure, being an α,β-unsaturated ketone with the typical strong absorption at 240 millimicrons. Of all the known androgens, testosterone and the compounds related to it are the most potent. This potency is due primarily to the carbonyl group at C_3 with the double bond in conjugation with it. The configuration at C_{17} also has an important effect on activity (testosterone is more active than *epi*-testosterone, the compound with the 17-hydroxyl having the β configuration). And, even though the favorable condition is retained in ring A, introduction of alkyl groups at C_{17} modifies the biological activity so that both androgenic and progestational effects are produced. Certain modifications of rings A and B cause loss of androgenic potency and development of estrogenic activity.

The conversion of acetate-C^{14} to testosterone by testicular tissue has been demonstrated. Cholesterol is not a necessary intermediate in the biosynthesis of testosterone from acetate. Testicular tissue has been shown to convert pregnenolone, a steroid, to testosterone. Pregnenolone is thought to be an intermediate in the biosynthesis of the hormone.

As in the case of progesterone, study of the metabolites of androgen is complicated by the presence in urine of structurally related compounds that are products of the metabolism of adrenal cortical steroids. The administration of testosterone leads to increased amounts of

17-ketosteroids in the urine. A rather large number of metabolites are present, but quantitatively most important are androsterone and etiocholanolone, a stereoisomer of androsterone. Androsterone is about one-sixth as active as testosterone; etiocholanolone is inactive. Etiocholanolone is probably present in urine primarily as the glucuronide, whereas androsterone appears in about equal amounts as the sulfate and the glucuronide.

Most of the circulating testosterone is bound by serum albumin, which probably accounts for the fact that so little of this steroid ever appears in the urine; the complex is not filterable.

Inactivation of testosterone by the liver has been demonstrated both *in vivo* (spleen implants) and *in vitro* (liver slices). The liver enzymes that metabolize testosterone have been extensively studied. At least two enzymes are inolved, one requiring DPN as cofactor and the other being activated by citrate.

The kidneys also are capable of acting on the androgens; they bring about changes similar to those effected by the liver but more slowly.

Effectiveness of Exogenous Hormones

Mode of Administration

It is generally true that a dose of any hormone is less effective when it is given in a single injection than when it is divided into frequent smaller injections. In the latter method of treatment the end organ is exposed to repeated stimulation by lower levels of circulating hormone, a condition that more nearly approximates the action of endogenous hormones than does the flood of high concentration that is produced by giving the total dose in a single injection. To what extent the ability of estrogen to "hang on" to its target organ (as was mentioned elsewhere in this book) applies to other hormones, both steroidal and nonsteroidal, is not known.

The unphysiological condition of peaks of hormone concentration following daily injections can be overcome, in part, by the implantation of hormone pellets. Pellets release the hormone slowly and more or less continuously. Injections of microcrystalline suspensions of steroid hormones attain much the same end. The rate of absorption of hormones from pellets or injections depends, to an important extent, on the vascularity of the area in which they are placed. Occasionally pellets may become encapsulated by tough connective tissue, which reduces the rate of diffusion. In small animals, such as rats or chickens, one can prevent this by manipulating the skin over the implant at frequent intervals and breaking the tissue capsule. Hormones injected into thick layers of fat may be completely ineffective.

Usually a steroid hormone is given in the form of an ester rather than as the free steroid (estradiol benzoate, testosterone propionate, etc.). Steroid hormones are effective orally, but this mode of administration requires higher doses for effects comparable to those produced by parenteral injection. Intravenous injections are most effective because they bring the hormone concentration in the blood to a high level very rapidly. Because steroid hormones are fat-soluble and go into aqueous solution most unwillingly, it is usually not possible to inject them intravenously, since few animals tolerate intravenous injections of oil without showing ill effects. Most steroids are soluble in propylene glycol, which can be injected intravenously without harm. Next to intravenous injections, intraperitoneal, intramuscular, and subcutaneous injections—in that order—are most effective.

Protein hormones (except thyroglobulin) are ineffective when given orally because they are digested before they are absorbed into the blood stream. Otherwise the same rules hold for them: intravenous injection provides the most rapid effectiveness, but also the most rapid rate of destruction; subcutaneously administered protein hormones are absorbed more slowly and last somewhat longer. All protein hormones are water-soluble. Crude preparations must be injected as aqueous suspensions, but more highly purified hormones (such as FSH, LH, growth hormone, or PMS) can be obtained in lyophilized form, which goes into solution completely. All steroid hormones are heat-stable, but protein hormones are not and must be protected from thermal and bacterial decomposition if they are to retain their potency.

Refractoriness of end organs stimulated by exogenous steroid hormones is occasionally observed, especially after prolonged administration of steroids, even though no antihormones are formed against them. It is thought that this type of refractoriness may be due to the exhaustion of the end organ.

Augmentation and Synergism

When protein hormones are mixed with certain complex proteins, such as the heme of blood, or with milk, or with metals like copper and zinc, they show greater effectiveness than they do when injected alone. This phenomenon is called augmentation. It is probably due to the formation of a complex between the hormone molecule and the protein or the metal ion, the complex being less available physiologically than the free hormone and thus less subject to rapid destruction. The increased effectiveness of such complexes may be caused by their prolonged retention in circulation. Insulin is regularly combined with protamine zinc to augment and prolong its effectiveness.

Certain hormones administered together are found to have an effect that is much greater than the sum of the effects of the several hormones given separately. In one experiment, for instance, estrogen alone produced chicken oviducts weighing 1,800 milligrams; progesterone alone produced oviducts weighing 530 milligrams; when the same amounts of the two hormones were injected simultaneously, the oviducts weighed 5,700 milligrams, or considerably more than could have been expected from the simple additive effect of the two hormones. In another experiment FSH injected alone into rats produced ovaries weighing 75 milligrams; LH alone produced ovarian weights of 19 milligrams; combination of the two hormones at the same dosage produced ovaries weighing 152 milligrams. When the physiological response to a combination of hormones is greater than the sum of the effects of the same amounts of the hormones given separately, the hormones are said to synergize, and the phenomenon is called synergism. Synergizing hormones act in this way even if the two are injected by entirely different routes, such as subcutaneous and intramuscular.

Some hormones do not synergize; other synergize in some animals but not in others. It is possible that these differences may be due to dosage effects. In the investigation of the response of chicken oviducts to estrogen and progesterone, cited above, if the dose of estrogen was kept constant but the dose of progesterone was progressively increased, synergy resulted at the smaller doses of progesterone but inhibition of estrogen resulted at the larger doses of progesterone, and finally a point was reached at which the oviducts weighed only about 600 milligrams—much less than they would have weighed had the estrogen been injected alone. A similar change from synergism to inhibition is found in some combinations of FSH and LH.

Some Metabolic Effects of Hormones

In addition to their localized action on specific target organs, hormones may have general metabolic effects. Of the hormones considered in this chapter, the steroids are best known for these effects.

A number of the physiological effects of estrogen and progesterone have only an indirect relation to reproduction. It cannot be doubted that these side effects are of enormous significance in birds before the onset of egg formation or in mammals during gestation. In all the animals studied, estrogen has the ability to raise blood calcium levels much above the values found in males or females not under the influence of this hormone. This effect is spectacular in chickens approaching laying condition and in mammalian females in the late stages of pregnancy. In both instances, hypercalcemia coincides with the greatest need for calcium by the maternal organism—in the chicken for eggshell formation, in mammalian females for the bone growth of the fetus. Some of this blood calcium undoubtedly comes from feed, but much of it is mobilized by estrogen from the skeleton. In chickens, the increase in total serum calcium is all in the nondiffusible fraction. Coincident with this hypercalcemia there is an increase in certain serum proteins in birds under the influence of estrogen. Formation of vitellin, a phospholipoprotein, is actually induced by the hormone. This protein does not appear in the serum of male or immature female birds but can be produced in either by estrogen treatment. It has the property of binding calcium, and the protein-Ca complex is nondiffusible.

As birds approach the laying stage, a peculiar effect of estrogen on bone appears. There is bone growth in the long bones from the endosteum into the medulla, so that in laying birds the marrow cavities of these bones become almost completely filled with spongy bone. This is the fowl's means of storing calcium for the large amounts that are needed for eggshell deposition. During the laying period there is rapid turnover of this bone. The effect of estrogen in this respect is not just on calcification; the hormone stimulates the formation of bone matrix. Medullary bone formation can be produced in one mammalian species, the mouse, by administration of estrogen.

In laying hens, a spectacular lipemia is caused by the endogenous estrogen. All lipids are increased, but the most pronounced effect is on neutral fat. Liver fat also is increased. Both the hyperproteinemia and hyperlipemia due to estrogen in fowls are antagonized by treatment with thyroid hormone. The effect of estrogen on blood fat is less pronounced in mammalian females than in birds.

Folic acid is a specific requirement in chickens for the effect of estrogen on the oviduct. Deficiency of this vitamin causes estrogen to lose its ability to increase the size of the avian oviduct but does not interfere with its ability to cause hyperlipemia.

Estrogen and progesterone cause secretion of avidin and biotin by the avian oviduct.

Estrogen alone can bring about many of these metabolic effects, but its efficiency is enhanced by progesterone, which, given alone, is completely ineffective. Many of the metabolic effects of estrogen are probably results of its action on the liver. All of them can be induced in males and in hypophysectomized animals.

Administration of progesterone increases the rate of protein catabolism in human subjects. It also causes loss of sodium and chloride; this, however, it not a direct effect of progesterone but is due to its inhibition of certain adrenal cortical steroids.

Of interest and of some practical importance are the roles played by estrogen and progesterone in bacterial infections of genital organs and possibly even in general infections. It has long been known that vaginitis can be cured by local application of estrogen. Cattle reacting positively to tuberculin react negatively after massive doses of estrogen. They regain lost weight and show only inactive lesions in the lungs if estrogen treatment is continued for a sufficient length of time. In rabbits, and later in cattle, it was noted that infections of the genital tract occur much more commonly during pseudopregnancy or during the luteal phase than during the follicular phase of the cycle. Extension of these observations confirmed the suspicion that castrated females treated with estrogen resist artificially induced bacterial infection of the genital duct, whereas those treated with progesterone not only become infected but are actually more liable to infection than they would be without progesterone treatment. The mechanism of action of estrogen is not completely understood, but it now appears (Hawk, 1958) that the hormone acts by increasing the rate of migration of leucocytes into the uterine lumen and by increasing the bactericidal activity of the uterus. In contrast, in pseudopregnant females, the uterus has no bactericidal activity, and the rate of leucocytic infiltration of the uterus in infected, progesterone-treated females is much lower. Leucocyte-free uterine exudates from estrogenized infected females show significantly greater bactericidal activity even *in vitro*. This observation suggests that the defense mechanism evoked by estrogen treatment is due, not merely to an increased vascularity of the uterus and a resulting increase in leucocytic infiltration, but also to the ability of estrogen to induce the production of a bactericidal substance, which is contained in cell-free and uterine exudates of infected estrogenized females.

The most striking general metabolic effect of the androgens is an increase in nitrogen retention, which is an indication of increased protein anabolism. Creatine and creatinine metabolism is also influenced by androgens. Creatinuria results from the castration of rabbits, and the condition is abolished by treatment with androgens.

The Mechanism of Action of Hormones

The greatest mystery in the field of endocrinology is the mechanism of action of hormones at the cellular level. The observed physiological effects of a hormone are the result of a sequence of biochemical events in the stimulated tissue and tell us nothing of what the initial action of the hormone was—what "bottleneck" was opened to allow subsequent reactions to take place. Because hormones are substances that *in trace amounts* cause profound physiological changes, it has seemed likely to investigators that they are enzyme regulators of some sort. The possibilities that have been considered in this connection are that hormones may function as components of enzyme systems, that they may themselves be accelerators or inhibitors of enzyme systems or may act upon such accelerators or inhibitors, and that they may actually change the concentration of enzymes in tissues. A great deal of work has been done on hormone-enzyme relations, and it has been found that hormones do indeed influence the activity of enzymes in many instances, but never has the observed effect of a hormone upon an enzyme explained the physiological action of the hormone. Although the consequences of hormone action (such as proliferation of tissue) certainly involve many enzyme-catalyzed reactions, the primary action of the hormone may not involve an enzyme system. For the hormone whose mechanism of action is probably best understood, insulin, this has, in fact, been shown to be true if the effect of this hormone on the permeability of cells to sugars is its primary action.

Most hormones have the ability to promote growth of their specific target tissues. This involves the intracellular accumulation and incorporation of amino acids into the cells, which use them for the formation of new protein. Just as insulin can facilitate the entrance of glucose into cells, other hormones, for instance somatotrophin, can significantly increase the cell wall permeability to amino acids. Obviously this is not the only thing hormones can do, because after they are accumulated the building blocks must be put into proper sequence to permit synthesis of the protein typical of the cell and needed for growth and multiplication.

It is further known that some hormones can cause the multiplication of mitochondria, which play an important role in catalysis of aerobic oxidation in the Krebs tricarboxylic acid cycle, as well as in the energy transfer system. Any hormone action resulting in mitochondriogenesis must of course be important to the ability of the cell to fulfill its intended function. Thyroxin is generally mitochondriogenic, and estrogen has the ability to increase the number of these structures in the uterine muscle. The effects of other hormones on the number of mitochondria in their target tissues has not yet been studied.

After hypophysectomy there is a fall in the nuclear and cytoplasmic protein and in RNA of the liver, but both can be restored to normal or above normal values by the administration of somatotrophin. Furthermore, microsomal liver fractions obtained from hypophysectomized animals do not have the ability to synthesize protein from amino acid substrates *in vitro;* but this ability can be restored if the microsomal fraction is prepared from the livers of hypophysectomized animals that were previously treated with somatotrophic hormone.

Apparently, hormones also have the ability to "hang on" to their target tisuses; hormones that are nonspecific for such tissue do not. If tagged estrogen is injected into a mouse, the concentration of the labeled hormone immediately increases in liver, blood, muscle, spleen, uterus, etc., but the estrogen disappears with great rapidity from all of these except the uterus. While in the nonspecific tissues it remains in high concentration for only a few minutes, in the uterus and in the vagina its concentration continues to increase and to remain at a high level for as long as 6 hours. The exact mechanisms by which estrogen can show such an affinity for the uterus remains unknown. It should be remembered that estrogen causes profound changes also in liver metabolism (for instance, production of lipemia), and yet it is eliminated from the latter much more rapidly than it is from the uterus. The difference may lie in the fact that the liver does not "grow" in response to estrogen while the uterus does.

In all the cases studied there was a more or less prolonged latent period between the injection of the hormone and the first measurable effects on the target tissue. For example, in rat uteri, following a single injection of estrogen, seven different enzyme systems activating amino acids were found to increase quantitatively beginning 3 hours after treatment, the increase continuing for the ensuing 24-hour period.

Estrogen in this case is thought to act either by stimulating enzyme synthesis *de novo*, by activating already existing enzymes, or by uncoupling enzymes, which can, after being "released," participate in cellular metabolism. In other instances the latent period may be much longer, as in the case of the effect of somatotrophin on the synthesis of detectable amounts of nucleic acid.

Hormones also have the ability to influence the reproductive rate of cells. Thus, somatotrophin is known to increase the frequency of polyploid cells in the liver, just as estrogen has the well-known ability to increase the number of mitotic figures in estrogen-sensitive tissues such as the uterus and the vagina.

Although by no means exhaustive, this summary of the known effects of hormones on their target organs makes obvious that the role of hormones is not a simple one and that it is not restricted to single effects. Almost nothing is known about the action of hormones on biochemical reactions at the cellular level. Many hormones are known to increase the oxygen consumption of their target organs; this has led to the demonstration that slices of human placenta treated with estrogen can convert both acetate and pyruvate to CO_2. It has also been suggested that estrogen may participate in reactions of the tricarboxylic acid cycle; the estrogen-sensitive enzyme is thought to be a transhydrogenase that causes the transfer of hydrogen ions from TPNH to DPN.

In the rat uterus the following sequence of events has been established after a single injection of estrogen. During the first 2 hours there is a very significant water imbibition and an incorporation of glycine and formate into nucleic acid. During the next 18 hours there is an accumulation of RNA, which results in protein synthesis. During the next 40 to 72 hours, DNA synthesis takes place. It is interesting to note that during the first 6 hours after estrogen injection there is no increase in oxygen uptake of the uterine tissue, even though the uterus is far from being metabolically inactive during that interval.

Most and perhaps all trophic hormones have the very distinct ability to increase the vascularity of their target organs. For instance, the first visible effect of FSH on an atrophic ovary is hyperemia, which is seen 1 or 2 hours after FSH injection. Estrogen greatly increases uterine vascularity and, if it is applied locally on the skin, the vascularity of the treated patch becomes obviously greater than the vascularity of neighboring, but untreated areas.

SUMMARY

The hormones concerned with reproductive processes are either proteins or steroids. Protein hormones are water-soluble and heat-labile and are difficult to obtain in pure form. They are fairly stable in dry form but are destroyed or inactivated very rapidly in aqueous solution or after they are injected into animals. The major inactivation occurs in the liver. Because of this, the activity of these hormones is very short (lasting, probably, only minutes) once they enter the circulation. Antihormones are formed in response to the foreign hormone proteins injected, and after prolonged treatment the end organs are not able to respond to the injected hormone. Antibodies are hormone-specific and sometimes also species-specific.

In contrast, no antihormones are formed in response to the injection of steroid hormones. Steroid hormones are heat-stable and fat-soluble. They are also inactivated, primarily in the liver, and some of the inactivation is due to the fact that steroid molecules become conjugated with protein or glucuronate. As long as they remain bound, their biological activity is negligible.

Intravenous injection of either protein or steroid hormones permits most rapid action (but also most rapid inactivation); intramuscular injection is less effective, and subcutaneous injection is least effective, in rapidity of action. Protein hormones (except thyroxine) are completely inactive when fed (they are digested); steroid hormones are active orally but significantly less so than by injection. The action of hormones, especially of steroid hormones, can be prolonged if they are implanted in the form of pellets or are injected as microcrystalline suspensions.

Hormones are said to synergize when two hormones injected together produce a greater effect than is produced by the same doses of the two hormones injected separately. Synergy is known among steroid hormones and among protein hormones.

REFERENCES

R. I. Dorfman. 1948. "Biochemistry of the androgens" in *The Hormones,* Vol. I. Academic Press (New York).

R. I. Dorfman. 1950. "Physiology of androgens" in *The Hormones,* Vol. II. Academic Press (New York).

R. I. Dorfman. 1952. "Steroids and tissue oxidation" in *Vitamins and Hormones*, 10. Academic Press (New York).

R. I. Dorfman. 1955. "Steroid hormone metabolism" in *The Hormones*, Vol. III. Academic Press (New York).

H. M. Evans and M. E. Simpson. 1950. "Physiology of the gonadotrophins" in *The Hormones*, Vol. II. Academic Press (New York).

W. H. Fishman. 1951. "Relationship between estrogens and enzyme activity" in *Vitamins and Hormones*, 9. Academic Press (New York).

H. W. Hawk. 1958. "The influx of leukocytes and presence of bacterial substances in inoculated uteri of estrous and pseudopregnant rabbits." *J. Animal Sci.*, 17:416.

E. E. Hays and S. L. Steelman. 1955. "Chemistry of the anterior pituitary hormones" in *The Hormones*, Vol. III. Academic Press (New York).

O. Hechter. 1955. "Concerning possible mechanisms of hormone action" in *Vitamins and Hormones*, 13. Academic Press (New York).

H. Hirschmann. 1955. "The chemistry of steroid hormones" in *The Hormones*, Vol. III. Academic Press (New York).

Choh Hao Li. 1949. "The chemistry of gonadotrophic hormones" in *Vitamins and Hormones*, 7. Academic Press (New York).

W. H. Pearlman. 1948. "The chemistry and metabolism of the estrogens" in *The Hormones*, Vol. I. Academic Press (New York).

S. Roberts and C. M. Szego. 1955. "Biochemistry of the steroid hormones." *Ann. Rev. Biochem.*, 24:543–596.

L. T. Samuels and C. D. West. 1952. "The intermediary metabolism of the non-benzenoid steroid hormones" in *Vitamins and Hormones*, 10. Academic Press (New York).

W. H. Strain. 1943. "The steroids" in Gilman's *Organic Chemistry*, 2nd ed. Wiley (New York).

A. White. 1949. "The chemistry and physiology of adenohypophyseal luteotropin (prolactin)" in *Vitamins and Hormones*, 7. Academic Press (New York).

chapter 7

Reproduction in Male Mammals and Birds

It has been pointed out that females may be classified as continuous or seasonal breeders. A similar situation exists in males, and in most species the breeding behavior of the males corresponds to that of the females. Testes, as a rule, regress at the end of the breeding season at about the same time as ovaries. In most species the testes show signs of recrudescence at the start of the breeding season somewhat ahead of the awakening of the ovary. The testes and the duct system of some mallard drakes may be filled with mature spermatozoa at a time when the ovaries of none of the females show follicles larger than one-half millimeter in diameter. The majority of drakes are in full breeding condition between ten and twenty days before the hens are ready to ovulate their first egg. This synchronization of male and female reproductive functions is not surprising, for the basic controlling mechanisms in both sexes are identical, the relative seasonal precocity of males possibly being an expression of the greater sensitivity of male end organs to the external and internal stimuli involved.

There are exceptions to the rule that the breeding seasons of males and females coincide. In rams, spermatogenesis and libido are not restricted to the breeding season of ewes. Spermatogenesis in raccoon males is continuous throughout the year even though the breeding season of females is restricted to January, February, and March. A similar situation is found in domestic dogs and probably in several other species.

The endocrine control of reproductive phenomena in males is similar to that in females in that the same two pituitary hormones, FSH and LH, play the major role in the stimulation of the testes. The behavior of male rabbits even suggests that, within the breeding season of males, there is a cycle or rhythm of testicular function; but this rhythm (if it exists) is neither as accurately timed nor as well defined as the estrous cycle of the female.

Before considering the intricacies of the endocrine control of the testes, let us briefly review what happens in the normal development of the male gonad.

The Testes

The Seminiferous Tubules

Males, at birth or at hatching, possess tubules that have no lumina and are lined with a single layer of small nuclei. Gradually, as the male matures, the tubules acquire lumina, and the germinal epithelium progresses from the one-layered state to the complex state seen in sexually mature males, in which all cell types (spermatogonia, primary and secondary spermatocytes, and spermatozoa) are seen. There is considerable individual and species variation in the rapidity, in relation to age, with which these changes occur, the process being most rapid in species in which the males reach sexual maturity early. The ages as which these events occur are shown in Table 7-1. In animals with a short life

Table 7-1. Relation of spermatogenesis to age

	AVERAGE AGE AT APPEARANCE OF		
ANIMAL	PRIMARY SPERMATOCYTES	SECONDARY SPERMATOCYTES	SPERMATOZOA
Guinea pig	. . .	. . .	50–70 days
Rat	. . .	. . .	33–35
Boar	84	105	147
Bull	63	181	224
Goat	. . .	. . .	110
Ram	63	126	147
Chicken	42–56	70	84–140
Man	. . .	. . .	10–15 years

SOURCE: Compiled from the literature.

(chickens), spermatogenesis continues unabated until death, and the great majority of tubules appear to be functioning normally throughout life. In mammals with a long life (man, boars, bulls), spermatogenesis may continue normally throughout life, but past the middle age more and more tubules may atrophy, and eventually only a few may show normal spermatogenic activity.

Not infrequently individuals produce viable sperm and are capable of mating long before the majority of the members of the species or population to which they belong. Precocious sexual maturity in boys and other mammals is probably commoner than is generally assumed. Complete spermatogenesis, with sperm in the epididymis, was seen in the testes of one ram at the age of seventy-two days, and motile sperm were obtained from a Leghorn cock at the age of sixty-two days. That age at sexual maturity is genetically influenced is seen from the fact that there is considerable difference in this respect between breeds of domestic animals (among dairy cattle, Brown Swiss bulls mature from four to six months later than Jersey or Guernsey bulls). It has, in fact, been possible to select for early or late sexual maturity within the breeds of practically all domestic animals with which the attempt— either consciously or unconsciously—has been made.

In seasonally breeding males, the testes regress completely during the nonbreeding season, and the germinal epithelium returns to the state in which it is commonly found in young, sexually immature males. The tubules lose their lumen and are lined with a single layer of small spermatogonia. In many mammals the testes migrate from the scrotum into the body cavity, where they remain until shortly before the onset of the next breeding season; then they begin to go through the same changes through which they had gone in reaching puberty and through which they will go with the onset of each new breeding season. We commonly call this seasonal reawakening of the testes "recrudescence" to differentiate it from the prepubertal changes that occur in sexually immature males.

Of considerable interest and importance is the length of time required for the completion of the processes of spermatogenesis and spermiogenesis—that is, for the transformation of a spermatogonium into a finished sperm cell. It is possible to measure this time in a variety of ways. An older method was to destroy testicular and epididymal sperm by X-irradiation or heat, and then to determine the time required for repair of the germinal epithelium and formation of new sperm. A newer and more elegant method labels the nuclei of germ cells with P^{32} and takes advantage of the fact that the nuclei of cells in the different stages of spermatogenesis do not become radioactive. Thus it is possible to determine the interval elapsing between the uptake of P^{32} by nuclei in the initial stages of spermatogenesis and the appearance of radioactive mature sperm cells (Ortavant, 1956). There is good agreement between the figures obtained by the two methods: both show that spermatogenesis requires about 10 days in the mouse, 16–20 days in the rat, 39 days in the rabbit, 48 days in the bull, and 50 days in the ram. Injection of P[32] into rams also showed that the rate at which the different stages of spermatogenesis occur is extremely uneven, some being completed in a few hours and others in as long as 15 days.

That spermatogenesis is a slow process is frequently overlooked by those who are interested in studies of the rates of sperm and semen production. This fact should be especially remembered in experiments designed to study the rate of exhaustion of epididymal or testicular sperm after frequent ejaculation, and such experiments should run for 10–20 days for the smaller animals and 50–60 days for all the larger ones.

The Interstitial Tissue

The most important components of the intertubular tissue are the Leydig, or interstitial, cells, which secrete the male sex hormone, androgen. (A minority of investigators still feel that this question has not been settled; they favor the seminiferous tubules as the source of androgen. Because it is not possible to remove the tubules and the intertubular tissue separately, it is difficult to settle this question. The circumstantial evidence is all in favor of the Leydig cells as the source of androgen.)

Table 7-2.   Relation between age, testes weight, and rate of androgen secretion in bulls

AGE RANGE (months)	BODY WEIGHT (lbs)	WEIGHT OF BOTH TESTES (g)	ANDROGEN CONTENT OF BOTH TESTES (bird units)*	RATIO OF TESTES TO BODY WEIGHT	RATIO OF ANDROGEN TO TESTES WEIGHT
1–3½	137	16.8	2.18	0.122	0.13
4–6	236	52.6	5.33	0.223	0.10
7½–9½†	272	86.1	2.80	0.313	0.03
10–13	313	110.0	6.00	0.351	0.05
14–16	477	254.2	8.50	0.533	0.03
18–21	640	398.3	23.6	0.623	0.06
24–28	712	406.5	18.5	0.571	0.05
5 & 7 years	1,540	645.8	94.9	0.419	0.15
13½ & 15 years	1,365	483.3	16.4	0.354	0.03

SOURCE: Data adapted from a table by Hooker. 1944. *Am. J. Anat.*, 74:1.
* Androgen was measured in Gallagher-Koch bird units.
† Full spermatogenesis was noted at nine months of age. Note that testes show a relative decrease in weight after about two years of age and an actual decrease after five years of age; bulls up to six months of age secrete more androgen per gram of testis than older bulls (except one five-year-old bull, which accounts for the higher ratio in the older group).

Embryonal testes are known to contain enough androgen to cause local effects in androgen-dependent end organs (seminal vesicles), but the urine of month-old bull calves contains no measurable amounts of androgen. Androgen is present in the testes of bulls one and a half months old (Table 7-2). Testes contain (and presumably secrete) androgen long before full spermatogenesis, but the increase in androgen secretion is significantly slower than testicular growth. In bulls older than five years, however, the testes decrease in weight and in the rate at which they secrete androgen, even though bulls of these ages retain fertility and libido. The weight of the testes, the number of Leydig cells, and the rate of androgen secretion decrease in men past about thirty years of age (Fig. 7-1), in senile rats, and probably in the males of other species.

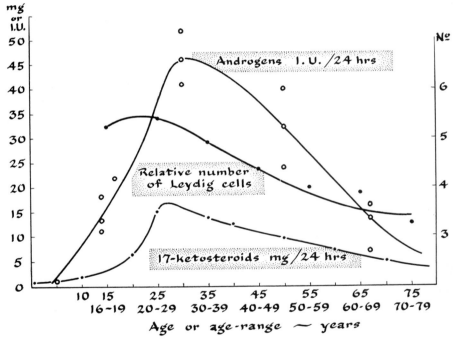

Figure 7-1. *Relation between number of Leydig cells and amounts of androgens and 17-ketosteroids found in 24-hour samples of urine of normal human males from infancy to old age. In comparison: eunuchs produce 4.0–7.7 I.U. and eunuchoids about 17.6 I.U. of androgen in 24 hours. (Androgen curve from Hamilton, 1954, J. Clinical Endo. and Metabolism, 14:452; 17-ketosteroid curve from Hamburger, 1948, Acta Endo., 1:19; Leydig cell counts from Tillinger, 1957, Acta Endo., Suppl. 30.)*

When a group of growing males of various ages is considered, there is very high correlation between size of testes and size of androgen-dependent end organs, such as the comb ($r = +0.98$) and, in rats, the seminal vesicles ($r = +0.87$). When the same comparison is made within an age group, the correlation coefficient continues to be significant but is considerably lower (in chickens, correlation between comb size and testes weight at fifty days was $+0.25$, at ninety days was $+0.56$). This indicates that some males with large testes produce less androgen and hence smaller end organs than males with smaller testes.

Androgen and the Secondary Male Sex Characters

Androgen develops and maintains the male sex characters. The degree to which absence of androgen affects the development of secondary sex characters depends on the stage in their development at which androgen is withdrawn. If, for instance, males are castrated after having reached sexual maturity, they may continue to show sex drive and erection. If juvenile prepubertal males are castrated, sex desire and related phenomena will, as a rule, not develop. The castration of boys causes them to retain a high voice; men castrated after puberty usually retain the pitch of their voice. The qualitative and quantitative changes produced by androgen deficiency are, in general, more intense when they occur before puberty.

One of the most frequently studied androgenic effects is growth of the comb in cocks. The comb regresses completely after castration, but it can be returned to normal size, texture, and color by the administration of androgen. Because the degree of growth is proportional to the amount of hormone injected, both immature males with small combs and castrated adults make excellent assay animals for androgen. (We mention here, parenthetically, a few paradoxical effects of androgen in birds. The blackness of the beak of male English sparrows is due to androgen, for the beak lightens after castration—and during the non-breeding season—and blackens after androgen injection. The beak of females is light but becomes black after androgen injection. This suggests that the ovary of female sparrows either does not secrete androgen or secretes it in very small quantities. In female chickens, comb growth is caused by androgen, which is secreted by the ovary. In starlings, however, androgen produces the yellow color of the beak; and in the black-headed gull it is responsible for the crimson color of the beak.)

Because of the well-known relation between libido and androgen, it was expected that the hormone would correct low sex drive or impotence in males. In general, however, androgen is able to correct low sex drive only if this condition is due to testicular hypofunction and deficiency of the hormone. Many cases of male impotence seem to be due to psychological involvements and cannot be corrected by androgen medication. If males are used as teasers over prolonged periods, during which they are not permitted to mate after they discover females in heat, they eventually lose their sex drive and even refuse to attempt to mate with females in heat. Such males do not regain potency even after massive doses of exogenous androgen, but they gradually recover their ability and willingness to mate without medication if they are permitted to attempt and eventually complete matings without interference. Such temporary loss of libido has been seen in bulls, boars, and rabbits, some individuals becoming discouraged much sooner and more easily than others.

Androgen and the Accessory Glands

We have noted that the effect of androgen on the secondary male sex characters, such as pitch of voice and libido, depends, to some extent, on factors other than the direct action of the hormone on end organs. In distinct contrast is the effect of androgen on the accessory glands, which include the seminal vesicles, the prostate, and the bulbo-urethral (Cowper's) glands. Morphologically and physiologically, all of these glands are totally dependent on androgen. Castration causes cessation of their secretory function and drastic reduction in their size and in the height of their epithelial linings (Fig. 7-2). Androgen given to normal males causes an increase in the size of the accessory glands beyond the normal; androgen given to castrated males rehabilitates those glands both in size and in secretory function. The degree of growth of the accessory glands of castrated males that can be caused by androgen administration is proportional to the amount of hormone injected. For this reason these end organs are valuable for androgen assays. If the concentration of androgen in the unknown to be assayed is small, the height of the epithelium of the accessory glands may be used as the end point. It is easier and usually more convenient, however, to use the weight of the accessory glands. The rat's prostate is a more sensitive indicator of most androgenic compounds than the seminal vesicles (Dorfman and Shipley, 1956, p. 123). (Seminal vesicles increase some-

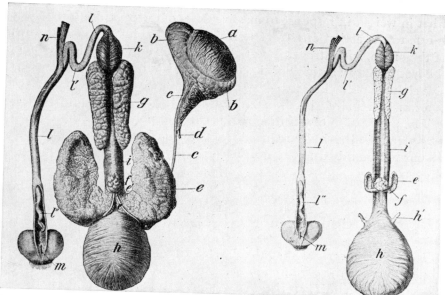

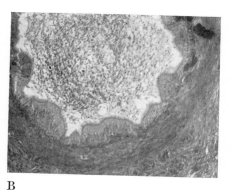

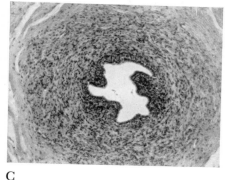

A

B

C

Figure 7-2. *Effects of castration on the genital organs.*

A. Genital organs of a normal and a castrated boar. (From *Handbuch der ver-gleichenden Anatomie der Haustiere* by permission of the Springer Verlag, Heidelberg.)

a—testis
b—epididymis
c—vas deferens
d—spermatic cord
e—seminal vesicle

f—prostate
g—bulbo-urethral gland
k—cavernosus muscle
l—penis
m—orifice of preputial pouch

B. Normal vas deferens of a bull ($\times$ 25). Note the tall pseudo-stratified epithe-lium and the sperm cells in the lumen.

C. Vas deferens of a steer 6 months after castration ($\times$ 25).

what in weight in response to massive doses of estrogen, but the increase is due to the action of estrogen on the fibromuscular connective tissue of the organ, and estrogen is not able to repair either the epithelium or the lost secretory activity of the seminal vesicle of castrates.) Retrogressive changes occur in the duct system of males after castration, and these too can be repaired by the administration of androgen.

The production of fructose, citric acid, and phosphatase by the accessory glands is drastically reduced by castration but can be brought back to normal or raised above normal levels by the administration of androgen.

Hormonal Control of the Testicular Function

It is almost certain that the LH of the gonadotrophic complex is responsible for the stimulation of Leydig cells, which respond by secretion of androgen. There is good evidence either that the LH secreted by chicken pituitary glands differs from mammalian LH or that there are actually two LH-like hormones secreted by avian pituitaries. This statement is based on the fact that mammalian LH is capable of inducing only temporary comb growth in hypophysectomized cocks, whereas chicken pituitary glands can sustain comb growth indefinitely. Furthermore, chicken testes that have lost their ability to respond to mammalian LH can regain this ability after a few injections with whole avian pituitary glands. This ability is again lost after a course of stimulation with mammalian LH, and a second interlude of treatment with avian LH is necessary before mammalian LH can cause further androgen production. Histological examination shows that mammalian LH is capable of stimulating the already differentiated Leydig cells, which soon become exhausted. Avian LH, in contrast, is able not only to cause androgen secretion by the Leydig cells already differentiated but also to cause the differentiation of new Leydig cells as the old ones become pycnotic. It will be noted elsewhere that a similar species-specificity is seen in female chickens, whose ovaries can respond to mammalian gonadotrophic hormone only to a limited extent.

The question of the hormonal control of spermatogenesis is much more complex than that of androgen secretion. Though it is true that FSH can cause a very significant increase in the diameter of the seminiferous tubules, it appears virtually certain that both LH and FSH are essential to full and complete spermatogenesis. It is not clear whether LH as such is necessary for this response or whether it exercises its effect on spermatogenesis by its ability to induce androgen secretion, the androgen in turn making complete spermatogenesis possible. The latter possibility is strongly supported by the following evidence. If sexually mature male rats are hypophysectomized, the testes regress very rapidly, and spermatogenesis ceases soon after the operation. If however, androgen is injected into the rats immediately after the operation, spermatogenesis is maintained for as long as forty days (but degeneration of the Leydig cells is not prevented). Still more significant is the fact that 30–80 percent of the rats hypophysectomized *before* the onset of spermatogenesis and immediately placed on androgen therapy show spermatogenesis even though the injected androgen does not stimulate the testes to increase in size. In contrast, if androgen treatment is delayed for a few days after hypophysectomy, complete testicular degeneration cannot be prevented, and spermatogenesis cannot be revived. The ability of androgen to maintain spermatogenesis in hypophysectomized males, and its inability to rehabilitate spermatogenesis, raise the question of the role of androgen in the gametogenic function of the testes. The experimental evidence suggests that androgen stimulates true spermatogenesis and does not simply maintain the sperm cells that had differentiated while the testes were under gonadotrophic stimulation. It seems reasonable to postulate that gonadotrophins (FSH? both FSH and LH?) are essential to some stages of spermatogenesis, but that the final differentiation can be accomplished by androgen. However, the intricacies of the hormonal interrelations remain unknown. It is noteworthy that androgen is able to prevent summer sterility in some rams but not in others. Whether the number of unresponsive rams can be decreased by a more careful adjustment of the dose of androgen remains unknown.

Like estrogen, androgen also is able to inhibit the pituitary. Injection of androgen into intact males causes a reduction in the size of the testes in proportion to the amount injected. Testicular damage is greatest if androgen injection is begun in animals a few weeks old; sexually mature male rats can withstand appreciable doses of the hormone. The testes of young males (rats) damaged by androgen injection recover very slowly; in some experiments testes were smaller and fertility was severely reduced as long as 130 days after androgen injections had been discontinued. This suggests that androgen may damage the testes directly; but injection of appropriate doses of gonadotrophic hormone along with androgen prevents such damage and indicates that the primary effect of androgen is on the pituitary rather than on the testes.

In view of the experimentally demonstrable ability of androgen to control the rate of the pituitary function, the question arises whether a "push-pull" mechanism, similar to the one operating in the female, controls the pituitary-testes relation in the male. Though there are no clear-cut experiments demonstrating cyclic functioning of the male, there is a "feeling" on the part of evaluators of semen from bulls and men that the volume, density, and quality of the semen of individuals vary in a cyclic fashion. If there are indeed cyclic variations in the male, they are not as clear-cut and distinct as in the female. The effect of season on the properties of the semen and on the fertility of cocks is shown in Figure 7-3.

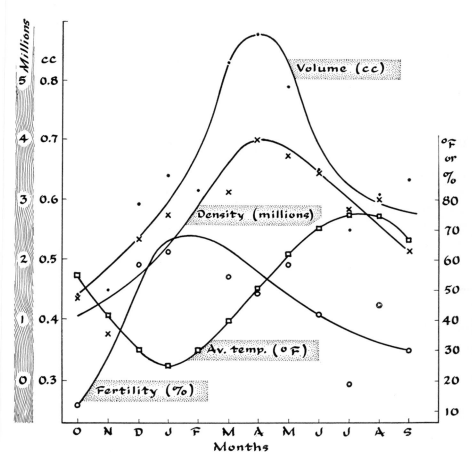

Figure 7-3. *Monthly changes in the properties of cock semen. The density and volume of semen are determined by the males alone; the fertility curve is determined by the interaction of males and females. (Data from Parker and McSpadden, 1943, Poultry Sci., 22:142.)*

We have already discussed in some detail the role of the "releasing factors" in the secretion of such hypophyseal hormones as ACTH, LTH, LH, and perhaps of growth hormone, and the evidence for a factor depressing the release of prolactin. Without doubt, the male has good use for releasing factors for ACTH and LTH, but what of releasing factors for LH and FSH? It has been found that LRF is present in the hypothalami of the pituitary glands of males, females, and castrated males, but no comparative studies have been made to determine the relative concentration of LRF in the hypothalami of males and females. There is one bit of suggestive evidence that there may be distinct "sex difference" between the hypothalami of males and females. As we know, there is no clear-cut male gonadal cycle comparable to the cyclic behavior of female ovaries. If one transplants the adenohypophysis from a male rat into the sella turcica of a female, the male hypophysis (after becoming established) will begin to function in the same cyclic manner in which its "female" predecessor had functioned. This suggests that the pituitary gland does not know its "sex" until the hypothalamic factors direct it to function—either as an acyclic male or as a cyclic female pituitary gland. At present there is no reason to argue either for or against the importance of the role of an LRF (and possibly of an FSHRF) in the normal function of the pituitary gland of males. The gonadotrophic releasing factors can be reconciled with a cyclic gonadal function if one assumes (as we have before) that the hormonal feedback system involves the action of testicular androgen on a steroid-sensitive hypothalamic center which responds either by withholding or by releasing the releasing factors. While such cyclicity would not be as sharply defined as the cyclicity of the female, it would very adequately account for the much more relaxed cyclic behavior of males mentioned earlier.

Miscellaneous Effects of Androgen

We have already noted that androgen plays an important role in determining the sexual behavior of the male toward the female. In addition to regulating the intensity of the male sex drive, androgen has a variety of other effects, which are only indirectly related to reproductive activity. Androgen has been shown to determine the so-called pecking order among chickens (and probably among birds in general), the social organization of fish schools, and the butting order among cows. Both males and females assume their places in the social organization of their group according to the degree to which they are being stimulated by the male sex hormone. Individuals that normally belong at the top of the social order and assume the right to peck or to boss all individuals below them lose this privilege if they are castrated and rapidly sink to the bottom of the order. Injection of androgen restores them to their previous position, which they maintain as long as they are given the hormone. A similar social order exists in other "group-living" animals, such as mice, in which the social position of males is determined by a series of elimination fights, the winners of which are presumed to be producing the largest amounts of androgen. Here again, males that are low in the social order can be caused to rise to higher levels by the injection of androgen.

Androgen also has a number of effects that bear no relation to reproduction. The erythrocyte count and the hemoglobin concentration are lower in females than in males. Castration of males lowers both these values, and androgen administration returns them to precastration levels. Androgen stimulates protein anabolism in many of the animals in which it causes increased nitrogen retention; this may account for the more rapid growth and the greater ultimate weight of males. The skeletal muscles of castrated males and of females grow less rapidly than those of intact males. Androgen administration increases the number and thickness of muscle fibers as well as the tensile strength and the working ability of muscles.

The Physiology of Sperm

In an earlier section of this discussion it was pointed out that testicular and epididymal sperm are nonmotile and that they become motile when they are suspended in a fluid. This occurs when the sperm come in contact with and become suspended in the fluids contributed by the male accessory glands—the seminal vesicles (when present), the prostate, and the bulbo-urethral (Cowper's) glands. The mixture of sperm cells and accessory gland fluids is known as semen. The most important attributes of the seminal fluids have been briefly discussed in Chapter 2 (pp. 49–51).

The Morphology of Sperm Cells

The normal sperm cell consists of a head, a neck, a middle piece, and a tail (Fig. 7-4). The head is covered by a protoplasmic cap (galea caput), which at one time was thought to be present only in immature sperm cells but is now known to be a normal component of the head. It is usually dissolved when sperm are treated with fat solvents for staining. The shape of the head varies with the species; it is ovoid in bull, ram, boar, and rabbit, round in man, and, when motile, swims fishlike through the suspending fluids. Only when dead does it present its flat surface to the viewer. In birds the head is an elongated cylinder; in the mouse and the rat it terminates in a distinct hook. The neck, the middle piece, and the tail do not consist of a single solid flagellum (as frequently depicted) but are composed of several strands or fibrils (9 or 18),

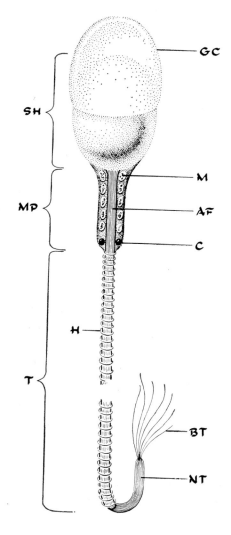

which are covered by a sheath. Only at the very tip of the tail, where the sheath ends, do these fibrils flare out into a naked brush. This anatomic detail was first seen under a simple light microscope and described in 1886 by Ballowitz, but it was not until 1941 that it was rediscovered by the use of an electron microscope (which is not so much a tribute to the power of magnification of the electronic gadget as it is to the thoroughness and the power of observa-

Figure 7-4. *Details of mammalian sperm cell structure as seen under the electron microscope (composite of several published pictures).*

SH—sperm head

MP—midpiece

T—tail

GC—galea caput

M—mitochondria

AF—axial filaments, which begin in midpiece, extend through tail, and emerge as a brush (BT) at tip of tail

C—ring centriole

H—helix, which coils round surface of tail but does not extend to tip of tail (NT).

tion of the earlier workers). Although this observation has been confirmed several times since 1943, when the original observation was published, sperm cells are still pictured in some of the newest texts as having a solid flagellum.

Several deviations from this normal morphology are regarded as abnormalities. Among them are giant or dwarf heads, double heads, headless or tailless sperm (this condition is frequently caused by rough treatment in preparation for staining or preservation, but such monsters are often seen in carefully treated preparations), multitailed heads, bent and coiled tails, and protoplasmic heads in the middle piece. These abnormalities should be absent or rare in normal ejaculates. When they occur in large numbers, they impair the fertility of the afflicted male; when their number approaches 50 percent of the total number of sperm cells in the ejaculate, the male is, as a rule, sterile— even though the normal-appearing sperm cells in the ejaculate should, theoretically, be more than enough to effect fertilization. Such sperm monsters commonly appear in rams suffering from summer sterility, in males suffering from fever, and in males used for mating too frequently or too young. Often there is no apparent reason for the appearance of abnormal sperm cells in the ejaculate, and this defect may correct itself with time. Certain deformities of sperm cells are also known to be genetic.

As a rule, ejaculates also contain a certain number of dead (nonmotile) sperm cells. Live and dead sperm cells can be distinguished by the use of vital stains, dead cells assuming the stain, live ones not. A few dead sperm do not interfere with normal fertility, but ejaculates containing a high proportion (approaching 50 percent) of dead cells show either impaired fertility or complete sterility.

In view of the known relation between the proportion of dead or abnormal sperm in an ejaculate and the fertility of males, it seems probable either that the dead or abnormal cells affect the fertilizing ability of the normal cells adversely or that the presence of abnormal cells is indicative of a constitutional weakness of the cells that show normal motility and appear normal on examination.

Survival of Sperm in the Epididymis

Elsewhere in this discussion it has been pointed out that the lifespan of ejaculated sperm is very short in the female reproductive tract (20–

30 hours), and that it rarely exceeds a few days if stored under optimal conditions *in vitro*. In contrast, sperm survive a long time, before ejaculation, in the epididymis. This can be demonstrated in several ways, among which experiments involving blockage of the ducts between the head of the epididymis and the testis have been the most popular. Since this operation prevents the entry of fresh sperm from the testis into the epididymis but does not prevent ejaculation, it is possible to measure the length of time over which epididymal sperm retain their ability to fertilize eggs. In this way it was found that epididymal sperm remain motile in bulls for 60 days. In contrast, sperm isolated in the ampulla of the vas deferens lose motility in less than 72 hours. In guinea pigs, epididymal sperm remain fertile for 20–35 days and motile for 59 days. In rats, the corresponding intervals are 21 and 42 days; in mice, epididymal sperm remain fertile for 10–14 days.

It should also be remembered that males may retain the ability to ejaculate fertile sperm for as long as four weeks after castration. Such observations are available for many species, reliable records indicating that stallions retain the ability to ejaculate fertile semen for as long as three weeks and men for as long as six weeks after castration. In castrated rats and guinea pigs, epididymal sperm may retain fertilizing ability for many months if the animals are kept on continuous androgen injection. It is not known what properties of the epididymis or of its secretions are responsible for the remarkable longevity of sperm in the epididymal lumen. Since sperm in the epididymis are nonmotile, it is possible but improbable that their longevity is attributable merely to their physical and metabolic inactivity—improbable because of the observation that androgen plays a role in determining the duration of survival of sperm by exerting an effect either directly, on the sperm cells, or indirectly, by acting on the epididymis and its secretion. Incidentally, the ability of castrated males to produce fertile sperm for several ejaculations following removal of the testes has been used by ancient and even modern naturalists as evidence against the assumption that the testes are the source of sperm.

In spite of the remarkable ability of the epididymis to maintain the fertilizing ability or at least the motility of sperm for a long time, sperm will eventually die even in that most favorable environment. For this reason males may ejaculate nonfertile sperm in the first two or three matings after prolonged sexual rest. In the order of their formation, and hence of their age, sperm in the tail of the epididymis may be dead while those in the head may still be motile and even capable of fertilizing ova.

Number of Sperm Needed for Fertilization

Because of the relatively large size of the female reproductive tract, the major portion of the ejaculate never reaches the oviduct. It has been calculated that, if 10–20 million sperm are introduced into a rabbit, only 5,000 reach the oviduct.

Only a few dozen sperm cells may reach the vicinity of the ovum; several may penetrate into the zona pellucida (polyspermy is much more common than is usually thought), but only one sperm enters the ovum proper and accomplishes fertilization. Because of this decline in the number of sperm from the time of the deposition of the semen in the vagina or cervix until the time the "sperm swarm" reaches the oviduct, it is usually thought essential that no less than 50 million living sperm be present to ensure fertility. Experimentally, however, sperm concentrations even below 100,000 have resulted in good and even maximal fertility. It has been found practical to dilute bull semen for artificial insemination as much as 1:100, and, with bulls of very high fertility, even greater dilution has given good results. At these rates of dilution the total number of sperm inseminated varies between 5 and 15 million. Some of the species differences in the characteristics of semen are summarized in Table 7-3.

Table 7-3.   Species differences in characteristics of semen

SPECIES	RANGE OF NORMAL VOLUME OF EJACULATE (ml)	RANGE OF NORMAL DENSITY OF EJACULATE (1,000 sperm/mm³)*	RANGE OF pH
Cock	0.2–1.5	50–6,000 (4,000)	6.3–7.8
Turkey	0.2–0.8	7,000 (7,000)	6.5–7.0
Boar	150–500	20–300 (100)	7.3–7.9
Bull	2–10	300–2,000 (1,000)	6.4–7.8
Ram	0.7–2	2,000–5,000 (3,000)	5.9–7.3
Stallion	30–300	30–8,000 (100)	6.2–7.8
Rabbit	0.4–6	100–2,000 (700)	6.6–7.5
Dog	2–14	1,000–9,000 (3,000)	6.7–6.8
Fox	0.2–4	30–300 (70)	6.2–6.4
Man	2–6	50–200 (100)	7.1–7.5

SOURCE: Data compiled from the literature.
* The most commonly observed values are in parentheses.

Preservation of Semen

The increase in the practical importance of artificial insemination is due to two factors: the development of sperm diluters, or extenders, which make it possible to inseminate several females from a single ejaculate, and the ability of semen to withstand storage for from two to four days. In general, the semen of chickens, stallions, and boars cannot be stored satisfactorily, but bull semen withstands dilution and storage very well. (Under proper conditions bull sperm may remain motile for as long as three weeks, but it loses its ability to fertilize after from seven to ten days. Similarly, chicken, boar, and stallion sperm may, when stored, retain motility for several days, but they lose fertilizing ability within forty-eight hours after ejaculation.) Within the last few years much work has been done on the freezing of sperm for prolonged storage. Chicken and human semen, and particularly bull semen, withstood freezing to $-79°C$ (the temperature of Dry Ice) and then, after prolonged storage, were found, on being thawed out, to have retained unimpaired their ability to fertilize. This advance in semen preservation has become possible through the finding that the addition of glycerol to the yolk-citrate diluter prevents crystal formation and hence the rupturing of the cells when they are frozen and thawed before use. This finding is potentially of great significance, for it makes it possible to preserve the semen of outstanding sires and to use it for artificial insemination after their genetic value has been adequately evaluated, possibly even after their death. Freezing apparently has no adverse effects on the sperm cells or on their fertilizing ability. Neither boar nor stallion semen retains its fertilizing ability after freezing.

The latest development in semen preservation may become important in the artificial insemination of cattle. Recent studies at the University of Illinois have shown that cattle semen may retain its motility and fertlizing ability for seven or even fourteen days at room temperature if the sperm cells (in a proper diluent) are exposed to carbon dioxide and are stored under the gas in sealed ampoules. In the presence of the gas, the sperm cells become nonmotile. It is possible that the gas acts as a narcotic, immobilizing the cells and reducing their metabolic rates. This may account for their ability to survive at room temperature for a long time.

Dimorphism of Sperm

The perennial attempts to separate, mechanically, the X- and Y-bearing sperm cells, as a means of controlling sex determination, appear justified on the assumption that X-bearing cells are heavier than the cells bearing the smaller Y chromosome. Measurements of a large number of sperm cells of many species of mammals have provided evidence of a dichotomous distribution of the length of the heads. These measurements, however, may not be valid; for, even though the dichotomy may be real, it may be due to the measurement of sperm cells of varying ages and stages of maturity.

More recently, Lindahl in Sweden has attempted to separate sperm according to size by ultracentrifugation. He found, unfortunately, that at lower speeds no separation is effected (as shown by an equality of the sexes in litters of young born from mothers inseminated by sperm thus treated), and that at higher speeds the sperm cells suffer so much damage that they lose their ability to fertilize eggs.

In spite of repeated claims that the two types of sperm can be separated by electrophoresis, no satisfactory demonstration has ever been made that young of predominantly one sex or the other are produced from sperm cells that aggregate at the cathode or the anode of the electric field to which they are exposed.

SUMMARY

The important components of the testes are the seminiferous tubules, which secrete sperm, and the Leydig cells of the interstitial tissue, which secrete androgen. It can be easily demonstrated that LH alone (except in chickens) can stimulate Leydig cells to secrete androgen, but for complete spermatogenesis FSH, LH, and probably androgen are needed. Androgen maintains the secondary male sex characters (beard, voice, horns, comb, pugnacity) and the accessory glands (prostate, seminal vesicles, Cowper's glands). The secretions of the accessory glands are essential components of semen. A brief outline of sperm morphology is given, and the relation of abnormal sperm to fertility is discussed. Of the many millions of sperm ejaculated, only a few hundred reach the oviduct, and only a few reach the vicinity of the ovum.

REFERENCES

E. Blom and N. O. Christensen. 1947. "Studies on pathological conditions in the testes epididymis and accessory sex glands in the bull." *Skand. Veterinartidskrift.*

R. I. Dorfman and R. A. Shipley. 1956. *Androgens: Biochemistry, Physiology and Chemical Significance.* Wiley (New York).

C. W. Hooker. 1944. "The postnatal history and function of the interstitial cells of the testes of the bull." *Am. J. Anat.,* **74:**1.

T. Mann. 1954. *The Biochemistry of Semen.* Wiley (New York).

C. R. Moore. 1944. "Hormone secretion by experimental cryptorchid testes." *Yale J. Biol. Med.,* **14:**203.

R. Ortavant. 1956. "Autoradiographie des cellules germinales du testicule de bélier: durée des phénomènes spermatogénétiques." *Arch. Anat. Microscopique Morphol. Exp.,* **45:**1.

V. A. Rice, F. N. Andrews, E. J. Warwick, and J. E. Legates. 1957. *Breeding and Improvement of Farm Animals,* 5th ed. McGraw-Hill (New York).

H. Selye. 1943. "Factors influencing development of scrotum." *Anat. Record,* **85:**377.

C. D. Turner. 1955. *General Endocrinology,* 2nd ed. Saunders (Philadelphia).

A. Walton. 1955. "Sexual behavior" in *Progress in the Physiology of Farm Animals,* Vol. II. Butterworth (London).

8

The Germ Cells

The importance of the egg was recognized by the ancients, who asserted: "Every living thing comes from an egg." But the realization that the egg, like all living things, goes through periods of youth, adulthood, and senility is recent. The implications of this seemingly obvious statement are important; they will be discussed and documented at some length because at least part of the high embryonal mortality that is treated in Chapter 11 is probably due to the inability of eggs fertilized during senility to complete intrauterine life normally. The male germ cell also ages, but the experimental evidence for the aging of the sperm is not as plentiful as that for the aging of the ovum.

The Viability and Aging of Germ Cells

Before we present the data, a few remarks are needed to introduce the subject. Reference to Table 4-2 (p. 124) will remind us that in subprimate mammals the period of sexual receptivity lasts from a few hours (rats and mice) to several days (pigs and mares). When left to themselves, males and the females in heat pair off and copulate frequently and repeatedly. Rats copulate almost incessantly during heat, although ejaculation does not occur at each intromission. Under domestication the breeder has taken over the task of determining when, during the sexual receptivity of the female, the single mating or artificial insemination shall take place. If insemination (either natural or artificial) occurs early in heat, the sperm arrive in the oviduct before ovulation and have to wait for the arrival of the egg. If insemination occurs late in heat, the reverse is true: the egg is waiting for the sperm, which may have to ripen in the oviduct before it is capable of penetrating the egg.

Nonprimates have the advantage of having periods of sexual receptivity, which synchronize, roughly, the arrival of the germ cells in the place of their union. Primates do not have peaks of sexual receptivity; and, unless attempts are made to synchronize copulation and ovulation, copulation occurs without regard to the time of ovulation. Thus very young eggs may be fertilized by senile sperm, or aged eggs may be penetrated by sperm of varying ages. In view of these considerations, the question arises whether the age of germ cells bears any relation to their ability to form zygotes and to complete embryonal development to parturition.

In an experiment in which data were obtained to shed light on this question, female guinea pigs were artificially inseminated at various times after ovulation. Thus it was possible to study the fate of ova that were allowed to age for various periods from eight to thirty-two hours after ovulation before the sperm had an opportunity to fertilize them. The results of this experiment (Table 8-1) show that guinea pig eggs

Table 8-1.   Number of impregnations, normal pregnancies, and abnormal pregnancies, and litter size, following insemination before and after ovulation of guinea pigs

TIME OF INSEMINATION	NUMBER OF FEMALES INSEMINATED	PERCENTAGE OF		AVERAGE LITTER SIZE	PERCENTAGE OF ABNORMAL PREGNANCIES
		IMPREGNATIONS	NORMAL PREGNANCIES		
During heat*	77	83	88	2.6	12
8 hours after ovulation	78	67	66	1.7	34
14 hours after ovulation	79	56	27	1.6	73
20 hours after ovulation	94	31	10	1.3	90
26 hours after ovulation	86	7	0	0.0	100
32 hours after ovulation	48	0	0	0.0	0

SOURCE: After Blandau and Young. 1939. *Am. J. Anat.*, 64:303.
* Control group.

lose their ability to be fertilized gradually; as late as fourteen hours after ovulation 56 percent of the eggs could still be fertilized; even as late as twenty hours after ovulation 31 percent of them could still be fertilized. The important conclusion to be drawn from these data, however, is that aged eggs that had been fertilized did not develop to the stage where they could form embryos capable of completing development and being born. As the age of the eggs at fertilization increased, the size of the litter decreased and the number of abnormalities increased. Similar data have been obtained for rats and cows (Table 8-2).

Table 8-2. Effects of aging of the ovum in cattle

HOURS FROM OVULATION TO INSEMINATION	FERTILITY OBSERVED AT 2–4 DAYS		FERTILITY OBSERVED AT 21–35 DAYS	
	NO. OF COWS	PERCENT WITH FERTILE OVA	NO. OF COWS	PERCENT WITH NORMAL EMBRYOS
2–4	4	75	4	75
6–8	4	75	10	30
9–12	5	60	13	31
14–16	4	25	8	0
18–20	5	40	6	17
22–28	1	0	11	0

SOURCE: From G. R. Barrett, 1948. "Time of insemination and conception rates in dairy cows." Ph.D. Thesis, Univ. of Wisconsin.

The fact that eggs retain their ability to be fertilized without retaining the ability to continue normal embryonal development is of great importance. This fact is further emphasized if we compare the time of insemination with the propotrion of cows that conceive (Table 8-3).

Table 8-3. Effect of time of insemination in relation to ovulation and fertility in cows*

TIME OF BREEDING	NO. OF COWS BRED	PERCENTAGE OF COWS CONCEIVING FROM ONE SERVICE
Start of estrus	25	44.0
Middle of estrus	40	82.5
End of estrus	40	75.0
6 hours after estrus ended	40	63.4
12 hours after estrus ended	25	32.0
18 hours after estrus ended	25	28.0
24 hours after estrus ended	25	12.0
36 hours after estrus ended	25	8.0
48 hours after estrus ended	25	0.0
Routine breeding	194	63.4

SOURCE: From Trimberger and Davis. 1943. *Univ. Neb. Res. Bul.* 129.
* Cows ovulate fourteen hours after the end of heat.

These data demonstrate two important facts that play an important role in the reproductive efficiency of animals (a topic that will be discussed in greater detail later). First, senility in itself does not prevent an egg from being fertilized, from undergoing cleavage, and even from becoming implanted. Second, fertilization and implantation of eggs do not ensure that they will complete development and give rise to viable young. It is obvious, in fact, that the fertilization of aged eggs leads, at best, to the very early death of the zygote, even before implantation. It is probable, however, that fertilized senile eggs implant frequently but temporarily, and that they are aborted sometime during the gestation period.

These nonviable embryos resulting from the fertilization of aged eggs may be the cause of the low fertility that is conspicuous in some animals, especially in the monotocous ones. The fertilization rates of both mares and cows are 80–85 percent, but only 40–50 percent of the females that conceive produce living young. In a group of women who did not practice contraception, according to Pearl (1939), 254 copulations were required, on the average, to produce a living offspring. More recent and more optimistic studies find that only about 30 percent of women conceive at the first opportunity after exposure.

It is obvious that most senile eggs, if fertilized, produce zygotes that die before or shortly after implantation; the fate of the exceptions—zygotes that arise from senile eggs but do not die *in utero*—remains unknown. They may continue to be handicapped in postnatal life by the fact that they originated from senile germ cells, but convincing data on this point are lacking.

Similar, but less overwhelming, evidence is available for male gametes.

In mammals, the lifespan of sperm—and therefore the time during which they are able to fertilize eggs—is probably no longer than about twenty-four hours. Sperm live the longest time in the cervix and the oviducts and the shortest time in the vagina and the uterus. Some bats copulate in the fall but do not ovulate until spring. This fact was interpreted to mean that sperm remain alive in the reproductive tract of bats for several months, lying in wait for the arrival of the egg. According to more recent evidence, however, bats copulate in the spring as well as in the fall, and fertilization is accomplished by the fresh sperm ejaculate at the spring copulation. The only cases of very prolonged survival of sperm in the female reproductive tract have been recorded in birds, bees, and sea turtles. Sperm has been shown to survive for as long as thirty days after ejaculation in the chicken, for seven years in the queen bee, and for a few years in the turtle. In mammals, spermatogenesis occurs at the lower scrotal temperature, and sperm are ejaculated into an environment of higher body temperature, where they retain fertilizing ability for some hours. In chickens, however, sperm are formed in an environment of high temperature and are ejaculated into an environment of equally high temperature, where they live for many days. Whether this difference is due to secretions of the avian oviduct or to other causes remains to be determined. As far as the ability of the two types of sperm to survive *in vitro* is concerned, the situation is completely reversed. Mammalian sperm may be made to live *in vitro* for several days, but avian sperm die *in vitro* within a few hours after ejaculation. One feels intuitively that a significant clue to the physiological peculiarities of sperm may lie in the differences between avian and mammalian sperm cited here, but the meaning of these differences remains obscure.

The first evidence of the deleterious effect of aged sperm on the survival of the zygote was obtained in birds. Chickens were permitted to mate at will up to a certain date, after which the males were removed. The eggs laid after the removal of the males had therefore been fertilized by sperm that were, on the average, one day older on each succeeding day. The eggs were incubated, and the fertilization and hatching rates of the eggs laid each day were determined (Nalbandov and Card, 1943). The data obtained in this way showed that senile sperm retained some ability to fertilize eggs, but that hatchability decreased significantly faster than fertility. There was also a strong negative correlation between the age of sperm and the age of embryos at death. These data show that senile sperm do not lose their ability to fertilize eggs, but that fertilization, as such, is no assurance that embryonal development will be completed. Not only do eggs fertilized by senile sperm die, but they die at an increasingly earlier age as the sperm activating them become more senile. The data cited were obtained on semen aged *in vivo;* confirming evidence has also been obtained for avian semen aged *in vitro.*

Similar data have recently been obtained for bull semen that had been diluted, stored for various periods after ejaculation, and used for artificial insemination (Table 8-4). The proportion of cows that failed

Table 8-4.   Effect of storing diluted bull semen on pregnancy one month and five months after insemination

INSEMINATIONS AND PERCENT PREGNANCIES	AGE OF SEMEN AT INSEMINATION (days after ejaculation)				
	0	2	3	4	5+
No. of inseminations	12	726	756	970	56
% pregnant at 30 days	58	67	63	54	57
% pregnant at 150 days	50	57	51	42	39
% difference	8	10	12	13	18

Source: From Salisbury and others. 1952. *J. Dairy Science,* 35:256.

to remain pregnant increased with increasing age of the semen. It is concluded, from these and similar data, that the increasing embryonal mortality, which presumably resulted in abortion between 30 and 150 days of pregnancy, is due to the use of sperm of increasing senility.

The evidence presented in this section convinces us that germ cells do age and thus become physiologically less vigorous and that their senility may be one of the main causes of embryonal mortality in both mammals and birds. The changes due to aging may be either physical or chemical. Hartwig (1912) found that frog sperm treated with methylene blue, chloral hydrate, or strychnine changed their physiological constitution to such an extent that eggs fertilized by them formed only pathological larvae that were unable to complete development. Though the physiology of germ-cell gerontology remains unknown and unexplored, its existence should be constantly kept in mind. It is particularly important to time matings or inseminations in domestic animals and man in such a way as to minimize the deleterious effects of aging on eggs and sperm cells.

The Transport of Eggs and Sperm

Fertilization in all the mammals thus far studied occurs in the oviduct (not in the uterus, as is occasionally stated). Ever since Leeuwenhoek first saw sperm under the microscope, great significance has been attached to the fact that sperm are equipped with motile flagella. This fact seemed to make it mandatory to assume that sperm avail themselves of their locomotive power to swim from the place of their deposition to the meeting place with the egg. Even today, despite overwhelming evidence to the contrary, this notion has not been completely dispelled.

The latest evidence shows that sperm transport from the vagina to the oviducts takes only a very few minutes. This has been demonstrated in rats, sheep, guinea pigs, and cows and probably holds for all the species that have not been specifically investigated. The transport through the length of the female duct system is much too rapid to be accounted for by the locomotor ability of the sperm themselves. Furthermore, completely inert substances, such as dead sperm or particles of India ink, reach the oviducts as rapidly as live sperm. These facts led to the assumption that uterine contractions were involved in transporting the sperm through the duct system.

There is no complete agreement with regard to the spontaneous activity of the uterus during the cycle. In women and in certain other mammals there seems to be a peak of contractility during the follicular phase and especially shortly before ovulation, the contractility then gradually subsiding during the luteal phase (Reynolds, 1949). In contrast, no such differences were seen in cows (Hays and VanDemark, 1953), uterine motility being about the same in cows in heat and during the luteal phase. In both cattle and sheep, sperm reach the oviduct as fast during the luteal phase as they do during heat. Because it is known that oxytocin is released during the physical or psychological sexual excitation of females, it appears probable that sperm transport is accomplished by the action of oxytocin on the uterine muscle, which responds by a series of contractions greater than those normally seen in the sexually unexcited female. Experimental work leads to the conclusion that the act of mating or insemination causes the release of oxytocin.

Whereas sperm are transported to the oviduct extremely rapidly by muscular contractions of the duct system, the transport of the eggs through the oviduct requires several days. Fertilized or unfertilized eggs are propelled through the oviduct by means of the ciliary beat away from the ovary and toward the uterus. The length of time required to reach the uterus and the degree of development achieved during the journey are shown in Table 8-5. The rate at which eggs travel is not

Table 8-5.   Rate of travel of eggs through oviducts of some mammals

ANIMAL	DAYS SPENT IN OVIDUCT	STATE OF DEVELOPMENT ON ARRIVAL IN UTERUS
Ungulates	3(–4)	4–16 cells
Rat, mouse, rabbit	3	Morula or blastula
Guinea pig	4	8 cells
Ferret	5	16–32 cells
Cat	8	Blastocyst
Dog	10	Blastocyst
Primates	4	16 cells

uniform, three-fourths of the whole time being spent in the uterine half of the oviducts. The rate of descent may depend on the degree of estrogen stimulation. The rapid descent coincides with the time when the female is still in heat and with the period immediately after heat, when the amount of circulating estrogen is presumably greater than it is two or three days after ovulation. Large doses of estrogen, however, have an adverse effect on oviducal motility, the eggs being arrested in the oviducts ("tube locking") and degenerating there. (In constrast, eggs that are prevented from leaving the oviduct by surgical occlusion do not degenerate but proceed to form blastocysts.)

Fertilization

Even though it can no longer be doubted that sperm are transported through the female duct system by uterine and oviducal contractions and that some of them reach the oviduct within a few minutes after being deposited in the vagina, it remains unknown whether the first sperm to arrive can fertilize the egg. This becomes all the more problematic in view of the work of Chang (1951) and Austin (1951), who found in rabbits and rats, respectively, that sperm must be exposed for at least six hours to tubal, uterine, or vaginal secretions before they acquire the ability to fertilize eggs. This phenomenon, called "capacitation," is well illustrated in Table 8-6. Though previous attempts to

Table 8-6. Capacitation of rabbit sperm deposited in oviducts at various times before or after ovulations

TIME OF INSEMINATION RELATIVE TO OVULATION	HOURS	NO. OF RABBITS	NO. OF OVULATIONS	OVA RECOVERED	
				TOTAL	PERCENT FERTILIZED
After	2	5	58	40	0
After	1	2	14	10	0
Before	2	5	42	31	0
Before	4	5	39	34	6
Before	6	4	49	41	78
Before	8	5	50	47	55
Controls					75–100

SOURCE: After Chang. 1951. *Nature*, 168:697.

fertilize eggs *in vitro* were quite unsuccessful, fertilization of rabbit eggs *in vitro* has been achieved by sperm that were recovered from the rabbit oviducts in which they had become capacitated. The nature of the changes that sperm undergo in acquiring fertilizing capacity remains unknown.

Rabbit ova can be easily fertilized *in vitro*, the exposed eggs cleaving normally, and, if transferred into suitably prepared foster mothers, they implant and are carried to term. In one exhaustive study by Dauzier and Thibault, 7,605 ova from 1,954 does were studied and *in vitro* fertilization of 67 percent of the eggs was achieved. Their interesting study has yielded some evidence that the rabbit ovum may be coated with a substance they call "fertilizine," which repels even the capacitated sperm. If the eggs are frequently washed with Locke's solution (in which they are also cultured), fertilizine is removed from the egg surface and sperm penetration can occur within 3–7 hours after exposure. They further postulate that the Fallopian tube normally contains a substance they call "antifertilizine," which counteracts fertilizine and makes ova penetrable to sperm. The data do not completely convince one of the existence of these two substances, and the question arises whether the fertilizability of an egg may not simply depend on its age or physiological maturity.

For unknown reasons eggs from other mammals (sheep, pigs, and cattle) cannot be fertilized *in vitro* as easily and reliably as those of rabbits.

The Transplantation of Ova

Ever since W. Heape, in 1890, succeeded in transplanting fertilized eggs from a rabbit of a small breed into a foster mother of a large breed and obtained living young, this technique has excited the imagination of research workers. The potential uses of the technique appear great, but the difficulties encountered have kept it from becoming as useful as artificial insemination. It was hoped that one could shorten the length of generations of slowly maturing domestic animals by superovulating sexually immature females and transplanting the eggs thus obtained into foster mothers, thus determining the genetic worth of the donor long before it loses its ability to furnish more eggs. It was also hoped that, once genetically valuable females had been found, one could increase enormously the number of their progeny by relieving them of the time-consuming tedium of pregnancy, using them only as egg pro-

Table 8-7. Proportion of transplanted eggs developing into young

SPECIES	NO. OF ANIMALS	NO. OF OVA TRANSPLANTED	NO. OF YOUNG BORN	YOUNG AS PERCENT OF TOTAL OVA
Sheep	18	19	8	42
Rabbits	249	1,478	415	28

SOURCE: Data from Hunter and others, 1955, *J. Agr. Sci.*, 46:143, and Venge, 1950, *Acta Zoologica*, 31.

ducers, while other, genetically less valuable females were used as incubators. Today, in spite of intensive work, the method of ova transplantation remains only a valuable tool for basic biological research; its lack of success in the improvement of breeds has been uniform.

If ova transplants are to be successful, several basic conditions must be met:

1. The number of eggs ovulated must be greater (especially in monotocous species) than at normal ovulation.
2. Either the time of ovulation must be accurately known, or, preferably, ovulation must be made to occur at the convenience of the investigator.
3. The eggs must be obtainable without major surgical invasion of the donor and must be implanted in the recipient without surgery.
4. A recipient female must be in a stage in the reproductive cycle when the transplanted eggs have a good chance of finding a uterine environment favorable for implantation.

Although each of these conditions has been met separately, difficulties have been encountered, especially in larger animals, in making the technique easily applicable. Great individual variability in response to superovulating dosages of gonadotrophic hormone have been detected, so that the number of ovulations obtained in cattle may vary from none to fifty or sixty. Cattle also become refractory after one or two courses of treatment with gonadotrophins (possibly because antihormone is formed), and a long rest period must intervene before cattle ovaries again respond to hormone injections. Efforts to flush eggs from the duct system of cattle without surgical intrusion into the body cavity have also failed. The most reliable method of flushing eggs from cattle oviducts still requires the slaughter of the animals. By this method three calves have been obtained. From smaller animals, such as sheep and rabbits, one can obtain eggs by laparotomizing the female and flushing the eggs from the oviducts. Even in these smaller animals, however, only a small proportion of the transplanted eggs ever result in living young carried to term (Tables 8-7 and 8-8). At the present time there is little hope that ova transplantation will be of any practical significance as a tool in animal improvement, but it can be used to good advantage in studies of maternal influences (see the interesting study of Venge, 1950) and of the effect of the uterine environment on the survival of embryos.

Table 8-8. Success of super-ovulation, recovery of eggs, and rates of fertilization of eggs in ruminants

SPECIES	TREATMENT FOR SUPEROVULATION	NO. OF ANIMALS	AV. NO. OF CORPORA LUTEA	PERCENTAGE OF OVA	
				RECOVERED	FERTILIZED
Cattle	PMS—luteal phase	33	6	38	38
	PMS—follicular phase	15	12	22	44
	AP extract—follicular phase	10	6.5	74	92
	Controls	7	1.0	100	100
Calves*	Conadotrophic hormones	17	15.4	27	6
Sheep	Progesterone, PMS	10	5.1	45	84

SOURCE: Data from Dowling, 1949, *J. Agr. Sci.*, 39:374, Marden, 1953, *ibid.*, 43:381, and Hunter and others, 1955, *ibid.*, 46:143.
* From 29 days to 30 weeks old.

SUMMARY

Germ cells do become senile, and their age is directly related to the survival of zygotes. Eggs lose their ability to survive as embryos before they lose the ability to become fertilized and to start cleaving. Data are given to show that eggs fertilized by senile sperm cells have a lesser chance of completing normal embryonal development than eggs fertilized by young sperm.

Sperm are transported through the female reproductive tract, not by their flagella, but by the hormone-controlled contractions of the female duct system. Sperm cells undergo a period of capacitation in the oviduct before they are able to fertilize an egg.

In vitro fertilization of 60–70 percent and in some experiments even 100 percent of rabbit ova can be accomplished by capacitated sperm. For unknown reasons eggs of other mammals cannot be fertilized *in vitro* as reliably as those of rabbits, even with capacitated sperm.

REFERENCES

C. R. Austin. 1952. "The 'capacitation' of the mammalian sperm." *Nature*, **170**:326.

W. G. Black, L. C. Ulberg, R. E. Christian, and L. E. Casida. 1953. "Ovulation and fertilization in the hormone stimulated calf." *J. Dairy Sci.*, **36**:274.

R. J. Blandau and E. S. Jordan. 1941. "The effect of delayed fertilization on the development of the rat ovum." *Am. J. Anat.*, **68**:275.

J. D. Boyd and W. J. Hamilton. 1952. "Cleavage, early development and implantation of the egg" in Marshall's *Physiology of Reproduction*, Vol. II, 3rd ed. Longmans (New York).

M. C. Chang. 1955. "The maturation of rabbit oocytes in culture and their maturation, activation, fertilization and subsequent development in the fallopian tube." *J. Exp. Zool.*, **128**:379.

D. F. Dowling. 1950. "Problems of the transplantation of fertilized ova." *J. Agr. Sci.*, **39**:374.

R. J. Fitzpatrick. 1957. "On oxytocin and uterine function" in *The Neurohypophysis*. Academic Press (New York).

R. L. Hays and N. L. VanDemark. 1953. "Effects of oxytocin and epinephrin on uterine motility in the bovine." *Am. J. Physiol.*, **172**:557.

G. L. Hunter, C. E. Adams, and L. E. Rowson. 1955. "Inter-breed ovum transfer in sheep." *J. Agr. Sci.*, **46**:143.

W. G. R. Marden. 1953. "The hormone control of ovulation in the calf." *J. Agr. Sci.*, **43**:381.

S. R. M. Reynolds. 1949. *Physiology of the Uterus*, 2nd ed. Hoeber (New York).

G. W. Trimberger and H. P. Davis. 1943. "Conception rate in dairy cattle by artificial insemination at various stages of estrus." University of Nebraska Research Bulletin 129.

O. Venge. 1950. "Studies of the maternal influence on the birth weight in rabbits." *Acta Zool.* (Stockholm), **31**:1.

W. C. Young. 1953. "Gamete-age at the time of fertilization and the course of gestation in mammals" in *Reproductive Wastage*. Thomas (Springfield, Ill.).

chapter 9

The Young Embryo

After fertilization and the early cleavages of the egg are completed in the oviduct, the young embryo, consisting of from eight to sixteen cells (the blastocyst stage), arrives in the uterus in search of permanent attachment. It is now only a small ball of metabolically very active cells. Because mammalian eggs do not have yolk stores such as those that supply energy for the growth of the young embryos of birds, reptiles, and other lower vertebrates, the early mammalian young must live off the environment in which it finds itself—the uterus. During the first days after its arrival in the uterus, the embryo is completely dependent upon uterine secretions for its energy. The uterine glands secrete "uterine milk," which is composed of protein, fat, and traces of glycogen. It is from uterine milk and the cellular debris from the epithelial lining of the uterus that the young embryo derives its sustenance until it implants itself and forms permanent placental connection with the maternal circulatory system.

Spacing and Uterine Migration

An interesting problem, which remains unsolved, is the mechanism that operates in the uterine horns of polytocous mammals and governs the spacing and distribution of the embryos in the uterus. Consider the problem: the embryos usually enter the uterine horn as a loose clump; as they are propelled inside the uterine lumen by irregularly myometrial contractions, one of them finds a suitable spot near the oviducal end of the uterine horn and remains behind while its mates continue on their way; other embryos drop out further along the lumen until all have found suitable endometrial folds in which to implant themselves. The distances between implantation sites are approximately equal, being shorter when there are many embryos to be accommodated than when there are few. Moreover, if more embryos find themselves in one uterine horn than in the other, the excess migrate from the one to the other. (This, of course, can occur only in females in which the two uterine horns are connected and not separated as they are in females that have duplex uteri.) The phenomenon is especially well illustrated by the pig, in which the left ovary functions with significantly greater frequency than the right. The frequency of ovulations in the two ovaries and the distribution of fetuses between the two horns are shown in Table 9-1. Though we do not know why some spots

Table 9-1. Comparison of frequency of ovulation from the two ovaries in sows and distribution of fetuses in the two horns

NUMBER AND PERCENT	CORPORA LUTEA		FETUSES	
	RIGHT OVARY	LEFT OVARY	RIGHT HORN	LEFT HORN
Number	2,289	2,830	1,936	1,932
Percent	44.7	55.3	50.0	50.0

SOURCE: Data from Warwick. 1926. *Anat. Rec.*, 33:39.

in the uterine lumen are attractive for implantation, spacing can be partly explained by the finding that, once a blastocyst becomes implanted, adjacent areas of the endometrium are no longer receptive to other blastocysts. This, of course, does not explain how the uterine lumen knows how many blastocysts it is expected to accommodate, how much space to allot to each of them, and how many of them should be shunted from one horn into the other.

Uterine migration occurs not only in polytocous, but also in monotocous, mammals. Implantations of blastocysts in the horn opposite to the ovary from which the egg or eggs were ovulated have been recorded in sheep (3–50 percent), goats, cattle, and horses, and also in the lower primates, in which it is rare. In rabbits, which have a duplex uterus, transuterine migration cannot occur, but eggs ovulated by one ovary may be picked up by the fimbria of the oviduct on the opposite side. Such external migration occurs in a few animals that have an open fimbria.

Implantation

If the zygote arrives in the uterus in a preblastocyst cleavage stage (Table 8-5, p. 226), it rapidly completes the development into a blasto-

Maternal vessels   Allantoic vessels   Chorionic   Endometrial
                                                   fossa   ridge

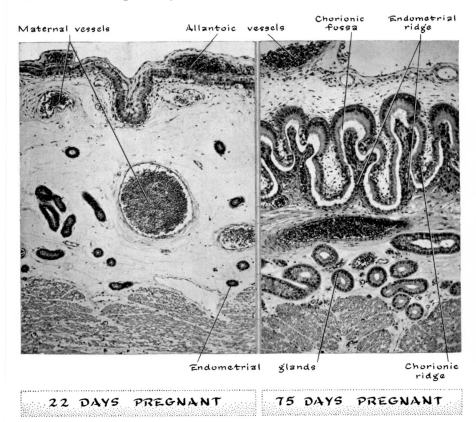

Endometrial   glands   Chorionic
                                          ridge

22 DAYS PREGNANT   75 DAYS PREGNANT

Figure 9-1. *Relation between the allantochorion and the endometrium in the sow early and late in pregnancy. (By permission of Professor E. C. Amoroso, F.R.S.)*

cyst. In ungulates and carnivores, the blastocyst elongates and enlarges until it fills a good part of the uterine cavity; this is known as central implantation. In rodents, the blastocyst remains small and becomes lodged in a fold of the uterine lumen, where it implants itself; this is eccentric implantation. In the guinea pig, insectivores, and man, the blastocyst implants itself interstitially by passing through the uterine epithelium and becoming completely cut off from the uterine lumen.

During its early life in the uterine lumen the blastocyst is unattached and free-floating. In animals in which implantation is eccentric or interstitial, the transition from the free-floating blastocyst to the definitely implanted embryo is rather clear-cut. In man it occurs in 6–8 days; in mice, 5 days; in guinea pigs, 6 days; in rabbits, 7 days; and in cats, 13 days after ovulation. In the mare, the cow, and the ewe, the transition is not so clear-cut. If the uterine horn of the pregnant mare is opened as late as eight weeks after mating, the much enlarged and elongated chorionic sac separates from the uterus quite easily and without tearing either fetal or maternal tissue; complete attachment occurs as late the fourteenth week of gestation. A similar equivocal situation exists in the cow, in which corancular attachment is said to take place as late as day 40 after ovulation. In sheep this happens on day 18. In the sow, blastocysts float free in the uterus until between days 11 and 20 of pregnancy. By day 11 the chorion is in apposition with the uterine epithelium, which by that time has formed irregular ridges into which the chorionic folds mold themselves. According to Corner, the corrugation of the uterine epithelium is helpful in anchoring the chorionic vesicle and making attachment of the embryo possible (see Fig. 9-1).

Placentation

As the blastocyst increases in size, it can no longer absorb enough nutritive material by diffusion, as it does during the early stages of its sojourn in the uterus. Implantation is a step toward the eventual formation of embryonic membranes that give the growing embryo access to the maternal circulatory system. Thus the transition from embryotrophic nutrition, during which the embryo subsists on "uterine milk" (a product of the uterine glands), to hemotrophic nutrition is made. During the hemotrophic stage the placenta (literally, "flat cake") is formed. Mossman characterizes the formation of the placenta as an "intimate apposition or fusion of the fetal organs to the maternal tissues for physiological exchange."

It is not within the scope of this book to provide a detailed discussion of placentation, which is a large, complex, and fascinating subject, and the reader is urged to consult the excellent summary by Amoroso (1952). In animals with centrally implanting blastocysts, there is no

Table 9-2. Classification of types of placentation according to Grosser

TYPE OF PLACENTA	GROSS SHAPE	ANIMALS IN WHICH FOUND (EXAMPLES)
Epitheliochorial	Diffuse	Pig, horse, donkey
Syndesmochorial	Cotyledonary	Sheep, goat, cow
Endotheliochorial	Zonary or discoid	Cat, dog, ferret
Hemochorial	Discoid or zonary	Primates
Hemoendothelial	Discoid or spheroidal	Rat, rabbit, guinea pig

destruction of the surface epithelium of the uterus where the apposition of epithelium and vesicle occurs. In animals with eccentric and interstitial implantation, however, the uterine epithelial cells that are in contact with the trophoblast appear to erode. Shortly after attachment, the organization of placental membranes begins, and the chorion, amnion, and allantois are formed.

The different types of placentae found in mammals can be classified in several different ways, one of which is summarized in Table 9-2 (see also Figs. 9-2 and 9-3). The epitheliochorial and syndesmochorial types fall into the class of "apposed," or "nondeciduate," placentae, in which

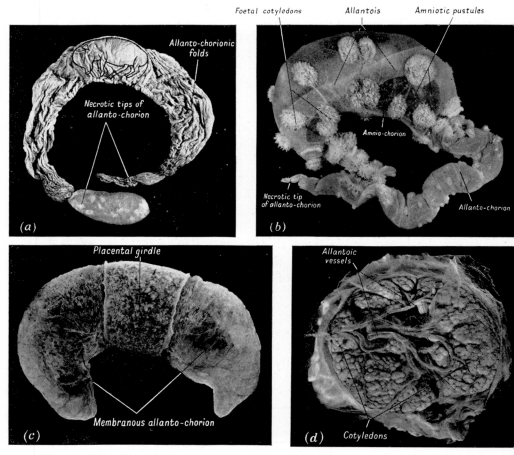

Figure 9-2.   *Types of placenta. (By permission of Professor E. C. Amoroso, F.R.S.)*

a—epitheliochorial-diffuse, from a sow

b—syndesmochorial-cotyledonary, from a cow

c—hemochorial-zonary, from a cat

d—hemoendothelial-spheroidal, from a rabbit

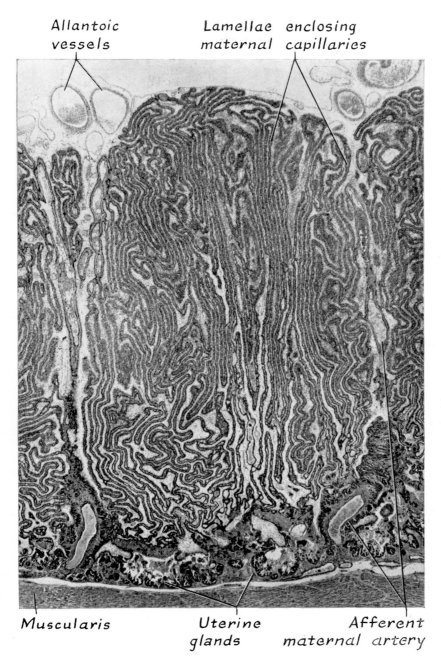

Allantoic
vessels

Lamellae enclosing
maternal capillaries

Muscularis

Uterine
glands

Afferent
maternal artery

Figure 9-3. *Section through the chorio-allantoic placenta and uterine wall of a cat near term. Compare the intricacy of this system with the simplicity of organization in the sow (Fig. 9-1) and the cow (Fig. 9-4). (By permission of Professor E. C. Amoroso, F.R.S.)*

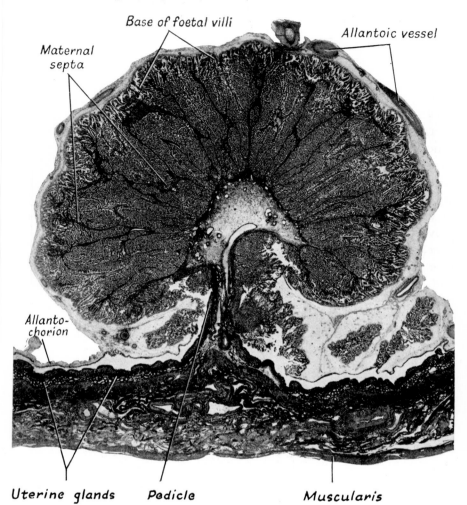

Figure 9-4. *Vertical section through a cotyledon of a cow on day 90 of pregnancy. Note the relation between the maternal tissue and the fetal villi. Compare with Figure 9-3. (By permission of Professor E. C. Amoroso, F.R.S.)*

there is no intimate fusion between the maternal and fetal placentae. At parturition the fetal placenta of these types separates easily, without bleeding or major damage, from the uterine endometrium. The other three types of placentation are "conjoined," or "deciduate." In them an intimate connection is established between fetal and maternal tissues, leading, at parturition, to difficult separation, tearing of maternal tissue, and bleeding. In marsupials and in the mole, the placenta is not shed at parturition but is gradually absorbed.

There appears to be no obvious correlation between the type of placentation and the readiness of females to conceive after parturition. Animals with apposed placentae, in which practically no uterine damage occurs when the placenta is sloughed off at birth, fall into two categories. Mares and sows (provided the latter do not lactate) have post-partum heats and ovulations in 3–10 days after parturition and can conceive if bred; cows have no heats or ovulations for 30–60 days after parturition, and during this interval the uterus involutes. It should be remembered that ruminants have large, specialized corancular areas, at which attachment of the embryo occurs; in the pregnant cow these may reach the dimensions of a hand, but in the nonpregnant they are only about 1–2 centimeters in diameter (Fig. 9-4). The relation between the enormous corancular development in ruminants and the need for their involution, on the one hand, and the absence of heats and ovulations after parturition, on the other hand, is not clear. (See the discussion, on pp. 104–105, of the effect of beads implanted in the uterine horns of sheep during the estrous cycle.)

In contrast, both rats and mice, which have conjoined placentae and suffer severe uterine trauma at parturition, can conceive within twenty-four hours after giving birth to a litter (provided they are not allowed to nurse the young). Similarly, women not infrequently are known to conceive from one to three weeks after giving birth to a child at term. It is possible, of course, that the job of repairing the damage inflicted on the uterus by placentation is greater in imagination than in reality and that the repair is easily accomplished by a vigorous organism in a short time.

Nutrition of the Embryo

Both the mare and the pig have epitheliochorial placentation, and in both of them embryotrophe continues to play an important role in that the uterine milk secreted by uterine glands furnishes a good share of the nutrients that diffuse through the placental membranes and enter the fetal circulation. In advanced pregnancy in these species, however, and throughout pregnancy in the species with other types of placentation, the nutrients must come from the maternal circulatory system and pass through the placenta into the fetal circulation.

The sheep fetus weighs about 1,000 grams at 80 days and 8,000 grams at 140 days of gestation; the rabbit fetus weighs less than 1 gram at 16 days and 64 grams at term (32 days). In view of this extremely rapid growth of the fetus and the corresponding, though less spectacular, in crease in weight of the fetal membranes, the question arises how the conceptus manages to divert so much nutrient material from the maternal circulation to its own use. It is possible that, in all physiologic systems, tissues with a higher metabolic rate have a prior claim to the available nutrients. It is known that the fetal and placental cells have a higher metabolic rate than the cells of the maternal tissues, and that fetal red cells have a greater oxygen-carrying capacity than maternal red cells.

This concept of metabolic gradients caused by a difference in met-abolic rate between mother and fetus has been expanded by Huggett and Hammond (1952) to establish a system of priorities even within the growing fetus. Arranged in the order of decreasing metabolic activity and rapidity of their growth we find the central nervous system, bone, muscle, and fat. This theory is well illustrated in experiments in which pregnant females are fed severely deficient diets: although the mother loses weight, the young increase in weight. It is found, further-more, that the nervous tissue of young gestated under severe dietary restrictions is the least affected (highest metabolic level); after that comes bone; and muscle tissue, with its lower metabolic level, is af-fected most adversely.

Different types of placentae show varying degrees of permeability to minerals, carbohydrates, fats, and proteins. In both pigs and cows (epi-theliochorial and syndesmochorial placentations), the fetal blood shows a significantly higher concentration of blood glucose than the maternal blood. In contrast, in all the other animals studied (dog, rabbit, rat, guinea pig, and man), the fetal blood is always lower in blood sugar than the maternal blood. The significance of these differences is not known, but it is noteworthy that the babies of diabetic women are significantly heavier at birth than the babies of normal women, and that the blood-sugar level of diabetic women is higher than that of normal women. Whether the higher growth rate of the fetus and the ultimately greater size of the infant are the result of the abnormal carbohydrate metabolism of the mother or whether they are due to other causes is not known.

It is now well established that fetal size and the birth weight of the young, up to the "normal" size and weight, depend on the plane of nutrition during the second half of gestation. A low plane of nutrition during the first half of pregnancy does not affect ultimate fetal weight adversely, provided the dietary intake is adequate during the second half. An inadequate plane of nutrition during the second half of pregnancy, or competition for available nutrients between twins in monotocous animals or among very large litters in polytocous animals, reduces the size of the young at birth. Excessive food intake by the mother, however, does not cause fetal growth beyond the "normal" size.

In both rats and sheep, injection of progesterone throughout gestation or during part of it causes an increased size of the embryos. In this connection it should be mentioned that rats maintained on a completely protein-free diet carry gestation to normal completion if they are injected with progesterone throughout. They lose much weight, and the young are much smaller than normal at term, but the size of the litter is not affected.

Placental Permeability to Hormones and Agglutinins

Placental permeability increases with advancing gestation. The placenta is probably permeable to all hormones and certainly permeable to insulin, steroids, and gonadotrophins. The ease of passage of all substances (including vitamins) is determined by their solubility. Steroid hormones pass through the placenta in sufficient quantities to cause enlargement of the fetal end organs that are responsive to them (male accessory glands, vaginal epithelium, mammary glands, etc.). The passage of both steroid and gonadotrophic hormones is beautifully demonstrated by the reproductive tracts and organs of fetal Equidae, in which one can see successive stimulations, first by gonadotrophic hormones, coincident with the peak in PMS secretion, and later by estrogen, when this is secreted in large quantities by the placenta itself (see Fig. 11-3, p. 264).

Somewhat out of context, we mention here the unique case of freemartins. In about eleven out of twelve cases in which a female is gestated as a twin to a male in cattle, the reproductive system of the female is modified to a greater or lesser degree, and she is made completely sterile by intersexuality. This condition was first described in 1792, but it was not until 1917 that Lillie advanced an explanation for the intersexuality of the female. Lillie found that, in all cases of cattle twins of different sex in which an anastomosis of the chorionic vessels occurs, a modification of the female comes about. This is thought to occur because androgen secreted by the testes of the male twin passes directly through the anastomosed chorionic vessels into the sexually undifferentiated female twin and modifies its reproductive system to the point of intersexuality. Though this explanation is still generally accepted, there is some unhappiness over the fact that anastomoses of chorionic vessels occur in other animals, notably in cats and in marmoset monkeys, in which no intersexuality is noted in spite of careful searches for it. Recent work of Ryan may provide a possible explanation for this discrepancy. He found that the bovine placenta is relatively unable to convert androgen to estrogen, while the placenta of the marmoset monkey can do so readily. This fact may explain why no intersexes of the freemartin type are known in this species, even though anastomoses of chorionic vessels are frequently seen.

To return to placental permeability: Young placentae are generally impermeable to bacteria and molecules much beyond 4–5 microns in size. The fact that young are frequently born infected with bacterial diseases is generally ascribed to placental senility or to placental lesions, which are used as a port of entry for organisms and protein molecules. There is an interesting case in which a fetal agglutinogen immunizes the mother and the maternal agglutinin crosses the placenta to the fetus. This is the celebrated case of the Rh factor or the erythroblastosis fetalis, which causes the fetus to die *in utero,* or shortly after birth, of anemia and jaundice. The condition is brought about by a combination of genetic and physiologic factors. The fetus inherits from the father an agglutinogen that is absent from the mother. This fetal Rh factor passes through the placenta (damaged or senile?) and causes the mother to form antibodies to Rh. Maternal iso-agglutinins for Rh return to the fetus and react with fetal Rh agglutinogens, which cause destruction of blood cells and erythroblastosis.

The immunology and genetics of this situation have been worked out only for primates, but they are potentially applicable to all proteins and to other species. Factors similar to the Rh factor may play a role in the fetal mortality of mammals other than primates (see Chapter 10).

SUMMARY

This chapter touches very briefly upon the important and complex problems of the spacing of embryos in the uterus and their migration from one uterine horn to the other. The mechanisms causing the remarkably even spacing of embryos in the uteri of polytocous mammals remain unknown. The processes of implantation and placentation are reviewed, and the fundamental processes of uterine nutrition of the embryo are introduced.

REFERENCES

E. C. Amoroso. 1952. "Placentation" in Marshall's *Physiology of Reproduction,* Vol. II, 3rd ed. Longmans (New York).

B. G. Böving. 1956. "Rabbit blastocyst distribution." *Am. J. Anat.,* 98:403.

J. F. Burger. 1952. "Sex physiology of pigs." *Onderstepoort J.,* Suppl. No. 2, pp. 2–217.

E. L. E. Hafez and G. Pincus. 1956. "Hormonal requirements of implantation in the rabbit." *Proc. Soc. Exp. Biol. Med.,* 91:531.

A. St. G. Huggett and J. Hammond. 1952. "Physiology of the placenta" in Marshall's *Physiology of Reproduction,* Vol. II, 3rd ed. Longmans (New York).

B. L. Warwick. 1926. "Intra-uterine migration of ova in the sow." *Anat. Record,* 33:29.

L. M. Winters, W. W. Green, and R. E. Comstock. 1942. "Prenatal development of the bovine." University of Minnesota Technical Bulletin 151.

chapter 10

Efficiency of Reproduction

The number of young born depends on the number of eggs ovulated, the number of eggs fertilized, the number of fertilized eggs that are capable of cleaving and implanting themselves, and the number of implanted blastocysts that are able to survive through the whole gestation and to be born as live young. A variety of factors, which will be discussed forthwith, play a role in each of these critical events. Some of the factors are of purely maternal concern (such as ovulation rate and uterine environment); others depend on the interaction between male and female germ cells (fertilization); and still others depend on the contribution of the parents' germ plasm to the embryo (lethals or semilethals may cause the death of the embryo). We shall consider these factors and present the available data on each.

Ovulation Rates

We already know that the rate of secretion of gonadotrophic hormone determines the number of follicles ripened and the number of eggs ovulated. Later (Chapter 12) we shall consider the possibility of increasing natural ovulation rates by the use of exogenous hormones. For the present, only natural ovulation rates will be the subject of discussion.

As Table 10-1 shows, the litter sizes of some common domestic animals show great variation within the same species. Some breeds of domestic pigs have an average litter size of about seven (Mangalitza), but others average eleven (Norwegian Land Race). An example of what can be accomplished by genetic selection in a polytocous animal is presented by MacArthur (1949). Starting with a strain of mice weighing 23.2 grams, he began to select for great and small body weight without paying attention to any other characteristic. By the twenty-first

Table 10-1. Litter sizes in some common domestic animals

| ANIMAL | AVERAGE LITTER SIZE OF STRAIN | |
	LOW	HIGH
Pig	6.6*	11.2
Rat	6.1	11.1
Mouse	4.5	7.4
Rabbit	4.0	8.1
Dog	3.0	12.0

* The average litter size of the wild pig is 4.0.

generation he had two strains, one of which weighed 40 grams and the other 12 grams. Since nothing except body weight was being selected for, it was startling to learn that by the twenty-first generation the heavy strain ovulated 14.1 eggs and had a litter size of 10.5 while the light strain ovulated 7.2 eggs and had a litter size of 5.3.

We see that the ovulation rate is genetically controlled in monotocous animals also if we compare the fecundity of different breeds of sheep (Table 10-2), in some of which twins are commoner than single births (Table 10-3), and take note of the twinning rate in the various breeds of domestic cattle (Table 10-4). It is interesting to speculate on the way the genes bring about these effects. The genetic differences noted are probably due to an increased rate of secretion of gonadotrophic hormone, but this cannot be the only effect produced by genetic selection, for a higher ovulation rate alone does not necessarily result in a greater litter size. Harmonious interplay of all the hormones concerned with reproduction is necessary for high rates of implantation and embryonal survival. MacArthur, in his experiment on mice, increased body weight, growth rate, and prolificacy simultaneously by selecting for only one character: body size. Because this characteristic is controlled by another

Table 10-2. Fecundity of sheep

BREED	LAMB CROP (percent)	BREED	LAMB CROP (percent)
Cheviot	89.1	Suffolk	144.3
Scottish Blackface	93.1	Corriedale (Canadian)	146.0
Karakul	110.0	Shropshire	162.0
Corriedale (U.S.)	118.0	Leicester	163.0
American Shropshire	126.2	East Frisian Milk Sheep	205.1
Dorset	127.4	Romanov	238.0
Lincoln	138.9		

SOURCE: After Adsell. 1946. *Patterns of Mammalian Reproduction.*

Table 10-3. Illustration of greater fecundity of ewes from multiple births of the Romanov breed

EWES BORN OF	AVERAGE LAMBS PRODUCED BY THEM
Singles	2.17
Twins	2.36
Triplets	2.63
Quadruplets	3.01

SOURCE: From Lopyrin. 1940. *Sovetskaia Zootechnika*, 7:88.

pituitary hormone (somatotrophin), the question arises whether, by selecting for the rate of secretion of one hormone, one speeds up the functioning of the pituitary gland as a whole. This possibility is supported by the data shown in Table 10-4, which deals with the rate of twinning in domestic cattle, and in Table 10-2, which deals with fecundity in sheep. Table 10-4 shows that the breeds with the highest twinning rate are, in general, the greatest milk producers and are also the heaviest breeds. In Table 10-2 the two breeds showing the highest twinning rate are breeds that have been selected for high milk production. It seems, therefore, that selection proceeded simultaneously for rate of secretion of growth hormone, thyrotrophic hormone, prolactin, and gonadotrophic hormone, even though the original intention was to select for only one trait—say, high milk yield. The low twinning rate of beef cattle does not necessarily upset these speculations, for their genetic selection was probably in the direction of an entirely different endocrine environment from that, for instance, of Holstein cattle. Similar relations roughly hold for other species, such as dogs and rabbits, in which there is a good correlation between body size and prolificacy. It would be interesting to test the possibility of combining small body size with large litter size, or vice versa, and thus demonstrating that genetic selection for more rapid secretion of one hormone does not necessarily have to be coupled with the rapid secretion of other pituitary hormones.

Table 10-4. Rate of twinning in domestic cattle

Percentage of twins in Swedish Red and White cattle	1.85	Percentage of twins in Ayrshires	1.62
Percentage of twins in Frisian cattle	3.35	Percentage of twins in Jerseys	1.03
Percentage of twins in Guernseys	2.78	Percentage of twins in beef cattle	0.44

SOURCE: Compiled from the literature.

Effect of Age on the Ovulation Rate

The ovulation rate is significantly affected by age. As Marshall observed many years ago, the ovulation rate, starting from adolescent sterility, rises rather rapidly to its highest point and gradually falls with advancing age to senile sterility. This generalization appears to apply to many of the animals studied. A few examples of the relation between ovulation rate and age follow.

Less than 0.5 percent of Negro and white human mothers seventeen years old give birth to twins. In Negroes thirty-seven years old the proportion of twin births rises to 2.0 percent; in whites of that age it is 1.3 percent. These are statistically significant differences.

In pigs, two separate effects of age are noted. At the third and fourth heats after puberty, ovulation rates are significantly higher than at the first and second. After the fourth or fifth cycle the ovulation rate becomes stable. The second effect of aging shows up after the females have gone through one or more pregnancies. In the second pregnancy pigs produce 0.68 more young than in the first. The effect of the age of dams on their prolificacy is shown in Table 10-5.

Table 10-5. Relation between parity and prolificacy in pigs

No. of litter	1	2	3	4	5	6	7	8	9
Excess of young over first litter	0.0	0.68	1.36	1.58	1.90	1.92	1.89	1.71	1.45

SOURCE: Data from Lush and Molln. 1942. USDA Tech. Bul. 836.

It will be noted that prolificacy reaches its peak with the fifth litter, remains unchanged until the seventh litter, and then declines slightly to the ninth litter. The increase in reproductive efficiency seems to be an effect, not of age, but of previous reproductive experience. This is brought out by the finding (Asdell, 1941) that sows bred for the first time late in life produced about three pigs per litter less than sows bred at the normal time. Similarly, rats bred very early in life produced an average of 5.8 young per litter, those bred at the normal time 6.2, and those bred for the first time late in life 4.9. These and other experiments on sheep, rabbits, and guinea pigs support the data presented in detail for the pig and emphasize the fact that the increased prolificacy of polytocous females of increasing parity is probably not a function of age (or of greater body weight) but depends primarily on previous reproductive experience. It is also a well-established fact (and a vexing one for the commercial egg producers) that pullets first coming into production lay eggs which are significantly smaller than those which the same pullets will lay two or three weeks after the initial egg. The size of the finished egg is largely determined by the size of the ovum ovulated, and the increase in the size of the ovum cannot be accounted for by increasing body size of the pullet.

It is possible that, while acquiring "reproductive experience," animals find the best adjustment of the neuroendocrine niveau, which, as we emphasized earlier, involves all the glands. Thus, the proper adjustment of the rate of function of the thyroids, adrenals, pancreas, etc. may require trial-and-error periods during the time when the organism is first exposed to the new experience of producing ova, of gestating, or of lactating. These are all situations sufficiently different from each other to require a readjustment of the neurohumoral feedback system to bring all the glands involved into proper and optimal interrelation with each other.

The data shown in Table 10-6 further illustrate the effect of age on

Table 10-6.   Effect of age on reproductive efficiency of rabbits

			AVERAGE NUMBER			
TIME OF BREEDING	NO. OF DOES	EGGS SHED	ATROPHIED BEFORE 10TH DAY, OR UN-FERTILIZED	ATROPHIED AFTER 10TH DAY	NORMAL YOUNG	PERCENT NORMAL YOUNG
First bred at early age	12	10.2	3.9	0.8	5.5	55
First bred at 20 months	19	10.2	3.8	2.6	3.6	36

SOURCE: From Hammond. 1953. *Zootecnica e Veterinaria*, pp. 3–8.

prolificacy and suggest that, in rabbits at least, the effect is due to increased intrauterine mortality during the second part of gestation in older mothers.

A perfect example of the phenomenon discussed above, and of the trajectory of reproductive performance mentioned in the opening paragraph of this section, is found in Pearl's ewe, whose amazing reproductive record is shown in Table 10-7. The decrease in fecundity toward the end of the reproductive life of this unique female, as well as that

Table 10-7.   Trajectory of reproductive performance as it is affected by
               age

Reproductive year	1	2	3	4	5	6	7	8	9	10	11	12	13	14	15	16	17	18	19
No. of lambs*	1	1	2	3	3	3	3	3	3	2	2	2	2	2	2	1	1	0	0

SOURCE: From Pearl. 1913. *Science*, 37:226.
* Total: 36 lambs.

shown by the data on pigs cited earlier, seems to apply to monotocous as well as to polytocous species.

That the nutritive state has an important relation to fecundity has been recognized for many centuries. General malnutrition, as well as specific deficiencies, such as that of certain vitamins (B, E), is known to impair or to stop reproduction completely, but mild restrictions only impair reproductive efficiency. In general, when low nutritive states are improved, the ovulation rate rises. This is probably the reason why wild animals are usually more prolific in captivity, if they reproduce at all. Experiments on domesticated animals have shown, in the majority of cases, that improved nutrition improves prolificacy. The best-known example of this is the "flushing" of sheep, the ovulation rate and the rate of twinning being significantly increased by the practice of feeding ewes more intensely shortly before the onset of the breeding season. In swine restricted energy intake (about 70 percent of normal) causes a lowered ovulation rate, but it also usually reduces embryonal mortality. For practical purposes it may be advisable to feed pigs a high-energy ration soon after mating. Thus, the intensive feeding before breeding should increase ovulation rate, while the reduced energy intake should insure a reduced embryonal mortality during gestation.

According to experiments conducted at Cornell, dairy heifers on a low plane of nutrition reached sexual maturity (as measured by first heat and ovulation) at 65 weeks of age, those on a medium plane at 47 weeks, and those on a high plane of nutrition at 37 weeks.

Restricted feeding of males (boars and bulls), even to the point of causing distinct retardation in growth, has no significant effect on their fertility even though the total volume of semen produced by boars on 60-percent *ad libitum* feeding is significantly lower than the volume produced by full-fed boars.

The effects of other factors, such as light and temperature, have already been discussed in Chapter 3 (breeding seasons). The modification of ovulation rates by hormones will be discussed in Chapter 12.

Fertilization Rates

The fertilization of ovulated eggs obviously depends on the meeting of germ cells in the oviduct at a time when sperm and eggs are able to fertilize and to be fertilized. We have already seen what happens when either of the germ cells is allowed to age (Chapter 8), and we shall consider here only the optimal situation, in which aging is avoided by synchronization of ovulation and insemination. This situation exists only in animals in which psychological heat is so short that neither of the germ cells has to wait for the arrival of the other. This condition is met only in animals whose frequency of mating is not restricted (most wild animals, laboratory animals, chickens, and sheep). Induced ovulators have an ideal timing device in this respect: ovulation depends on mating, and hence the sperm arrive in the oviduct at the best time in relation to ovulation.

If the timing is proper and adequate quantities of viable sperm are present, the fertilization rates of all polytocous animals approach 100 percent. In rabbits, guinea pigs, rats, and mice, the rates rarely drop below 95 percent, according to most studies, the average for the species named being 98.6 percent. In pigs, also, fertilization rates are very high, and, if individuals in which none of the eggs is fertilized are excluded, the rate approaches 100 percent. If all females are considered, the fertilization rate of pigs ranges from 85 to 95 percent.

At this point, a word of caution is in order. It is known that in swine and in other mammals, unfertilized ova frequently fragment, often showing such perfectly "normal" clearage patterns that even an experienced observer may conclude that he is viewing normally cleaving ova. To what extent such "normally" fragmenting ova contribute to the impression that fertilizability in pigs approaches 100 percent remains unknown. The presence of sperm in the zona pellucida can not be taken as proof that the ovum is cleaving normally because sperm have been found in the zonas of eggs that did not cleave at all as well as in eggs that were obviously undergoing disorderly fragmentation. This observation underscores the necessary precaution that each egg be examined carefully under the microscope, with special attention to the orderliness of cleavage planes. The presence of many disorderly cleaving eggs, even if the others show orderly cleavage, should raise the suspicion that the whole lot may be undergoing fragmentation rather than normal division.

In monotocous females the story is somewhat different. The species that have been studied most intensively—cows and sheep—show fertilization rates varying from 60 to 85 percent, the majority of workers finding a figure below 80 percent. No such figures are available for primates or horses, but it is probable that the same situation exists in these monotocous species. There is no obvious explanation for this difference between monotocous and polytocous females. The low fertilization rate of monotocous animals may be due, at least in part, to a lowered fertility of the males.

Loss of Eggs and Embryonal Mortality

Ever since it was established that each follicle produces one egg (leaving the possibility of multiovular follicles out of consideration for the present), comparisons have been made between the number of eggs ovulated and the number fertilized, the number of embryos implanted and the number of young born. Such comparisons are not easily made in one individual, but they can be made in groups of females provided enough of them are available to permit statistical treatment and provided the experimental design makes such comparisons valid. A common method consists of sampling one group of females either by laparotomy or at autopsy within two or three days after breeding. At that time, usually, all the eggs can be recovered by flushing of the oviduct with a few drops of saline solution. The eggs can be counted and examined for signs of fertilization under low-power magnification. As a rule, and especially in the larger animals, the number of eggs recovered corresponds to the number of corpora lutea counted in the ovaries. Thus it is possible to determine the average rates of ovulation and fertilization.

The time at which the second group of females should be sampled will depend on the kind of comparison desired by the investigator. If an estimate of early embryonal mortality is wanted, the sampling of the second group can be made shortly after the females have gone beyond the first expected heat after breeding. This timing is desirable because it eliminates the females that did not conceive at the previous mating. Comparison between the number of embryos found in the second group and the number of fertilized eggs found in the first group provides an estimate of early embryonal mortality. Modifications of this method can be used for estimates of reproductive efficiency during different phases of gestation. Most of the information to be discussed here was obtained by the method described.

It has already been pointed out that the fertilization rate of litter bearers approaches 100 percent but that the implantation rate and the number of young carried to term, in the great majority, are significantly less than the number of eggs fertilized. The discrepancy between the number of eggs fertilized and the number of embryos found in the uterus varies greatly between the individuals of one species, but it is nearly constant for all polytocous species. Several studies of rats, rabbits, pigs, and other litter bearers have shown that 30–50 percent of the fertilized eggs are lost sometime during gestation. Most of the fetal mortality occurs during the first third of pregnancy, and probably most of the losses occur between fertilization and implantation. One illustration of the situation, taken from work on a large number of litters in pigs, includes the post natal losses as well as those occurring during gestation (Table 10-8). The physiological factors

Table 10-8.   Fate of ova shed by sows during heats at which they were mated

FATE OF OVA	IN SOWS PRODUCING LITTERS (percent)	IN ALL SOWS BRED (percent)
Loss from failure to conceive	. . .	36.4
Loss during gestation	31.3	19.9
Loss at parturition	3.2	2.0
Loss from birth to weaning	22.9	14.6
Live pigs at weaning	42.6	27.1

SOURCE: From Phillips and Zeller. 1941. *Am. J. Vet. Res.* II, 5:439.

responsible for embryonal mortality are not known, but several suggestive leads have been obtained and are worth mentioning.

It was pointed out in another connection that the aging of germ cells leads to increased embryonal mortality. It is quite possible that a large share of the average intrauterine mortality occurs at the expense of the zygotes and embryos that manifested effects of the aging of either germ cell. It is also possible that the females that show a very low embryonal mortality are those in which, the timing being perfect, sperm of maximal vigor fertilized eggs of optimal age. Another factor that is definitely known to increase embryonal mortality is infection, such as brucellosis. In most of the data to be presented here, however, this factor has been excluded or, at least, was not present to the best knowledge of the workers.

Data presented by Hammond (1921) and in more recent studies show that, among pigs, embryonal mortality is higher in animals with higher ovulation rates. These data should not be interpreted to mean that high ovulation rates are undesirable, for, despite the higher mortality, the group with the high ovulation rate produced one pig more than the group with the lowest ovulation rate and the lowest embryonal mortality (Table 10-9).

Table 10-9.   Relation between number of eggs ovulated and embryonal mortality in pigs

| NO. OF FEMALES | AV. NO. OF CORPORA IN BOTH OVARIES | PERCENT OF EGGS WHICH BECAME | | | NO. OF NORMAL EMBRYOS |
		NORMAL FETUSES	ATROPHIC FETUSES	MISSING OVA	
5	22.6	54.0	14.2	31.9	12.20
5	18.8	64.9	14.9	20.2	12.20
4	16.7	71.6	16.4	11.9	11.96
5	14.8	74.3	10.8	14.9	10.99

SOURCE: After J. Hammond. 1921. *J. Agr. Sci.*, 11:337.

It seems significant that in about 15 percent of the 2,800 reproductive tracts of swine obtained at slaughter the number of corpora lutea corresponded exactly to the number of embryos found in the uterus. Similarly, in about 40 percent of rat pregnancies none of the eggs or embryos is lost. This observation suggests that loss of eggs and embryonal mortality are not inevitable features of pregnancy in polytocous animals. The study of pigs included animals with both high and low ovulation rates, ranging from 10 to 20.5 eggs ovulated, and suggests that under certain, as yet unknown, optimal conditions all the eggs can be fertilized, implanted, and carried nearly to term, regardless of the total number of embryos to be accommodated. In 90 percent of the females that lost some of the eggs or embryos, there was no significant correlation between the number of eggs ovulated and the number of embryos lost. In the group with the highest ovulation rate (more than 20 corpora in the two ovaries), embryonal mortality was 33 percent; in the group with 10–20 corpora, the loss was 35 percent; in the group with less than 10 corpora, the loss was 31 percent. These findings suggest that "crowding" does not contribute to the loss of eggs or to embryonal mortality. Other workers, however (see Perry, 1955), suggest that pigs and other polytocous animals do show a positive correlation between "crowding" and embryonal mortality.

It was pointed out earlier that optimal feeding is known to increase ovulation rates in the animals in which it was studied (pigs and sheep). The same type of feeding, however, also increases embryonal mortality in pigs. It may become practical, eventually, to full-feed pigs in order to take advantage of the effect on the ovulation rate and then to reduce the food intake immediately after conception in order to prevent the undesirable effect of maximal food intake on embryonal mortality.

Attention is called, finally, to the "case of the unfriendly uterine environment," uncovered by Fekete (1947) in mice. A comparison of the normal reproductive performance of two strains of mice, dba and C57 black, is presented in Table 10-10. It is striking that, in spite of a lower ovulation rate, C57 blacks have a bigger litter size than the dba's. These data permit of two obvious interpretations: (1) that dba eggs are less viable; (2) that dba uteri are less hospitable. The latter possibility was tested in a most painstaking manner by the collection and transfer of 5,000 mouse eggs within and between the two strains (Table 10-10). Although the percentage of eggs that developed into

Table 10-10.   Normal reproductive performances of two strains of mice (compare ovulation rate and litter size) and effect of reciprocal ova transplants between these strains on survival of young

STRAIN	AVERAGE NO. OF EGGS PER OVULATION	AVERAGE NO. OF YOUNG PER LITTER	NO. OF LITTERS	EGGS DEVELOPING INTO YOUNG (percent)
dba	8.2	4.8	220	58.3
C57bl	6.7	5.6	236	83.9

STRAIN OF DONOR	STRAIN OF RECIPIENT	TOTAL NO. OF EGGS TRANSFERRED	EGGS DEVELOPING INTO YOUNG (percent)	RECIPIENTS PREGNANT No.	RECIPIENTS PREGNANT Percent	EGGS DEVELOPING INTO YOUNG No.	EGGS DEVELOPING INTO YOUNG Percent
dba	C57bl	1,928	18.3	134	44.7	352	40.3
dba	dba	647	7.1	26	26.0	46	28.9
C57bl	C57bl	600	12.8	33	33.0	77	28.1
C57bl	dba	1,871	11.4	102	34.0	213	30.1

Source: After Fekete. 1947. *Anat. Rec.*, 98:409.

young after transplantation was low (7–18 percent), the data obtained suggest that the dba uteri were equally inhospitable to their own eggs and to those coming from the C57bl strain. In the C57bl uteri, however, a significantly higher proportion of the young from either donor were carried to term. Because of the low rate of conception following transplantation of eggs, it appears desirable to obtain additional data of this type, but the preliminary conclusion that certain intrauterine factors may be conducive to greater embryonal mortality appears justified. What these factors are remains unknown.

Another case that appears to involve unfavorable uterine environment has been encountered in certain cattle that have an embryonal mortality of 52 percent between days 16 and 34 of gestation (Hawk and others, 1955) despite a fertilization rate of about 80 percent—a rate that indicates that there is nothing amiss with the viability and fertilizability of the eggs shortly after ovulation. It is possible, however, that factors other than uterine inhospitability are responsible.

During the remainder of gestation, however, the embryonal mortality of these cattle is only 5–7 percent, and it appears to be spread at random through the remaining 200 days. Similar figures for other mammals show that for most of them the peak of embryonal mortality occurs during the first third of gestation—usually during the first 20–30 days.

Efficiency of reproduction depends, then, on the ovulation rate, the quality of the ovulated eggs, the ability of the eggs to become fertilized and to develop into a viable zygote, and the ability of the uterus to receive and implant the embryos and carry them through pregnancy. The fact that some females are able to turn in a perfect reproductive performance, at least once in their lifetime, is considered significant. The repeatability of such perfect performances cannot be studied, for, without laparotomy, there is no good and simple method of comparing the ovulation rate, fertilization rate, and implantation rate with the litter size of the same female over several pregnancies. It therefore remains unknown whether perfect or nearly perfect records are unique accidents in the reproductive life of females or whether some females are more able than others to produce eggs of high fertilizability and survival ability and to provide them with optimal intrauterine environments. The ability of some females to show perfect reproductive efficiency presents the research worker with a most challenging and important problem and poses the question: If some females can do it, why can't they all?

Embryonal Mortality of Birds. The embryonal mortality of birds appears to be comparable to that of mammals in only two respects: it, too, depends, to some extent, on the fertilization rate and on the aging of sperm cells. Environmental factors such as the temperature of incubation and the humidity make valid comparisons between mammals and birds impossible. Two peaks of embryonal mortality occur during the 21-day incubation of chickens, the birds that have been studied most intensively. The first peak occurs during the second, third, and fourth days of incubation; the second and by far the largest peak occurs during the last two or three days of incubation. Why these particular periods are so critical is not known, but it is assumed that the physiological processes occurring then place the greatest stress on the embryo.

SUMMARY

The rates at which reproductive phenomena occur are controlled by hormones, and the rates at which hormones are secreted are controlled by genes. All hormone-controlled phenomena, such as rate of growth, rate of milk secretion, and rate of ovulation, are therefore subject to genetic selection. This is the basis for the improvement of domestic animals by genetic selection; selection is actually for rates at which glands function, but the results of selection are measured in rate of growth, egg production, etc.

The ovulation rate also depends, to no mean degree, on age ("trajectory of reproductive performance"), previous reproductive experience (parity), and the nutritional state.

Although, in most polytocous animals, the fertilization rate approaches 100 percent, very few females manage to go through gestation without embryonal mortality. About 60–70 percent of all the eggs ovulated result in viable young. The embryonal mortality is due to an "unfriendly" uterine environment, senile eggs or sperm, and, in the pig at least, overfeeding.

REFERENCES

See the end of Chapter 11.

chapter *11*

Pregnancy, Parturition, and Lactation

Preparation of the Uterus for Pregnancy

Pseudopregnancy

We know that during each cycle the uterus undergoes changes in preparation for the possible arrival of a young embryo, and that these changes consist primarily of the progestational proliferation of the uterine glands and the secretion of uterine milk. In females with long cycles there is plenty of time between heats (or menstruations) for the development of the luteal tissue that secretes the progesterone that brings about the progestational uterine changes. But some mammals, such as rats and mice, have very short cycles (lasting four or five days), and in them, during the normal cycle, the luteal phase of the ovary is so short that the uterus does not undergo the changes usually associated with progesterone action. In rats and mice, furthermore, it takes eggs about three days after ovulation to arrive in the uterus. If a rat or a mouse mated and the eggs were fertilized, they would arrive, one might think, in a uterus that was unready for their reception because at that time the female would be hormonally preparing for the onset of the next cycle, with its heat and ovulation. This, however, does not happen, for mating, in rats and mice, causes pseudopregnancy. Pseudopregnancy is characterized by the fact that corpora lutea from the last ovulation are maintained well beyond the time when they would normally have regressed; in some species, in fact, they may be maintained for an interval equal to the normal length of pregnancy. In most animals pseudopregnancy lasts about half the time of the normal pregnancy.

Pseudopregnancy in rats and mice has been shown to follow stimulation of the cervix during copulation. It appears probable that cervical stimulation causes nervous impulses to act upon the hypothalamus, which releases neurohumoral substances that are carried via the pituitary portal system to the anterior pituitary, where they are instrumental in releasing luteotrophic hormone, which is essential to the activation of corpora lutea; but another mechanism, to be discussed later, may be responsible for the continued maintenance of the corpora.

That the mechanism activating pseudopregnancy depends on neural transmission is supported by the following observations: pseudopregnancy can be induced by stimulation of the cervix with a glass rod or with an electrical current (or even by irritation of the nasal mucosa of rats with silver nitrate). Under deep anesthesia rats do not become pseudopregnant after mechanical or electrical stimulation. Neither do they become pseudopregnant if the cervical innervation is destroyed.

In rats and mice, then, pseudopregnancy serves the purpose of holding the next cycle in abeyance and allowing ample time for the preparation of the uterus for the expected implantation. If the mating was infertile and no pregnancy resulted, the corpora of pseudopregnancy wane about twelve days after ovulation, and the estrous cycle is reestablished. During their life the corpora lutea of pseudopregnancy cause an increase in uterine size and a very significant proliferation of the mammary glands, which, in some animals, such as the bitch, may actually lactate. Nest building is also frequently noted toward the end of pseudopregnancy. Thus, except for the fact that there is no conceptus in the uterus of a pseudopregnant animal, the condition is very similar to true pregnancy.

In rats, mice, and hamsters, pseudopregnancy occurs only after copulation (or other cervical stimulation); in other animals it follows ovulation in the absence of mating. The bitch and the vixen, both of

Table 11-1.   Comparison of animals showing pseudopregnancy

SPECIES	TYPE OF OVULATION	DURATION OF PSEUDOPREGNANCY (days)	DURATION OF NORMAL GESTATION (days)
Cat	Induced	30–40	65
Dog	Spontaneous	About 60*	58–63
Fox	Spontaneous	40–50*	52
Ferret	Induced	35–40	42
Mink	Induced	Variable	Variable†
Hamster	Spontaneous	7–13	16–19
Rabbit	Induced	16–17	30–32
Rat	Spontaneous	12–14	22
Mouse	Spontaneous	10–12	19

* Pseudopregnancy follows even without copulation.
† Delayed implantation.

which ovulate spontaneously, automatically undergo pseudopregnancy following every ovulation. In the vixen, pseudopregnancy lasts as long as gestation itself would have lasted, but in the bitch there is considerable variation in the duration of pseudopregnancy, depending on the breed. In the absence of accurate data it appears that in the less "perverted" breeds of dogs (such as the German shepherd) the length of pseudopregnancy equals that of gestation; in the smaller breeds it may last as long, or it may be much shorter, in some breeds lasting only a week or two (Table 11-1). In rabbits and cats, both of which are induced ovulators, the immediate cause of pseudopregnancy is ovulation, not mating. This is seen from the fact that in both these species, in the absence of mating, pseudopregnancy follows an injection of LH, which causes ovulation and initiates the formation of corpora lutea.

Maintenance of Corpora Lutea Without Pseudopregnancy

As we have seen above, in some animals pseudopregnancy automatically follows copulation or ovulation. In others there must be some mechanism that acts, when pregnancy is probable, to maintain the uterus in progestational condition and to prevent subsequent heats or menstruations and ovulations. What this mechanism may be is not yet clear, but the following chain of events may participate in notifying the ovary that the uterus is now pregnant and that the corpora lutea should be maintained. It is probable that the physical presence of embryos in the uterus releases a neural signaling mechanism, which, either directly or via the hypothalamus, causes the release of a luteotrophic substance from the pituitary gland. It has already been pointed out that this luteotrophic substance is prolactin in rats, but what it is in other animals remains to be seen.

That a neural link exists between the uterine lumen and the pituitary gland is demonstrated by the following experiment. If beads are implanted in the uterine lumen of sheep, the length of subsequent cycles is significantly modified. That this modification is mediated neurally is seen from the fact that the cycles remain normal in length if the uterine segment containing the bead is completely denervated. A difficulty in interpreting these results arises because the presence of beads in the uterine lumen shortens the cycle (that is, has a luteolytic effect) if the beads are implanted on about the fourth day of the cycle but prolongs the cycle (that is, has a distinct luteotrophic effect) if the beads are implanted during the late luteal phase (days 8–10 of the cycle). Though these observations demonstrate a neural link between the uterus and the pituitary gland, it remains unclear just how the uterine contents control the life-span of corpora lutea. It seems probable that the presence of a conceptus in the uterus during the late luteal phase sets in motion the events that cause the corpora lutea to persist much longer than they normally would. We have also mentioned that the participation of uterine contents in the control of the release of certain hypophyseal hormones is not restricted to sheep but also operates in cattle and guinea pigs. However, neither the pig nor the rat responds by a modification of the length of the estrous cycle to the presence of foreign bodies in its uterus.

The Role of Hormones in Pregnancy

Though the mechanism involved in maintaining the corpora lutea in pregnant females remains incompletely understood, the general role of progesterone during gestation is well known. Progesterone is essential for keeping the blastocysts alive before implantation, during the time when they are floating free in the uterine lumen. If pregnant females are castrated before implantation, death of the blastocysts is inevitable. Castration after implantation, during the first third or the first half of pregnancy, generally leads, in the majority of species, to resorption of fetuses or to abortion. Some mammals, after this crucial period, can do without the ovaries and their secretions, but others must have the ovaries throughout gestation.

In rats, the ovary is essential throughout the major part of pregnancy; abortion occurs if they are castrated even as late as five or six days before the expected parturition. But rats can be hypophysectomized ten days after conception—according to some reports, even earlier—without aborting. The fact that pregnant rats tolerate hypophysectomy but not castration without aborting suggests that in this species the corpora lutea are the major—perhaps the only—source of progesterone. The pituitary gland may initiate the growth and functioning of the corpora lutea but may not be essential to their continued functioning throughout gestation.

The ovary has been found to be essential throughout pregnancy not only in the rat but also in the opossum, hamster, thirteen-striped ground squirrel, mouse, rabbit, and goat. In the cow, it may not be necessary after the seventh month. Pigs abort if castration is performed before day 90 of the 115-day gestation period. The ewe, bitch, mare, cat, guinea pig, monkey, and woman do not abort after castration if the operation is performed during the second half or, in some species, during the last trimester of gestation. Castration leads to fetal resorption in the majority of viviparous snakes, whether they are castrated early or late in gestation.

Failure of implantation, or abortion, can be prevented in all castrated animals by the administration of progesterone. Rabbits require 1 milligram of progesterone daily for implantation and 2–3 milligrams daily for the remainder of gestation. Pregnancy can be maintained in mice with 1–1.5 milligrams of progesterone; sheep require 5–10 milligrams, goats 10 milligrams, and cows 50–75 milligrams daily. All available evidence shows that pregnancy can be maintained in castrates with progesterone alone but that much smaller amounts of progesterone are needed if small amounts of estrogen also are injected.

In all Equidae, apparently, but certainly in mares, the corpus luteum formed after ovulation of the eggs that were fertilized and implanted degenerates during the early part of gestation and is replaced by "accessory" corpora lutea (Fig. 11-4). These result from the ovulation of follicles that are caused to mature by the secretion of "equine gonadotrophin." The accessory corpora persist until about day 180 of gestation.

The question arises why females of some species continue pregnancy in the absence of corpora lutea whereas others abort soon after removal of the ovaries. The answer apparently lies in the fact that the placenta, as an endocrine organ, certainly secretes estrogen and progesterone and possibly other hormones as well. It is therefore probable that, in ewes, women, and others, the placenta provides the progesterone that is necessary for the maintenance of pregnancy even if the ovaries are removed after implantation has been accomplished. It is inferred that, in rats, goats, and the other species in which abortion occurs in the absence of ovaries, the placenta secretes no progesterone or amounts inadequate to the maintenance of pregnancy. Progesterone has been demonstrated in the placentae of some species (women) and in the blood during the pregnancy of others (ewes), but, because of the difficulty of assaying for progesterone, not enough work has been done to permit authoritative generalizations on the subject of placental secretion of progesterone.

Hormone Levels During Pregnancy

Estrogen and Progesterone

Though it is well established that both estrogen and progesterone are secreted by the fetal placenta during pregnancy, it is not known which cells are responsible for the production of these hormones. Estrogen has been extracted from the placentae of several species soon after placentation has occurred. In cattle, estrogen can also be demonstrated in the urine, and the reasonable assumption is made that it is of placental origin. In early pregnancy the amounts of estrogen secreted by the placenta are small, but they rise rapidly during the last trimester. Immediately after parturition, urinary levels of estrogen drop very abruptly if the placenta has been expelled (Table 11-2). As long as the

Table 11-2. Amount of estrogen found in the urine of pregnant cows

STAGE IN PREGNANCY (days)	RAT UNITS OF ESTROGEN IN 24 HOURS
31–57	0–41
128	307
167	960
188	186
214	215
256–261	483–3,250
270–280	3,242–6,616
Postpartum	
19 hours	112
25 hours	0

SOURCE: From Hisaw and Meyer, 1929. *Proc. Soc. Exp. Biol. Med.*, 26:586.

placenta is retained, the urinary titers continue to be high. This is taken as additional evidence that the placenta is the source of estrogen.

Placental progesterone follows a similar pattern. Its concentration in the blood of pregnant sheep increases four- or fivefold from the beginning to the end of gestation, and within about eight days after parturition it returns to its prepregnancy level (Fig. 11-1). Since ovariectomy during pregnancy has no measurable effect on the blood level of progesterone in sheep, it seems probable that only a minor portion of that hormone is produced by the ovaries in pregnancy. In contrast, the castration of pregnant rabbit does seven days before parturition causes

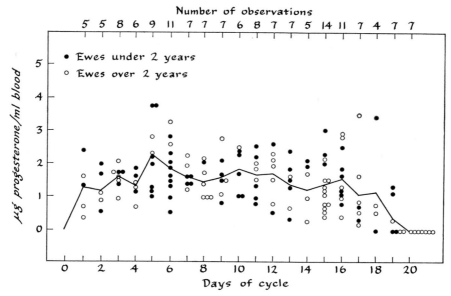

Figure 11-1. *Concentration of progesterone in ovarian venous blood of ewes during pregnancy. Compare with Fig. 11-2. (Redrawn from Edgar and Ronaldson 1957. J. Endocrinol. 16:378.)*

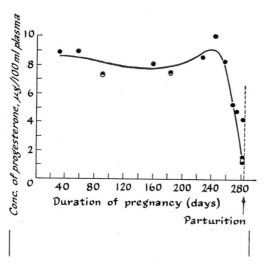

Figure 11-2. *Concentration of progesterone in the plasma of pregnant cows. Compare with Fig. 11-1. (Redrawn from Short 1958. J. Endocrinol. 16:426.)*

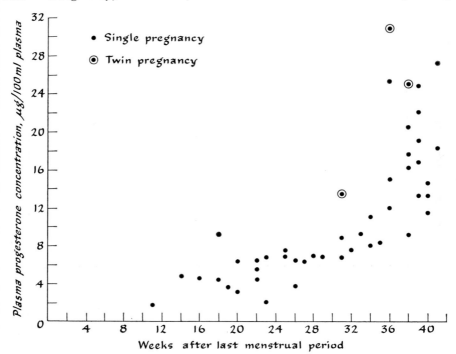

Figure 11-3. *Concentration of progesterone in the plasma of pregnant women. Note that in women the progesterone level does not drop toward the end of pregnancy as it does in sheep and cattle. (Redrawn from: Short and Eton, 1959. J. Endocrinol. 18:418.)*

a precipitous drop in the levels of blood progesterone and leads to immediate abortion. These facts are interpreted to mean that in sheep the placenta produces progesterone during pregnancy but that in pregnant rabbits the ovaries are the major (or sole) source of this hormone.

It is interesting to note that although the progesterone concentration in the blood of ewes (Fig. 11-1) and cows (Fig. 11-2) drops toward the end of pregnancy, no such decrease seems to occur in the blood of pregnant women (Fig. 11-3). It also appears that women carrying twin pregnancies produce more progesterone than those carrying singles (Fig. 11-3).

As for cattle, it has been known for some time that large quantities of androgen are contained in the feces of pregnant cows, but that no androgen, or a very insignificant quantity, is demonstrable in the feces of nonpregnant females or of bulls. Recent work has shown that the fecal androgen of pregnant cows may be a conversion product of placental progesterone.

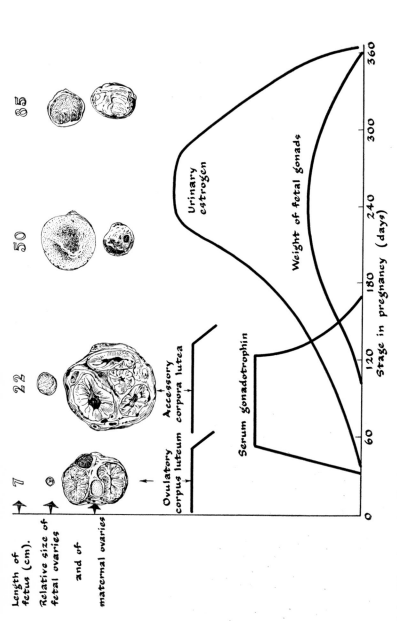

Figure 11-4. *The rise and fall of serum gonadotrophin and urinary estrogen in pregnant mares, and the effect of these hormones on the maternal gonads. Note that ovulatory corpora lutea degenerate and that accessory corpora are formed when the serum gonadotrophin level rises. Fetal ovaries (upper row) grow in response first to gonadotrophin and later to estrogen and become larger than the atrophic maternal ovaries. (Data adapted from Cole and others, 1933, Anat. Rec., 56: 275, and other literature.)*

Length of fetus (cm).

Relative size of fetal ovaries

and of

maternal ovaries

7   22   50   85

Ovulatory corpus luteum

Accessory corpora lutea

Serum gonadotrophin

Urinary estrogen

Weight of fetal gonads

Stage in pregnancy (days)

0   60   120   180   240   300   360

Gonadotrophic Hormones

The placenta of rats is said to secrete luteotrophic hormone, which may be responsible for the maintenance of the corpora lutea of pregnancy in this animal. There is no evidence for (or against) the secretion of luteotrophic substances by the placenta in other species.

The endocrinology of the other gonadotrophic hormones—pregnant mare's serum (PMS) and human chorionic gonadotrophin of pregnancy—has been discussed elsewhere. We shall confine ourselves here to a discussion of the circumstances of their secretion during pregnancy.

Pregnant Mare's Serum.   Equine gonadotrophin, as its discoverer, H. H. Cole, prefers to call it, appears in large quantities in the blood of pregnant mares at about day 40 and remains high until day 120 of gestation (Fig. 11-4). This hormone is made in the so-called endome-

Figure 11-5. *Section through an endometrial cup* (C) *of a mare pregnant 63 days. The space between the cup and the allantois* (A) *is filled with uterine milk* (U). *Note the uterine glands* (G). (*By permission of Professor E. C. Amoroso, F.R.S.*)

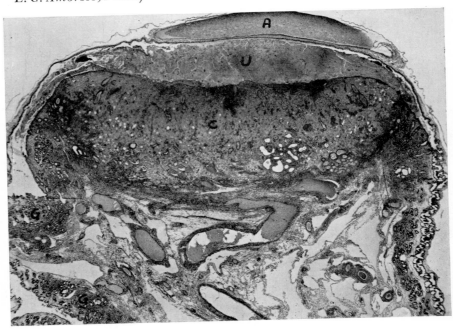

trial cups of the uterine epithelium (Fig. 11-5) and is thus not a placental hormone. By the time it appears, the ovulatory corpus luteum has diminished in size, and the ovaries of the mare are stimulated by the uterine gonadotrophin to form large follicles. Many of these follicles ovulate (eggs can be recovered from the oviducts) and form corpora lutea, while other follicles become luteinized without ovulating. These structures, called accessory corpora lutea, persist until about day 180 of gestation; then they in turn degenerate, leaving the pregnant mare without ovarian lutein tissue for the remainder of gestation. Recently it has been found that elephants, too, form accessory corpora lutea, but only from about the end of the sixth to the ninth month of the twenty-four months of gestation. It is inferred that elephants secrete a gonadotrophin similar to the one produced by pregnant mares. Accessory corpora lutea are also formed in the nilgai (*Beselaphus tragocamelus*), which is an antelope and a ruminant. Again the implication is that a serum gonadotrophin is present to permit follicular development and ovulation. No serum or urinary gonadotrophic hormones have ever been found in other ruminants (cattle and sheep), nor do these species form accessory corpora lutea.

Whether the secretion of gonadotrophic hormone and the formation of accessory corpora lutea are just artifacts, without physiological significance to implantation and subsequent gestation, remains unknown. In mares, gonadotrophic hormone also acts on the gonads of the fetuses of both sexes, causing them to increase in size. The ovaries of female fetuses, in fact, become larger than the ovaries of the mother, and fetal testes are larger than the testes of newborn foals (Fig. 11-4). As the influence of the gonadotrophin on the fetal gonads wears off, because of decreasing amounts of the circulating hormone, the gonads, the duct system, and the accessories come under the influence of estrogen and progesterone. The uterus of female fetuses becomes enlarged, and the endometrium proliferates. The connective tissue of the sex apparatus of both sexes is especially sensitive to the increasing titer of estrogen. This is particularly apparent in the seminal vesicles, which greatly enlarge because of the enormous growth of their estrogen-stimulated connective tissue. Soon after parturition, after the duct system of the newborn has been removed from the environment of the high estrogen and progesterone titers to which it is exposed *in utero,* the duct system and the accessory glands are drastically reduced in size. Whereas the enlargement of the fetal gonads is typical of fetuses exposed to high levels of serum gonadotrophins, the duct systems and accessory glands, in all species, are affected by the high maternal titers of estrogen and progesterone. The vaginae and vulvae of newborn females are greatly enlarged and lined with stratified-squamous epithelium, but they regress to a simple form very shortly after birth.

Chorionic Gonadotrophin.   This hormone is not in any way comparable to the gonadotrophic hormone found in the blood serum of mares. The endocrine properties of chorionic hormones were discussed earlier. Unlike PMS, chorionic gonadotrophin is secreted by the placenta and not by the uterine endometrium. It is thought that the chorionic villi are the site of its formation. We have pointed out that HCG is luteotrophic in a variety of species, including women, rats, rabbits, pigs, and others. For this reason it is tempting to ascribe to it the role of maintaining the corpora lutea during early pregnancy in women. If the hypothesis concerning the mechanism of maintenance of corpora lutea proves to be approximately correct, then we may find that the corpus luteum immediately after ovulation gets enough impetus from hypophyseal luteotrophic factors to remain physiologically active until the chorionic gonadotrophin begins to be formed in sufficient quantities to assume significance as a luteotrophin. Measurable amounts of HCG appear in the urine of pregnant women as early as 5–16 days after ovulation, but the urinary HCG titer does not reach a peak until 35–50 days of pregnancy (see Table 3-3, p. 89).

Intermedin

The placenta contains (and probably secretes) extractable amounts of intermedin, a hormone normally secreted by the intermediate lobe (also called the pars intermedia) of the posterior pituitary gland. Intermedin extracted from that source is frequently contaminated with ACTH (adrenocorticotrophic hormone), and ACTH obtained from the anterior lobe usually contains intermedin. Intermedin has been extracted from the placentae of women, mares, cows, and bitches, and its concentration in the chorion increases with advancing pregnancy. In lower vertebrates this hormone causes the expansion of the chromatophores of the skin, but its physiological role in mammals remains unknown. It may be responsible for the pigmentation of the areolas, the nipples, and the linea alba of women during pregnancy.

Heats and Ovulation During Pregnancy

It is generally thought that estrous cycles are suspended by the onset of pregnancy and that ovaries are inactive during all of gestation. Recent work has shown that pregnant females frequently have psychological heats and accept the male throughout pregnancy. This occurs much more frequently than is commonly thought. Ewes in which pregnancy was verified at autopsy showed heat indistinguishable from that observed in nonpregnant females. These heats last about eighteen hours and are noted early during gestation and as late as five days before parturition. In one group of sheep that were checked for heat daily, it was noted that about 30 percent of the pregnant ewes showed heats, some as many as five times. It seems almost certain that no ovulations occur at these pregnancy heats, even though some of the ewes have follicles of ovulatory size. About 10 percent of cows show one or more heats while pregnant, and this figure might be even higher if cattle presumed to be pregnant were regularly checked for heat. It is not known whether cows ovulate at pregnancy heats. The intervals between heats during gestation deviate significantly from the intervals typical of nonpregnant females. There appears to be no rhythm in the occurrence of these heats.

The fact that pregnant cows come in heat has practical significance: if they are artificially inseminated, and if the cervical seal is broken by the inseminating tube, abortion or mummification of the fetus usually results unless infection is prevented by the simultaneous injection of antibiotic drugs.

Heats during pregnancy are common in all laboratory mammals; matings have been observed in all of them throughout gestation. Infrequently some of the laboratory animals—and probably some of the larger domestic animals—ovulate during gestation, for superfetation has been recorded for rats, mice, rabbits, cattle, and sheep, two parturitions occurring a few days or weeks apart and fully formed young being born at each. Better proof of superfetation lies in the observation that the young born at two parturitions that are less than a full gestation period apart may bear color markings relating them to two different sires. It was noted in another connection that mares, as a rule, ovulate during pregnancy and that ovulations during pregnancy may also occur in women.

During the first third or even half of pregnancy, the ovaries of all species examined show considerable follicular development, follicles of ovulatory size being frequently found in female swine, cattle, and sheep (Table 11-3) in numbers typical of the species. Little support

Table 11-3.   Relation between stage in pregnancy, follicle number, and follicle size in ewes

STAGE IN PREGNANCY (days)	FOLLICLES PER EWE	FOLLICLE SIZE (mm)			TOTAL
		2–4	5–7	8–10	
3–8	Average No.	9.5	4.0	2.0	15.5†
18–30	Average No.	15.1	4.6	3.0*	22.7†
45–115	Average No.	17.0	4.3	0.0*	21.3†

SOURCE: From Williams and others. 1956. *J. Animal Science*, 15:978.
* Decrease significant at 1%.
† Increase significant at 1%.

is found in these species for the contention that during pregnancy follicles grow and become atretic in about the same rhythm as during the normal cycle. Though follicular atresia undoubtedly takes place during gestation, the lifetime of follicles seems to be longer then than during the cycle. During the last half of gestation, and especially toward its end, the follicles diminish in size and in number, and at parturition there are no follicles larger than 1 or 2 millimeters in diameter. It is assumed that this reduction in ovarian activity is due to suppression of the pituitary gonadotrophins by the increasing amounts of estrogen and progesterone secreted by the placenta. This interpretation is supported by the finding that the injection of gonadotrophic hormones (PMS) into sheep and pigs shortly before parturition causes pronounced follicular growth, ovulation, and even cyst formation, which show that the ovaries are capable of responding to hormone stimulation.

How heats and ovulations are held in abeyance in the majority of pregnant females is not clearly understood. The fact that follicles of ovulatory size are found in the ovaries of pregnant females shows that the pituitary-ovarian axis is not materially upset by pregnancy. It is possible that the best FSH-LH ratio for normal follicular development and ovulation does not usually exist in pregnant females but is achieved occasionally. Why females do not show psychological heat regularly and even continuously during late pregnancy, when placental estrogen reaches levels much higher than those necessary to bring nonpregnant females into heat, remains unknown. It is possible that the absence of heats is due to the well-known antagonism between estrogen and progesterone.

Delayed Implantation

In a number of species there is a hiatus between the activation of the egg by the sperm and the implantation of the zygote.

The best-known case of delayed implantation occurs in rats and mice. Females of these species show a postpartum heat, including ovulation, within twenty-four hours after parturition. If copulation is permitted at this heat, the subsequent gestation is significantly longer than the normal twenty-one days, the young being born thirty, forty, or even fifty days after mating. If the female is not permitted to nurse the first litter, the new gestation is of normal duration. Analysis of this situation shows that the eggs ovulated at the postpartum heat are fertilized normally but that the resulting blastocysts, instead of implanting themselves at the normal time, float free in the uterine lumen. The actual growth period of the embryo is twenty-one days, just as it is in normal pregnancies. The blastocysts can be caused to implant themselves at the proper time, in spite of concurrent lactation, by injection with estrogen. These observations are interpreted to mean that failure of implantation is caused by insufficient quantities of estrogen, which is presumed to be excreted in the milk. If the litters are large, more milk is secreted, the demands for estrogen are greater, and delay in implantation is longer than it is in females with smaller litters.

Recently new light has been shed on the possible role of estrogen in causing implantation in these species. It has been found that the local application of estrogen to a portion of the uterine endometrium of rats is sufficient to make this particular portion hospitable to a blastocyst, and only a blastocyst near such an estrogen-sensitized area will implant, while the other blastocysts remain free and unattached. What effect the application of estrogen has on a particular patch of uterine endometrium is unknown but it does emphasize the strictly local responses that hormones can apparently cause. A similar situation is illustrated by an observation on a bilaterally ovariectomized rat: a pellet of progesterone implanted into the lumen of only one of the horns will prevent abortion of fetuses in the horn containing the hormone but not in the contralateral horn; furthermore, if the progesterone pellet is very small, only those fetuses adjacent to the pellet survive, while those further away in the same horn die.

Delayed implantation is known in other species, in some of which implantation can be forced by estrogen injection; other species (for instance, the European badger) are completely nonresponsive to this or any other steroid tried. The local action of estrogen can even produce embryos of two or three distinctly different ages in the same uterine horn of rats. Although this experiment can be done in a variety of different reproductive conditions (and even in castrated females), it is easiest to use postpartum lactating females which have just ovulated and in which the resulting blastocysts will not normally implant for a period of up to 2 weeks after postpartum ovulation. If such females are given a local injection on the 5th day of as little as 0.005 microgram of estradiol, it can cause the immediate implantation of one or two blastocysts, the others remaining free. The local injection, repeated a few days later, causes the implantation of additional blastocysts, and a still later injection can bring about the implantation of more free blastocysts. Thus, fetuses of three different ages are found in the same uterus—the oldest young weighing 5 grams, those resulting from the second implantation 1 gram, and those from the last weighing only 0.25 gram. Such experiments can obviously be used in studies of mechanisms of implantation and of mechanisms of parturition.

Martens copulate in July or August (in America), and the eggs progress to the blastocyst stage, but implantation does not .occur until January. The young are born in March about 50 days after implantation, but 250 days after fertilization. In the mink, which, of all the mustelids, has received the greatest attention (Hansson, 1947), the average length of gestation is about 50 days, but it varies from 39 to 74 days. In some females implantation occurs without delay; in others a significant delay is noted, the interval between mating and implantation being dependent on many factors, of which frequency of mating and environmental temperature are the most important.

Delayed implantation also occurs in the armadillo and in the roe deer. The rutting season of the latter is in July or August, although other members of the family do not mate until November or December. The eggs of roe deer are fertilized at mating but lie dormant until about December; then they implant themselves, the fawns being dropped in May. The interval from mating to parturition is 40 weeks, but true gestation lasts only 20 weeks.

The physiological significance of delayed implantation in animals other than the rat is not clear. Just as in the rat, it seems to be controlled by endocrine factors, for one can shorten the gestation period of martens and mink by exposing them to prolonged light. It is assumed that this treatment works by stimulating pituitary activity, but attempts to bring about the same effect with gonadotrophic and steroid hormones have been equivocal or unsuccessful.

Parturition

Basically, the problem of birth is a simple one: when the period of embryonal growth is ended, the conceptuses are expelled from the uterine lumen. When the details of parturition are analyzed, however, it becomes apparent that the initiation of the birth process, if not birth itself, involves events that are complex and, at the present time, incompletely understood.

First, a few facts to set the stage for subsequent discussion. None but minor contractions of the uterus occur during the major part of gestation, but the process of birth is precipitated by increased uterine motility and contraction. It is probable that the process is initiated by a combination of factors that lead to an increased sensitivity of the uterine muscle to hormones. An older theory held that the fetus itself might be secreting substances (accumulation of waste products) that initiated birth. It was also thought that the size of the fetus might give the signal for parturition. There are two experimental observations that cast serious doubt on the validity of these theories. When the roles of both fetal size and fetal secretions are tested by experiments in which the fetuses are removed and the placentae are left *in situ*, pregnancy continues after removal of the fetuses, and the empty placental membranes, which continue to grow, are carried for the length of time of normal pregnancy (21 days in rats and 31 days in rabbits). At term, when birth of the young would have occurred, the empty membranes are delivered.

Prolonged gestation sometimes occurs in many species (women, mares, pigs, etc.). Of greatest interest is a study of prolonged gestation in dairy cattle. Here abnormally long gestation is known to be a genetic character, which causes calves to be carried long beyond the normal period of 278–290 days. Gestations as long as 330 days have been recorded, the calves continuing to grow *in utero* and reaching sizes much greater than normal (up to 200 pounds). The fetuses frequently become so large, in fact, that normal birth becomes impossible, and the calves must be delivered by surgical intervention. In normal pregnant cows, blood progesterone levels are known to drop a few days before parturition, but no such drop occurs in animals with prolonged gestation.

Since, however, it is not possible to prolong gestation in normal cows with exogenous progesterone, why the progesterone level does not drop in cows with prolonged gestation remains unclear.

Another variant of prolonged gestation has recently been described: in a California herd, fetuses of smaller than normal or normal size are carried long beyond normal term. In this case (which appears to be due to a recessive character) the fetuses completely lack both lobes of the pituitary gland.

Prolonged gestation, the resulting large fetuses, and the delivery of membranes, after removal of the fetuses, at the expected time, all argue against the assumption that either the size of the fetus or a stimulus coming from the fetus has any effect on the onset of labor. It is also significant that in all monotocous species male fetuses are carried *in utero* significantly longer than female fetuses. It is not quite clear whether the longer gestation of males is the cause of their larger size at birth or whether they must have a longer gestation to become physiologically ready to be born. In any event, it is quite clear that fetal size itself does not determine the time of onset of labor.

A few observations on the positive side may shed light on the problem of parturition. The uterine muscle contracts rhythmically when it is under the influence of estrogen. These contractions can be converted into tetanic contractions by the injection of oxytocic hormone from the posterior lobe of the pituitary gland. These facts are basic for our understanding of the birth process, but a few difficulties remain to be ironed out. If oxytocin plays a major role in initiating the uterine contractions that lead to parturition, the question arises as to how the release of oxytocin is made to coincide with the readiness of the conceptuses for delivery. The fact that birth can occur normally in totally hypophysectomized females does not necessarily argue against the role of oxytocin in parturition, for, in the absence of the posterior lobe, the hormone may be secreted in sufficient quantities by the hypothalamus, its normal source.

The level of placental steroids may also be of importance in this connection. It has been pointed out that estrogen increases in amount toward the end of gestation. It is also known that in some species pregnancy can be prolonged and parturition held in abeyance by the injection of progesterone. If the injection is discontinued, birth occurs within a short time. This indicates that the level of progesterone may be of major importance during the preamble to birth. It may be postulated that, to make parturition possible, the progesterone level must fall. If the placenta is regarded as the major, if not the only, source of progesterone during late pregnancy, no known mechanism could explain a decrease in the secretion of placental progesterone. It becomes necessary to postulate that, even if the progesterone level itself does not fall, the effectiveness of the hormone is reduced by the well-known antagonism between estrogen and progesterone. According to this theory, the level of placental progesterone remains unchanged while the level of estrogen continues to rise until it reaches a level sufficiently high to antagonize progesterone. At this point the uterine muscle would be under the influence of the estrogen-progesterone ratio that is most conducive to its sensitivity to oxytocin. Under this theory it is not necessary to assume that oxytocin is released in response to a signal from the uterus or its contents, the onset of labor being brought about only by the normal increase of only one of the hormones involved in parturition. This theory is compatible with the known physiological facts and has the advantage of being simpler than the theory that calls for juggling two hormones instead of one.

The cervix, which remains tightly closed during the whole of pregnancy, opens shortly before parturition, presumably under the influence of relaxin, which is known to be secreted by the placenta as well as by the corpus luteum. Whatever the detailed mechanism of parturition may be, it is obvious that it depends on the occurrence of many synchronized events. For instance, injection of a large dose of oxytocin shortly before the expected onset of labor may precipitate an immediate onset; but, unless the cervix has relaxed, thus permitting expulsion of the fetuses, the violent uterine contraction may result in the rupture of the uterine wall rather than a normal birth process. If all the physiological events permissive of parturition have taken place, the onset of labor may be hastened with oxytocin. Attempts to hasten birth by many days have not been uniformly successful. Much additional study is needed before all the factors entering into this event are understood.

Lactation

Lactation may be considered the culmination of the reproductive process and as much a part of this process as the estrous cycle or gestation. It can be discussed best under two aspects: (1) the basic anatomy of the gland and its preparation for lactation; (2) the initiation and maintenance of milk secretion. Much research has been expended on this subject, but no general agreement has been reached on the physiological control of lactation. The summary presented here has been extracted from the outstanding works of C. W. Turner, W. R. Lyons, S. J. Folley, and their collaborators and students. For different points of view, and for important details that cannot be discussed here, the student is urged to study the contributions of these men.

Basic Anatomy of the Gland

Mammary glands are compound glands and are, basically, highly modified and specialized sebaceous glands that secrete milk. They are present in both sexes but become functional, as a rule, only in the female. The mammary glands of males are capable of becoming functional; in fact, much of the research work on the physiology of lactation has been done on males whose mammary glands had been developed by appropriate treatment. Occasionally development of the breast occurs in males spontaneously (called gynecomastia), especially in men and in male goats. There is at least one authentic case of a he-goat having produced enough milk to raise two kids.

Although the number of breasts may vary, they are invariably ventral and lateral to the midline. In some animals (elephants, sirenians, primates, etc.) they are located in the thoracic, in others (ungulates, cetaceans) in the inguinal region; in litter-bearing animals they extend from the thoracic to the inguinal region. In all species (except the monotremes) each breast has its own excurrent duct, the nipple, which may be single, as in cows, or may have 12–20 individual canals, as in women.

In the embryo, the mammary lines, which form on each side of the midventral line, mark the location of the future mammary glands. In animals in which only two breasts are characteristic of adults, supernumerary teats or even breasts may form along the mammary line; women and men with three, four, or even six breasts arranged in a fashion typical of litter-bearing animals are not rare.

Along the mammary line, centers of proliferation of the Malpighian layer, called mammary buds, appear in the areas of the future breasts and in numbers characteristic of the mature individuals. Next primary sprouts are formed as invaginations of the mammary buds. The primary sprouts give rise to side branches, which branch in turn, giving rise to secondary, tertiary, and further sprouts. As a rule, breast development stops at the stage of primary sprouts in embryos, subsequent development occurring postnatally.

Between birth and sexual maturity the mammary glands continue to increase in complexity, acquiring a more extensively branched duct system together with a good amount of adipose tissue, which accounts for most of the visible increase in the size of the breast. The most extensive growth of mammary glands occurs during pregnancy or pseudopregnancy, when the now elaborate duct system acquires terminal lobules, which consist of subdivisions called alveoli.

Though this account of the development of the mammary gland is by no means exhaustive and should not satisfy those who are especially interested in lactation, it is satisfactory for the purposes of the present discussion. We now are aware of the basic architecture of the gland: the alveolar cells that secrete the milk, the ducts that conduct the milk toward the nipple canal and hence to the milking machine, be it living or mechanical; and we are now ready to consider the endocrine control of the gland. We have deliberately ignored transformation into milk of the milk precursors conducted to the breast by the blood, not because it is not important, but because its details are not understood.

Endocrine Control of Lactation

Because of the obvious dependence of the growth of the mammary gland on sexual development and, later on, pregnancy, it soon became apparent that the hormones secreted by the glands concerned with reproduction control the development of the breast. A striking demonstration of this fact is seen in newborn babies, whose mammae, stimulated by the hormones of the mother during gestation, not only show greater development than they do a few weeks after birth, but also contain at birth a secretion resembling milk (called "witches' milk").

Controlled experiments on laboratory animals have shown that two hormone systems are involved in lactation: one preparing the gland for secretory activity anatomically, the other acting on the developed gland to cause secretion of milk. We are already familiar with this concept, for two hormone systems were found to be necessary to the mammalian uterus and the chicken oviduct, one for morphological development, the other for precipitation of secretory activity.

There is considerable variation among the species in the effect of estrogen and progesterone on the development of the mammary glands. We shall assume an otherwise euhormonal organism, for it is well established that both the thryroid and the adrenals play an important role in making optimal functioning of the mammary gland possible. It is true, in general, that estrogen, when given alone, produces only duct growth, although in some species this hormone, especially when given in large doses and over long periods, induces growth of the alveolar system as well. Estrogen injected into ruminants (most of the work has been done on goats) produces complete udder growth, including lobo-alveolar growth and lactation. Because most of these experiments were done on intact goats in possession of their ovaries and pituitaries, the conclusion that estrogen alone produced these effects is not justified. Progesterone alone, in the majority of species studied, produces alveolar growth without having any significant effect on duct development. As might be expected, combinations of these two steroids produce much more extensive development of the secretory tissue than either hormone alone. However, in species in which estrogen alone can cause both duct growth and alveolar development, addition of progesterone is either ineffective or only mildly synergic.

Androgen and possibly the adrenal steroids can also induce growth of mammary tissue, including duct and alveolar development. It is not clear whether it is androgen itself or a conversion product of that hormone that is gynecogenic.

There is a theory that estrogen and progesterone produce their stimulatory effect on the breast indirectly, by inducing the release from the pituitary gland of a mammogenic substance (or substances), which acts on the mammary gland, causing duct and alveolar growth. This theory finds little support, however, in view of the fact that complete mammary growth can be induced by the steroids in hypophysectomized animals. Furthermore, estrogen applied by inunction to only one breast of intact males causes the proliferation of only the treated breast and not of the contralateral breast. If the estrogen effect were mediated by the pituitary gland, both glands should develop in response to the hypophyseal mammogenic agent.

Secretion of Milk

Since hypophysectomy of lactating animals always causes rapid and complete cessation of lactation, it is evident that the pituitary gland elaborates a hormone or hormones that are essential for continued milk secretion. After the two steroids have prepared the mammary gland anatomically, a pituitary hormone acting on the ready gland causes it to secrete milk. It was earlier thought that this pituitary hormone was the lactogenic hormone prolactin, but more recent studies tend to focus attention on the growth hormone (GH). If unpurified pituitary

preparations are injected into lactating cows, a substantial increase in
the rate of milk production results. Subsequent attempts to determine
which pituitary hormone is responsible for this increase are summarized in Table 11-4. It will be noted that the growth hormone raised

**Table 11-4.   Effects of single injections of hormones on milk yield of
cows (two days before injection compared with two days
after)**

| TREATMENT (SINGLE INJECTION) | NO. OF COWS | PERCENT CHANGE IN YIELD | |
		ACTUAL	COMPARED WITH SALINE
Saline	12	−1.89	. . .
Growth hormone			
15 mg	4	2.78	6.30
30 mg	12	6.31*	8.20*
60 mg	8	3.42	6.68
Crude pituitary gland extract			
5 ml	4	2.87	6.03
10 ml	7	6.60*	9.90*
Prolactin			
40 mg	4	−2.34	0.82
40 mg + 30 mg growth hormone	3	7.94*	11.10*
ACTH			
7 mg	7	−6.61	−5.54
28 mg	4	−10.31†	−6.61
7 mg + 30 mg growth hormone	3	4.28	7.80

Source: Data from Cotes and others. 1949. *Nature*, 164:992.
* Significant at the 2% level.
† Significant at the 5% level.

the rate of lactation, prolactin alone was ineffective, and ACTH lowered the rate. Other studies have confirmed the data presented in this
table by injecting 25–100 milligrams of GH at different stages of lactation and obtaining increases in milk yield of 25–50 percent and in
fat yield of as much as 120 percent.

Table 11-5 presents data obtained with GH on nine pairs of identical
twin heifers, one heifer of each pair being injected with 50 milligrams
of GH daily for fourteen days before and fourteen days after parturition. All animals calved in July and August, 1955, and, aside from the
injection with GH, were treated identically. A substantial increase in
the average production rate was achieved during postpartum therapy.
Because there were no obvious effects of the GH during the first five
days of lactation (following fourteen days of prepartum GH therapy),
the conclusion is reached that GH has no direct effect on the milk-
producing ability of the mammary gland.

Table 11-5.   Effect of GH on milk production of nine pairs of identical heifer twins (treated twins were injected with 50 mg/day of GH, fourteen days before and fourteen days after calving)

AVERAGE YIELD (POUNDS) OR PERCENTAGE	INTERVAL AFTER CALVING (days)					
	7	14	21	28	35	42
Milk yield						
Treated twins	147	191	186	177	179	180
Control twins	139	174	180	181	179	176
Fat test						
Treated twins	4.4	4.4	4.1	4.3	4.6	4.0
Control twins	4.3	4.0	4.1	4.2	4.2	4.4
Butterfat						
Treated twins	6.3	8.0	7.5	7.5	8.2	7.2
Control twins	5.9	7.1	7.3	7.6	7.5	7.8

SOURCE: Data from Brumby. 1956, *N. Z. J. Sci. Technol.*, Sec. *A*, 38:152.

These observations raise a most important question—the mode of action of GH as a galactopoetic substance. GH has been shown to be diabetogenic in many mammals (but not in chickens), and the possibility arises that it may be galactopoetic by virtue of its ability to raise the blood glucose level. ACTH is also diabetogenic, however, but it has severely depressing effects on milk yield. Furthermore, in Shaw's experiments, in which single injections of GH have been found effective in increasing milk secretion, it is highly unlikely that the transitory diabetogenic effect of GH could influence milk production for as long as it does. Several workers who have used GH as a galactogogue have observed a very significant, and as yet unexplained, increase in the size of the udder of cows receiving injections of GH.

Thyrotrophic hormone (TSH) also has galactopoetic ability, but it is not as pronounced as that of GH and is quite temporary. Much additional work will be needed before the galactopoetic effects of pituitary hormones are understood. Whether they work on the level of the cells of the mammary glands by increasing their metabolic activity or whether they act on the systemic level by mobilizing precursors essential in milk formation remains to be determined.

Initiation of Lactation

From the preceding discussion we can now piece together some of the events that occur during the reproductive life of mammalian females.

Before puberty the mammary glands develop under the influence of estrogen and progesterone, and the breasts continue to respond to the cyclic ebb and flow of the steroids during the cycles. These cyclic changes remain unnoticed in most laboratory and domestic animals, but they are measurable in women, in whom the time of ovulation can be determined with a fair degree of accuracy from the changes in the size of the breasts and in their turgidity.

The changes that occur in the breasts during pseudopregnancy are much more profound and complete than those observed during the cycle. For all purposes they are indistinguishable from those taking place during pregnancy itself, except that mammary proliferation does not culminate in lactation in most females showing pseudopregnancy; but pseudopregnant bitches may even lactate.

During pregnancy the major role in causing the growth and proliferation of breast tissue is played by estrogen and progesterone, which are elaborated by the placenta in increasing amounts toward the end of pregnancy. Toward the end of gestation the secretory activity of the mammary gland begins with the secretion of colostrum, but really prolific lactation does not, as a rule, occur until after parturition. When prolactin was generally thought to be the hormone that precipitated the flow of milk, much effort was expended on determining what mechanisms controlled the release and the rate of secretion of pituitary prolactin. It appeared that an inhibitor kept prolactin secretion in check until after parturition, and it was thought that this inhibitor might be estrogen. The same question remains to be answered, but now it pertains to GH and possibly TSH rather than prolactin.

After initiation of lactation the rate of milk secretion rises rapidly to a peak and then declines slowly until the young are weaned. It appears that continued pituitary stimulation is necessary to continued milk secretion, for hypophysectomy brings lactation to an abrupt end. Other factors, however, such as the stimulus of suckling, play a role in maintaining lactation. If the breast is not emptied of milk by suckling, it involutes rapidly, and lactation stops. If only part of the breast is suckled while the rest of it is not, the whole mammary system is maintained. This suggests that suckling induces a neural stimulus of the pituitary, which secretes the hormone necessary for maintenance of the whole gland, including its unsuckled parts. Accumulation of milk as a factor in the involution of the unsuckled breast is less important than the absence of the neural stimulus obtained from suckling.

Although the role of neural stimuli appears to be important in rats (and perhaps in rabbits), it is much less clear in larger mammals. In goats it is possible to denervate one-half of the udder or even to transplant the whole breast to the neck, where it is certainly deprived of any nervous connections. Both the suckled or milked denervated half of the breast or the whole transplanted gland produce amounts of milk comparable to intact glands. These observations, of course, raise the important question whether in large animals other feedback mechanisms exist than those which control lactation in laboratory animals. Perusal of the pertinent literature makes it abundantly clear that important species differences exist with regard to the hormone requirements for the preparation of the gland for lactation, for initiation of lactation, and for the maintenance of milk synthesis. Generalizations are therefore not possible.

"Let-down" of Milk

If one cannulates the teat canal of such large animals as lactating goats or cows, only the milk stored in the cistern and in the larger ducts is obtained. This is a very minor portion of the total amount of milk present in the whole gland. If, however, such a stimulus as suckling or milking is provided, milk begins to flow freely. At present the theory formulated by Gains and by Petersen and his co-workers seems to explain this phenomenon of milk "let-down" best. It is postulated that a neurohumoral mechanism is ultimately responsible for the contraction of myoepithelial cells around the alveoli, squeezing out the milk contained in the alveolar cells. The stimulus obtained at suckling (or any mechanical manipulation of the breast or teat, such as milking) causes a neural reflex to go to the hypothalamus and thence to the posterior lobe of the pituitary, which responds by releasing oxytocin; this, in turn, causes contraction of myoepithelial tissue in the breast. The assumption can be verified in a variety of ways. Injection of oxytocin into a female, without physical stimulation of the mammary gland, or into females whose mammary glands have been denervated, causes milk let-down. That this is mediated through the hypothalamus is seen from the fact that, in females whose pituitary stalks have been cut, suckling does not lead to let-down. Electric stimulation of the hypothalamus in goats, without manipulation of the gland, also causes milk let-down, further supporting the theory of a neurohumoral pathway between the mammary gland and the posterior lobe of the pituitary.

Stimulation of the mammary gland is not the only phenomenon that induces milk let-down. In cattle, such events as the rattling of milk pails, the presence of calves, and the arrival of the scheduled time for milking, are enough to initiate the neurohumoral chain leading to milk let-down. Furthermore, an event completely unrelated to milking or to nursing, such as manipulation of the external genitalia, artificial insemination, copulation, or even the presence of the male, is sufficient to induce the phenomenon. Because in all these cases uterine motility and contractility increase, it is postulated that sexual excitation, whether it is connected with nursing or with mating, leads to the release of oxytocin. For centuries men have taken advantage of this chain of events by manipulating the vulva of cows to cause milk let-down. Even today, a street milk vendor in India inserts a stick into the vagina of his cow and rotates it a few times after he has found a buyer for the milk and before he milks the cow.

SUMMARY

An important question, "how the ovary knows that the uterus is pregnant," is discussed, but no final and satisfactory answer is given. It seems certain that the maintenance of corpora lutea for the duration of pregnancy is initiated in the uterus by the implanted embryo and is transmitted by the nervous system through the hypothalamus to the anterior pituitary gland, which responds by releasing a luteotrophic substance. In some animals the ovary is the sole source of progesterone and is therefore essential throughout pregnancy; in other animals the placenta takes over secretion of progesterone sometime during pregnancy, and the ovaries can be removed from these without causing abortion. Estrogen also is secreted by the placenta.

Gonadotrophic hormones are produced during pregnancy by the endometrial tissue of Equidae and by the placentae of primates. The role of these hormones is not known in either case.

Heats occur frequently during pregnancy in many species; ovulations during pregnancy are not nearly as common.

The size of the conceptus and the accumulation of waste products of fetal origin are discounted as the primary causes of the onset of parturition. While the final answer to this problem remains to be found, it appears that the onset of parturition is caused by the action of estrogen, progesterone, and oxytocin on the uterine muscle. How the signal for expulsion of the conceptus is given remains unknown.

In preparation for lactation, the breast is prepared anatomically by the interaction of estrogen and progesterone; milk secretion itself is caused either by the lactogenic hormone (prolactin) or by the growth hormone. Let-down of milk is caused by oxytocin, which is released from the posterior pituitary gland by a variety of stimuli, such as suckling, sexual excitation, and manipulation of the genitalia.

REFERENCES

C. R. Austin and A. W. H. Braden. 1953. "An investigation of polyspermy in the rat and rabbit." *Australian J. Biol. Sci.,* **6:**674.

H. J. Bearden, W. Hansel, and R. W. Bratton. 1956. "Fertilization and embryonic mortality rates of bulls with histories of either low or high fertility in artificial breeding." *J. Dairy Sci.,* **39:**312.

A. W. H. Braden. 1953. "Distribution of sperms in the genital tract of the female rabbit after coitus." *Australian J. Biol. Sci.,* **6:**693.

H. H. Cole, G. H. Hart, W. R. Lyons, and H. R. Catchpole. 1933. "The development and hormonal content of fetal horse gonads." *Anat. Record,* **56:**275.

A. T. Cowie and S. J. Folley. 1955. "Physiology of gonadotropins and the lactogenic hormone" in *The Hormones: Physiology, Chemistry and Applications,* Vol. III. Academic Press (New York).

L. Dauzier, R. Ortavant, C. Thibault, and S. Winterberger. 1954. "Résultats nouveaux sur la gestation à contre-saison chez la brebis et chez la chèvre, possibilité d'utilisation pratique." *Ann. Zootechnie,* **2:**89.

S. J. Folley and F. H. Malpress. 1948. "Hormonal control of mammary growth" and "Hormonal control of lactation" in *The Hormones: Physiology, Chemistry and Applications,* Vol. I. Academic Press (New York).

S. J. Folley. 1955. *The Physiology and Biochemistry of Lactation.* Oliver and Boyd (London).

O. T. Fosgate and V. R. Smith. 1954. "Prenatal mortality in the bovine between pregnancy diagnosis at 34–40 days post insemination and parturition." *J. Dairy Sci.,* **37:**1071.

A. Hansson. 1947. "The physiology of reproduction in mink, with special reference to delayed implantation." *Acta Zool.,* **28:**1–136.

H. W. Hawk, J. N. Wiltbank, H. E. Kidder, and L. E. Casida. 1955. "Embryonic mortality between 16 and 34 days post-breeding in cows of low fertility." *J. Dairy Sci.,* **38:**673.

A. Jacobson, H. A. Salhanick, and M. X. Zarrow. 1950. "Induction of pseudopregnancy and its inhibition by various drugs." *Am. J. Physiol.,* **161:**522.

J. H. MacArthur. 1949. "Selection for small and large body size in the house mouse." *Genetics,* **34:**194.

R. L. Murphree, W. G. Black, G. Otto, and L. E. Casida. 1951. "Effect of site of insemination upon the fertility of gonadotrophin-treated rabbits of different reproductive stages." *Endocrinol.,* **49:**474.

G. M. Neher and M. X. Zarrow. 1954. "Concentration of progestin in the serum of the non-pregnant, pregnant and post-partum ewe." *J. Endocrinol.,* **11:**323.

M. M. Nelson and H. M. Evans. 1054. "Maintenance of pregnancy in the absence of dietary protein with estrone and progesterone." *Endocrinol.,* **55:**543.

J. S. Perry. 1955. "Reproductive wastage: prenatal loss" in *Collected Papers:* Vol. III, *The Breeding of Laboratory Animals.* Laboratory Animals Bureau, M.R.C. Laboratories (London).

T. J. Robinson. 1950. "The control of fertility in sheep: Part I, Hormonal therapy in the induction of pregnancy in the anestrous ewe." *J. Agr. Sci.*, **40**:275.

T. J. Robinson. 1950. "The control of fertility in sheep: Part II, The Augmentation of fertility by gonadotrophin treatment of the ewe in the normal breeding season." *J. Agr. Sci.*, **41**:6.

T. J. Robinson. 1957. "Pregnancy" in *Progress in the Physiology of Farm Animals,* Vol. III. Butterworth (London).

I. W. Rowlands. 1949. "Serum gonadotrophin and ovarian activity in the pregnant mare." *J. Endocrinol.*, **6**:184.

E. L. Wiggins, R. H. Grummer, and L. E. Casida. 1951. "Minimal volume of semen and number of sperm for fertility in artificial insemination of swine." *J. Animal Sci.*, **10**:138.

M. X. Zarrow and G. M. Neher. 1955. "Concentration of progestin in the serum of the rabbit during pregnancy, the puerperium and following castration." *Endocrinol.*, **56**:1.

chapter **12**

Fertility and Sterility

We have discussed various conditions under which animals show impaired fertility, and we have noted that deviations from maximal efficiency of reproduction are common and may be ascribed to a variety of causes. A variable proportion of male and female mammals and birds show, not impaired fertility, but complete sterility. It is the purpose of this chapter to discuss some of the common causes of sterility (other than infection by microorganisms) and to consider the possibilities of repairing the damage. The question of improving the average levels of fertility of normal animals will also be given consideration.

We have excluded sterility due to infection by microorganisms, not because it is unimportant, but because this cause of sterility can be detected and treated with relative ease. Though such conditions as vaginitis, brucellosis, leptospirosis, and vibriofetus profoundly affect the reproductive performance of most mammals, they do not fall within the sphere of competence of the reproductive physiologist but are a matter of concern for the clinician. It is important to be aware of the role played by infectious diseases in reproductive physiology and not to confound sterility and impaired fertility caused by bacteria with those that are due to endocrine or anatomic aberrations.

Sterility

All cases of total sterility of both sexes can be divided into two categories: those due to anatomical defects, and those caused by endocrine imbalance or malfunction.

Anatomical Defects in Females

There is considerable variation among the species in the frequency with which anatomical defects of the reproductive system can be blamed for sterility. Various surveys involving large numbers of animals of known reproductive history indicate that anatomical abnormalities are rare in goats, sheep, mares, cows, rabbits, and rats, and that they are common in pigs, in which they account for about half of the cases of total sterility or greatly impaired fertility. Though no exact figures are available, anatomical abnormalities seem to be an important cause of sterility in women.

The situation of the pig has been analyzed most completely, both in the United States and in Europe, and permits some rather interesting comparisons. Populations studied in the United States involved about 10,000 animals, including both slaughter-house material and animals whose reproductive histories were accurately known. The results obtained in Wisconsin and in Illinois are in close agreement. The Illinois data will illustrate the problem involved.

Of seventy-nine "sterile" females purchased from farms that were known to be free of infectious diseases affecting reproduction, 53 percent conceived at the first opportunity after they were brought to the University Farm. The females that conceived had been bred by their owners from three to ten times before being culled as "sterile." At autopsy only 7.1 percent of these females showed abnormalities, which, however, were not sufficiently serious to account for their failure to conceive to previous breedings. Neither is there an explanation for the failure of the remaining females that conceived on the University Farm to conceive before their inclusion in the experiment, for no improvement in their nutritive state or their general well-being was brought about by the move from their original environment. From the point of view of the breeder, these females were, of course, sterile, since to rebreed them as often as necessary to cause them to conceive was neither economical nor practical. Neither is it usually practical to provide them with a change of scenery in order to determine which are truly sterile and which only require repeated matings (see also Chapter 4, "Bizarre phenomena related to the estrual cycle").

The remaining thirty-six females (45.6 percent of the total) did not become pregnant. The reasons were determined at autopsy and are summarized in Tables 12-1 and 12-2 (see also Fig. 12-1). Almost half of the females failed to conceive because occlusion and distention of their oviducts made the passage of eggs or sperm impossible. Other abnormalities, such as unilaterally blind uterine horns, brought the total incidence of sterility due to anatomical aberrations to 64 percent. Theoretically, there is no reason why an animal having a unilaterally blind horn should not conceive. Actually, though fertilized eggs have

Table 12-1   Anatomical findings in thirty-six gilts and sows that failed to become pregnant

CONDITION OF REPRODUCTIVE TRACT	GILTS (percent)	SOWS (percent)	TOTAL	
			NUMBER	PERCENT
Abnormalities found	52.9	32.1	36	45.6
Endocrine aberrations			9	25.1
Cystic follicles (corpora lutea)	7.8	7.1	6	16.7
Cystic follicles (no corpora lutea)	0.0	7.1	2	5.6
Infantalism	2.0	0.0	1	2.8
Anatomical abnormalities			23	63.9
Hydrosalpinx, pyosalpinx	31.3	3.6	17	47.2
Unilateral blind horn	7.8	3.6	5	13.9
Unilateral missing segment*	2.0	3.6	2	5.6
Blind uterine body	2.0	0.0	1	2.8
Miscellaneous abnormalities	0.0	7.1	2	5.6

SOURCE: From Nalbandov. 1952. *Fertility and Sterility*, 3:100.
* This abnormality does not preclude pregnancy.

been recovered almost invariably from the patent side, pregnancy in such animals is extremely rare. Those in which half of the uterus is missing are fertile, but their litter size is, of course, much smaller than that of normal females.

A similar study conducted by European workers (Perry and Pomeroy, 1956, and Goethals, 1951) revealed anatomical abnormalities to be a minor cause of sterility in the populations they studied. Goethals, in Belgium, for instance, did not find a single case of occlusion of the oviduct in the 1,000 animals included in his sample. Perry, in England, found, among 83 animals, only three that had abnormalities—presumably including anatomical defects—other than cystic ovaries. His findings with regard to cystic ovaries will be treated later.

Table 12-2.   Anatomical findings in seventy-nine gilts and sows that were bred from three to ten times to boars of known fertility

RESULT OF BREEDING	GILTS		SOWS		TOTAL	
	NO.	PERCENT	NO.	PERCENT	NO.	PERCENT
Pregnancy	23	45.1	19	67.8	42	53.2
No abnormalities	21	41.1	18	64.3	39	49.4
Abnormalities	2	4.0	1	3.6	3	3.8
No pregnancy	28	54.9	9	32.2	37	46.8
No abnormalities	3	5.9	1	3.6	4	5.0
Abnormalities	25	49.0	8	28.6	33	41.8

SOURCE: From Nalbandov. 1952. *Fertility and Sterility*, 3:100.

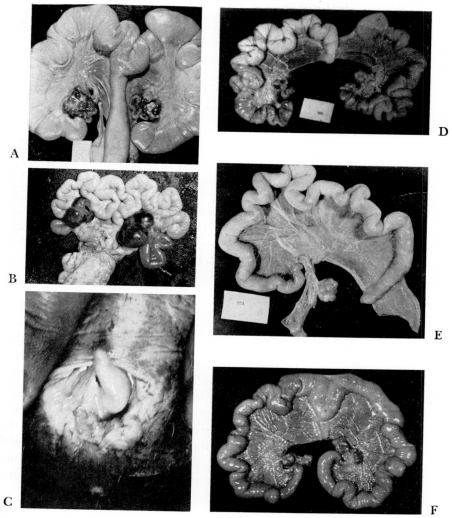

Figure 12-1. *Endocrine and anatomical causes of sterility in swine.*

A. Multiple small cyst. There are 32 cysts measuring 1.5 cm in diameter in the left ovary; the right ovary has a few small cysts and corpora albicantia.

B. This pig was sterile because she had large ovarian cysts and bilateral hydrosalpings (compare their size with the normal oviduct in A).

C. Enlarged clitoris (3.5 cm long, about 20 times the normal size), frequently found in cystic females.

D. Blind uterine horn. This usually causes sterility.

E. Right horn and ovary are missing. Such females are fertile.

F. Blind uterine body; the cervix and most of the vagina are missing.

All animals with anatomical defects have cycles of normal length and normal heats, and their condition cannot be diagnosed externally. It is possible, by injecting a starch suspension intraperitoneally and staining vaginal smears with iodine to show the presence of starch granules between twelve and twenty-four hours after the injection, to discover the cases of oviducal occlusion, but the method does not work on females with unilaterally blind horns.

Anatomical defects of the reproductive system are much less common in other mammals than in pigs. Cattle frequently have a complete or partial duplication of the cervix, but it does not interfere with fertility. Complete separation of the two uterine horns seems to be very rare in cattle but not infrequent in women, in whom each horn may also have a separate cervix. There are even records of several women who conceived separately in the two horns at two ovulations about twenty-eight days apart, two babies being delivered about thirty days apart. Such cases are interesting not only because they show that ovulation is not completely suppressed in pregnancy but also because they show that the readiness of the fetus to be born plays some role in the initiation of the mechanism of parturition.

Occlusion of the oviducts is a common cause of sterility in women. The condition in women is usually ascribed to infection, but attempts to produce hydro- or pyosalpinges in pigs by deliberate local infection of the oviducts were not successful. The fact that occlusion of the oviducts seems to occur in some families of pigs more often than in others suggests an underlying genetic mechanism, and the fact that it is found almost exclusively in gilts argues further against infection as the cause. These arguments are further supported by the finding that the condition is rare in European populations of swine.

Anatomical Defects in Males

In males, also, sterility is frequently caused by anatomical defects of the duct system. It occurs in all the species studied but is especially noted in men and bulls. The blockage may be found at any level of the duct system and may be unilateral or bilateral. Missing segments also are frequently noted.

Bilateral blockage of the duct system is easy to diagnose because no sperm are present in the ejaculate. Unilateral blockage is not so easy to diagnose, for the sperm count may be normal, and the fertility may range from none to normal.

Inflammations or degenerative changes of the accessory glands may also cause complete or partial sterility even though the sperm count and other characteristics of the semen may be normal. In three boars, of which two were completely sterile and one produced an occasional litter of greatly reduced size, the seminal vesicles (one or both) were found to be greatly enlarged, distended with atypical-appearing fluid, and distinctly inflamed. Sperm obtained from the vas, the epididymis, and the testes appeared normal in all three.

Endocrine Causes of Sterility

Cystic Ovaries in Swine.   In the Illinois study referred to earlier, 21 percent of the females that did not conceive in spite of frequent breedings were found to have cystic ovaries (see Fig. 12-2). We know already that two kinds of cysts were found in the pigs examined (Table 12-3)

Table 12-3.   Classification of cyst types found in swine and their effects on reproduction

| CYST TYPE | AVER. NO. OF CYSTS PER OVARY | HISTOLOGY OF | | EFFECT ON REPRODUCTION |
		CYST WALL	UTERINE ENDOMETRIUM	
Multiple, bilateral				
Large (2–5 cm diameter)	5.6	Granulosa heavily luteinized, thick	Progestational	Sterile, cycles very irregular, heat intense
Small	22.5	Granulosa normal	Estrogen type	But no nymphomania
Single or double (2–3 cm diameter)	1.2	Granulosa normal	Depends on stage in cycle	None; normal cycles
Normal follicles (0.7–0.9 cm diameter at ovulation)	5 9	Granulosa normal	Depends on stage in cycle	Normal cycles (21 days)

SOURCE: From Nalbandov. 1952. *Fertility and Sterility*, 3:100.

and that both large and small cysts are associated with sterility. It is noteworthy that cystic ovaries were much commoner in the European than in the American samples. The frequency with which cysts were found, and the apparently significant seasonal fluctuation in the occurrence of cysts in sows in England, are shown in Table 12-4. This tabulation, however, includes all types of cysts, including those that may have no effect on the fertility of the females examined (for example, retention cysts). Even if single cysts are omitted, however, the cystic degeneration of the ovaries of swine was significantly more frequent in England than in this country.

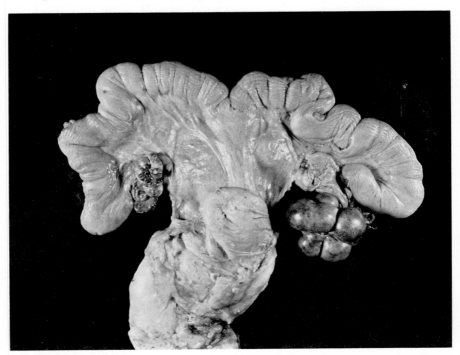

Figure 12-2. *Unilateral cystic ovary of a pig with a long history of sterility. The left ovary is normal and contains fresh corpora lutea; the right ovary has eight heavily luteinized cysts 3–4 cm in diameter (compare Figs. 5-1 and 12-1AB).*

Table 12-4. Seasonal changes in the occurrence of cystic follicles in sows. Arranged by months in which samples were available

MONTH	NO. OF SOWS	PERCENT CYSTIC	MONTH	NO. OF SOWS	PERCENT CYSTIC
February	22	32	September	49	20
March	34	35	October	147	14
April	68	35	November	150	14
May	115	36	December	85	18
June	147	30	January	5	20
Total	386	33.1	Total	436	13.3

SOURCE: Data rearranged from Perry and Pomeroy. 1956. *J. Agr. Sci* 47:238–248.

Cystic Ovaries in Cattle.   Estimates of the frequency with which cystic ovaries occur in cattle vary by conformation (rare in beef cattle, common in dairy cattle), by breed (Holsteins have more cystic ovaries than Jerseys), and by other factors (which will be mentioned). The cystic ovaries of cattle seem to differ significantly, in causes and effects, from those of swine. The only similarity between the two species is that both slight and great cystic degeneration of follicles is noted in both. In cows, ovarian cysts frequently lead to nymphomania, which causes afflicted females to assume several male secondary characters, such as coarseness of head and neck, male voice, and male sex behavior toward other cows. It is assumed that ovarian cysts secrete estrogen, then it must be postulated that estrogen in large quantities has an andromimetic effect. Since this is not supported by experimental evidence, it is possible that ovarian cysts in cattle secrete progesterone (just as they do in pigs) or that the cystic degeneration of the ovaries is a secondary effect. There is a strong suspicion that the primary difficulty may lie in an adrenal malfunction, which may lead to an upset in the pituitary-ovarian axis, culminating in cystic degeneration of the follicles. This possibility is supported by the finding that urinary 17-ketosteroids increase significantly in cows afflcted with nymphomania.

In a study involving 341 cows and 1,280 cow-service periods (Casida and Chapman, 1951), it was found that 18.8 percent of the cows had cystic ovaries. Confirming results obtained in Sweden and elsewhere, this study established the fact that the condition was inherited and that, in this particular herd, the heritability was 0.43. Of great interest is the fact that the frequency with which cystic ovaries occurred was significantly ($p = 0.01$) associated with the milk production (Table 12-5).

Table 12-5. Relation between milk production and incidence of cystic ovaries

GROUP NUMBER	NUMBER OF COWS	MANAGEMENT CONDITION	PERCENTAGE OF COWS CYSTIC
1	358	Not lactating	3.4
2	457	Lactating (in general herd)	6.8
3	106	Started on test but discontinued	8.5
4	359	On official test	10.6

SOURCE: From Casida and Chapman. 1951. *J. Dairy Science*, 34:1200.

With the exception of Group 1 (which includes heifers prior to their first parturition, in which age may be a factor), the groups are arranged in the order of the potential or actual ability of the cows to secrete milk, Group 2 being least productive and Group 4 most productive. It is tempting to ascribe the higher incidence of cystic ovaries in the animals of greater production to a rise in the rate of the pituitary function, which includes not only hormones responsible for the higher rate of milk secretion but most of the other trophic pituitary hormones. Though it is often stated that a high level of nutrition (high protein rations) is conducive to cyst formation, there is no good evidence for this contention. In a nutrition experiment conducted for many years in Oklahoma, in which cows were fed an abnormally high protein ration (cottonseed meal), the incidence of cysts was lower than it was in a control group fed a normal ration of protein.

The available data indicate that cysts are rare in other species, but they do occur.

Other Endocrine Defects.   In most mammalian species, infantilism of the reproductive tract of males or females is not uncommon. In females reaching the normal age of puberty, the ovaries remain very small and fail to produce follicles approaching ovulatory size. The duct system also remains immature, indicating an absence of trophic hormones. An infantile duct system responds to injections of estrogen by enlargement. The ovaries, as a rule, can be caused to enlarge and to form ovulable follicles. These observations indicate that infantilism is due to hypopituitarism, which is usually restricted to the secretion of the gonadotrophic hormones only, since such animals usually appear somatotypically normal. In human females, infantilism is frequently caused by hypothyroidism and can be corrected by appropriate medication.

In many domestic animals, quiet, or physiological, heats present a problem in that the females affected are not detected as being in heat and are not bred. Usually females having quiet heats ovulate normally at the expected time. It is probable that quiet heats are much commoner than is thought. If sheep are checked for heat daily with vasectomized males, it is found that certain females have intervals between heats that are multiples of sixteen days, the normal duration of cycles. That ovulations occur in these females has been determined by laparotomy. Quiet heats occur more frequently in some females than in others, and, furthermore, the propensity for quiet heats appears in the same females in successive breeding seasons. There is no indication that such ewes are less fertile than those not having quiet heats, but it should be kept in mind that such behavior restricts the control of the breeder over the time when females should conceive and is potentially dangerous if it is allowed to affect too many individuals. Similar observations have been made on cows, mares, and swine; but no good data are available on the repeatability of the condition in individuals, primarily because experiments have not been designed to differentiate between quiet heats and failure to show heat because pregnancy has been initiated but terminated shortly after breeding, through resorption or abortion.

Correction of Sterility

It is difficult to estimate the proportion of animals that are partially or completely sterile. Estimates of the occurrence of cystic ovaries in cattle vary from 1 to 20 percent and depend on a variety of factors, such as breed, family, and management practices. Estimates of the proportion of sterile swine vary from 5 to 17 percent of the total female breeding population. The divergence of these figures is undoubtedly due to the fact that causes of sterility are inherited (compare European and American data for anatomical abnormalities and cystic ovaries in swine) and that the proportion of cases is therefore determined by the prevalence of the genes governing the character.

Largely because the etiology of cyst formation is not understood, treatment is difficult and results are inconsistent. In cattle, luteinization of cysts can be accomplished by the injection of gonadotrophic hormone, such as LH-rich pituitary gland preparations or chorionic gonadotrophin. Not all cows respond to these treatments, however, and, even in those in which normal cycles are re-established as a result of treatment, cysts frequently recur. A further difficulty is that a high proportion of cystic animals (according to some estimates, 50–60 percent of them) recover spontaneously, complicating the interpretation of the efficacy of treatment. In women, a wedge-shaped resection of the cystic ovary has been found effective in re-establishing normal cycles and permitting subsequent conception. It is possible to induce normal reproductive performance and ultimate conception in all females afflicted with cystic ovaries after an appropriate expenditure of time and effort on various hormone treatments.

The most important question that arises in all discussions of corrective treatments of sterility in domestic animals concerns the wisdom of treating sterility and returning recovered females to the breeding herd or flock. There is a well-founded suspicion that anatomic abnormalities such as those described for swine are inherited. For this reason, it is fortunate that practically nothing can be done to overcome these defects; yet the mere elimination of the afflicted animals is not enough. It is necessary to eliminate as many of their relatives as the breeding program of the herd will allow. If that is not done, a gradual increase in sterility will take place. This had actually been seen in several of the herds from which sterile swine were obtained for the study discussed earlier in this chapter.

Similarly, we know that cystic ovaries in cattle have a hereditary basis. In contrast to anatomical abnormalities, nymphomania can frequently be corrected by endocrine treatment, or the afflicted females may recover spontaneously for sufficiently long periods to conceive. The available data indicate that it is not advisable to permit nymphomaniacs or related individuals to reproduce, and they should be eliminated from the herd, regardless of the initial investment in them.

An instructive example of what can happen when no attention is paid to certain types of sterility, and of how a high incidence of sterility can be corrected, is available in Swedish highland cattle (Eriksson, 1943). It was found, about 1935, that 30 percent of the cattle in these herds had hypoplasia of one ovary (usually the left) and that 5 percent had bilateral hypoplasia. The hypoplastic ovary was significantly smaller than the normal ovary and was completely nonfunctional, thus reducing the fertility of the afflicted animals. A campaign was instigated to detect the animals with hypoplastic ovaries and to remove them from the breeding herds, for it was found that the condition was caused by a recessive autosomal gene with incomplete penetrance. The initial prevalence of the condition and the success of the campaign to reduce its frequency in this Swedish breed of cattle can be seen in Table 12-6. The proportion of the totally sterile doubly hypoplastic cases was reduced from 5 percent in 1935 to approximately 1 percent in 1948. The

Table 12-6.   Incidence of ovarian hypoplasia in Swedish Highland cattle and effect of genetic selection against this trait

YEAR	NUMBER OF COWS STUDIED	COWS WITH HYPOPLASTIC OVARIES	
		NUMBER	PERCENT
1936	2,194	384	17.5
1937–39	1,173	179	15.2
1940–42	1,438	162	11.3
1943–45	1,588	176	11.1
1946–48	1,752	164	9.4

Source: After Lagerlöf and Settergen. 1953. *Cornell Veterinarian*, 43:51.

Table 12-10. Relation of conception rate and ovulation rate of sheep to season (which began late in September)

MATING PERIOD	NO. OF EWES MATED	PERCENT OF EWES CONCEIVING AT ONE MATING	NO. OF MATINGS PER CONCEPTION	NO. OF OVULATIONS PER EWE	EWES WITH QUIET HEATS
Oct. 20–30	22	73	1.5	1.9	3
Nov. 1–17	20	84	1.3	2.3	1
Nov. 18–30	19	90	1.2	2.4	0
Dec. 15–31	12	67	1.9	2.0	0
Jan. 20–31	22	54	1.9	1.9	2
Feb. 1–28	15	67	1.6	1.9	3
March 1 and later	20	65	1.7	1.8	4
Total or average	130	71	1.5	2.0	13

SOURCE: From Averill. 1955. *Studies on Fertility*, 7:139–148.

a man sits on the female's back or if manual pressure is exerted along the back. The female in heat responds by rigid immobility, but the nonestrous female escapes such overtures. Signoret has found that in the Large White breed of pigs about 50 percent of the females respond in this manner in the absence of the male and that the proportions of females responding can be significantly increased if a male is near enough to be smelled or heard. Du Mesnil du Buisson has classified the reflex behavior of 4,338 females, which were very calm (showed the rigidity reflex after physical contact with man alone), calm, or agitated (could be detected to be in heat only by the use of a boar). All of these animals were artificially inseminated; the numbers conceiving and giving birth to litters of pigs are shown in Table 12-11.

Table 12-11. Relation of conception rate in swine to their spontaneous ability to show the "immobility reflex"

BEHAVIOR	NULLIPARA		MULTIPARA		ALL FEMALES	
	TOTAL NUMBER	PERCENT CONCEIVED	TOTAL NUMBER	PERCENT CONCEIVED	TOTAL NUMBER	TOTAL CONCEIVED
Very calm	351	56.7	520	68.6	871	63.8
Calm	1,120	49.4	1,507	54.5	2,627	52.3
Agitated	345	31.3	461	36.2	806	34.1
No information	16	68.7	18	55.5	34	61.7
All	1,832	47.5	2,506	54.1	4,338	51.3

SOURCE: Du Mesnil Du Buisson. 1961. *Ann. Zootech.*, 10:57–67.

Examination of the data shows that the conception rate is 26 to 33 percent higher in those females that show the immobility reflex than it is in females not showing it. This very important difference implies that attention should be paid to gradations in intensity of estrual behavior and that only those animals with the strongest manifestations of estrual behavior should be used for breeding. Preliminary and incomplete data also suggest that the litter size of the females with the weak immobility reflex is lower than it is in the females with the strong reflex. Nothing is known about the possible neuroendocrine pathways involved in either the manifestation of the reflex or its connection with fertility and possibly fecundity.

Attempts to Increase Fertility

Earlier we made the generalization that fertilization rates in polytocous animals approach 100 percent but are, on the average, significantly lower in monotocous animals. In breeding populations of both types of animals the total loss of potential young, due to both failure of fertilization and embryonal mortality, is 30–50 percent. Most of this loss occurs very early in pregnancy, in all the animals studied. The fact that in many individuals, both polytocous and monotocous, there is no evidence of either loss of eggs or embryonal mortality raises the question whether the reproductive efficiency of females that do show reproductive waste can be improved.

The difficulty lies in the fact that it is not known why some females are reproductively so much more efficient than others. Since it is known that implantation does not occur in the absence of progesterone, attempts have been made to improve the reproductive efficiency of rats, pigs, and cattle by the administration of steroid hormones. The results obtained with progesterone alone are not promising; this hormone, at best, does not impair the reproductive performance of rats and swine if it is injected in small doses, but it is definitely detrimental to swine in doses of more than 200 milligrams per day. Combinations of estrogen and progesterone are detrimental to both rats and swine, presumably because the ratio of these two hormones in pregnancy is crucial and the correct ratio has not been found in the experiments.

The failure of attempts to preserve a larger proportion of zygotes raises the question whether raising the ovulation rate, by increasing the number of eggs fertilized and implanted, would increase the number of them that survive. A classical study of this question indicates that it is indeed possible to increase the fertility of sheep significantly by the injection of PMS (in this case given on day 14 of the cycle and again after the onset of heat). The dosage of PMS was intended, not to produce superovulation, but to increase the proportion of multiple ovulations at the expense of single ovulations (Table 12-12).

Table 12-12.   **Effect of gonadotrophin on number of young and on multiple birth in sheep treated with PMS**

TREATMENT	TOTAL LAMBING PERCENTAGE	PERCENTAGE			
		SINGLES	TWINS	TRIPLETS	QUADRUPLETS
Control	119.1	68	29	1.7	0.0
Injected with PMS	166.8	28	48	20.0	3.6

Source: From Lopyrin and others. 1940. *Sovetskaia Zootechnika*, 1 :82.

The most complete analysis of what happens in ewes in which super-ovulation is produced by varying doses of PMS has been made in two excellent papers by T. J. Robinson (1950). Table 12-13 shows that PMS

Table 12-13.   **Relation between ovulation rate and implantation rate in super-ovulated ewes**

NO. OF OVULATIONS	NO. OF EWES	PERCENTAGE CONCEIVING	MEAN NUMBER OF ATTACHMENTS IN EWES CONCEIVING	PERCENTAGE OF OVA ATTACHING
2	5	80	1.8	70
3	5	100	2.4	80
4	8	100	3.0	75
5	2	100	3.0	60
6	4	100	3.3	54
7	4	100	4.8	68
8–9	3	100	4.0	48
10–12	4	100	5.6	49
13–15	3	67	5.5	26
15	5	40	11.5	17

Source: From T. J. Robinson. 1950. *J. Agr. Sci.*, 41 :1–63.

significantly increases ovulation and that the implantation rate, though also increased, is not increased in proportion to the ovulation rate. Nothing in these data precludes the possibility of converting this particular monotocous animal into a polytocous animal by the use of hormones.

Much research work has been done on the possibility of bringing about reproduction in sheep during the nonbreeding season. It is easy to cause ovulation or heat in sheep during that season; the major problem, if out-of-season breeding of sheep is ever to become practical, is to synchronize these two events and induce them with only a small number of hormone injections. Treatment of ewes with progesterone or testosterone, followed by an ovulating dose of PMS, can, for a majority, cause synchronized heat and ovulation, followed by pregnancy, but the number of hormone injections required is at present too great to permit practical application.

Superovulation has been more or less successful in all species in which it has been tried. Cows respond to gonadotrophic hormones by multiple ovulations, but they rapidly become refractory to repeated treatments, probably because antihormones are formed. Even immature females of all laboratory species, as well as immature pigs, sheep, and calves, respond to gonadotrophic hormones by superovulation. In one study involving 17 calves aged 2.5–30 weeks, 262 corpora lutea were produced and 70 eggs were recovered, 23 of which had been fertilized (Marden, 1953). This is a very low fertilization rate, but it seems to be typical of eggs produced by juvenile females under the influence of gonadotrophic hormones.

Of extreme interest is the observation that, in both rabbits and ewes, eggs produced when the animal is under the influence of progesterone (pseudopregnancy in rabbits, luteal phase in sheep) show a drastically reduced fertilizability, whereas forced ovulations of eggs induced during the follicular phase show a fertilization rate that is about normal. The reason for the difference in fertilizability between eggs of the follicular phase and those of the luteal phase remains unknown, but it is not failure of sperm to reach the oviducts; the difficulty appears to lie in the physiological effect of progesterone on the ripening follicle and egg or in the effect of progesterone on the hormone system controlling follicular maturation.

Concluding Remarks

If we exclude sterility caused by anatomical defects or infections, the problem of gradations in fertility—from complete fertility through impaired fertility to total infertility—is among the most interesting, important, and difficult problems that the scientist and the practical gynecologist or breeder must face. Its importance lies in the fact that an appreciable number of all animals (including human beings) show some degree of impaired fertility, which reduces the breeding potential of the population to which they belong. The difficulty lies in the fact that the problem is multidimensional, being due to a variety of factors acting singly and to the interactions of factors acting together. We have seen that females showing reduced fertilizability of eggs also show increased embryonal mortality, and the temptation is strong to ascribe the two to the same cause. There is no evidence either for or against such a conclusion. The problem is further complicated by the fact that there are few if any clues that would permit an intelligent experimental approach. Though it is true, for instance, that the fertilizability of eggs in rabbits and in sheep can be reduced to almost zero by injections of progesterone, it is equally true that the fertilizability of eggs in sheep is also low very early in the breeding season and that at that time there are no functional corpora lutea in the ovaries. These observations are not necessarily contradictory, for it is possible that, though much progesterone is harmful, a little is essential. It is also becoming more apparent that we must learn to think of "physiological doses" and of the physiological ebb and flow of hormones before we can learn to imitate the conditions under which reproductive functions are at their optimum.

It is suggested that at this point the reader again refer to the discussion entitled "Bizarre phenomena related to the estrual cycle," Chapter 4. It is becoming increasingly clearer that not enough attention has been paid either by the research worker or by the practical breeder to so-called psychogenic factors, which seem to have such a profound effect on the breeding behavior of animals. The study of reproductive behavior of animals as it is affected by interaction with other animals, by the environment in which the animals live, and by the stresses to which they are exposed, seems a most promising and almost untouched area of research. Those who are less inclined toward reproductive animal psychology, and more toward physiology or endocrinology, can explore the mechanism of action of phenomena which appear to play such an important role in mice and pigs and—who knows?—perhaps in man. The chain of neuroendocrine events which can be modified by "odor" (whatever that may be, chemically speaking) must indeed be a fascinating area of research. In short, the field of the endocrinology of reproductive behavior—or, if you prefer, of behavioristic endocrinology—is wide open.

Attention is called, finally, to another important factor that is too frequently overlooked by clinicians and even by research workers. It has been found that, in subfertile females that show no evidence of anatomical abnormalities, the rate of spontaneous recovery is quite high. All hard-to-settle females conceive eventually if they are bred sufficiently often, and even females that are sterile because of cystic ovaries recover spontaneously and conceive if enough time is allowed them. Because of this spontaneous recovery, it is essential to include in any experimental design an adequate number of control cases from which treatment is withheld. Failure to provide adequate controls is largely responsible for the enormous number of meaningless reports that appear in the clinical literature.

SUMMARY

The majority of cases of sterility are due (1) to anatomical aberrations of the reproductive systems of males and females, and (2) to endocrine upsets. It is probable that both causes are hereditary; and therefore, at least in domestic animals, no attempt should be made to correct the anatomic or endocrine causes of sterility lest the condition be spread through a large part of the population.

More important than complete sterility is impaired fertility. In these cases the ovulation rate, the ovulation time, and the fertilization rate are normal, but embryonal mortality is far in excess of the "normal" 30 percent. The reasons why some members of a population show impaired fertility are obscure, since occasionally even such females reproduce normally if they are bred often enough.

Attempts to increase normal fertility rates by lowering "normal" embryonal mortality with the use of hormones (such as progesterone) have not been uniformly successful, but they show some promise. Similarly promising are attempts to increase the prolificacy of animals by increasing ovulation rates with hormones. In both instances much additional work will be required.

Attention is called once again to the role of little understood psychosomatic factors on the efficiency of reproduction. Data are presented to show that the intensity of psychological heat in pigs is inversely related to fertility and perhaps even fecundity. It is obvious that we need more intensive study of pheromones and of animal behavior as it affects reproductive phenomena.

REFERENCES

E. Blom and N. O. Christensen. 1947. "Studies on pathological conditions in the testes epididymis and accessory sex glands in the bull." *Skand. Veterinartidskrift.*

K. Eriksson. 1943. *Hereditary Forms of Sterility in Cattle.* Ohlsson (Lund, Sweden).

Otto Garm. 1949. "A study on bovine nymphomania." *Acta Endocrinologica,* Suppl. 3.

H. E. Kidder, W. G. Black, J. N. Wiltbank, L. C. Ulberg, and L. E. Casida. 1954. "Fertilization rates and embryonic death rates in cows bred to bulls of different levels of fertility." *J. Dairy Sci.,* 37:691.

N. Lagerlöf and I. Settergren. 1953. "Results of 17 years of control of hereditary ovarian hypoplasia in cattle of the Swedish Highland breed." *Cornell Vet.,* 43:51.

J. A. Laing. 1957. "Female fertility" in *Progress in the Physiology of Farm Animals,* Vol. III. Butterworth (London).

J. S. Perry and R. W. Pomeroy. 1956. "Abnormalities of the reproductive tract of the sow." *J. Agr. Sci.,* 47:238.

R. W. Phillips and J. H. Zeller. 1941. "Some factors affecting fertility in swine." *Am. J. Vet. Res.,* 2:439.

Index